Introduction to Abstract Algebra

Under the general editorship of
David Vernon Widder
Harvard University

INTRODUCTION TO
Abstract Algebra

Wilfred E. Barnes
Washington State University

D. C. Heath and Company Boston

Library of Congress Catalog Card Number: 63-13860

Printed March 1965

Preface

The study of abstract algebra has become an essential part of the training of every mathematician. This book treats those portions of the theory of groups, rings, and fields which will provide a reasonable background in these subjects for both the nonalgebraist and those wishing to pursue further studies in algebra. The level of the book should prove suitable for either advanced undergraduate or beginning graduate students.

The chapter on groups presents such topics as groups with operators, the Jordan-Hölder Theorem, composition series, direct product representation of finitely generated Abelian groups, and the Sylow Theorems. Ring and ideal theory is developed to the point of considering the effects of various finiteness conditions, elementary factorization theory, representation of ideals in Noetherian rings, and a brief introduction to modules and vector spaces. In field theory, following elementary results on transcendental and algebraic field extensions, the reader will be introduced to such notions as separability, reducibility criteria, finite fields (including the Wedderburn Theorem), and the Galois Theory.

For pedagogical reasons, certain topics are omitted or condensed. Most notable is the omission of linear algebra as a subject, with only those results needed for elementary field theory being considered in this book. This does not imply that linear algebra is not considered to be an extremely important and beautiful part of abstract algebra. Rather, it is omitted here because a number of excellent texts on this subject are available, and also it is often taught as a separate course, either preceding or following the material of such a book as this. In the author's opinion, linear algebra may well be presented first, as its subject matter seems to provide an easier introduction to the style and methods of abstract algebra and it develops more naturally out of topics with which the student is familiar. Thus, while this book is self-contained, it is designed for students whose algebraic maturity is roughly that to be expected after a semester's introduction to linear algebra.

Somewhat similarly, since the basic theory of sets, relations, functions, and the natural number system is often covered in other courses and has been treated by a number of authors, the first chapter of this book is intended merely to introduce the terminology to be used subsequently and does not pretend to be a rigorous treatment of these topics.

In the body of the book, no use is made of arguments based on the axiom of choice or equivalent axioms. However, in much of algebra these axioms play an important role. They are, therefore, introduced in Appendix I. A typical cyclic proof of the equivalence of the well-ordering axiom, the axiom of choice, and the two forms of Zorn's Lemma is given, followed by representative applications. Among the latter is a proof of the existence and essential uniqueness of an algebraically complete algebraic extension of an arbitrary field. Appendix II presents the properties of an ordered field and includes a construction (by the method of Cauchy sequences) of the real number field.

The text material has been divided into a number of small sections, more or less complete in themselves, both for convenience of reference and to allow the reader (or his instructor) to pick and choose a little. Since to learn mathematics it is necessary to do mathematics, a number of exercises (nearly 300 in all) have been provided following the individual sections. In some cases, these involve proofs of results stated in the section; in others, applications or extensions of such results are called for. However, such extensions are not used to develop further results in the text, and so a reader need not work all the exercises in order to read the rest of the book.

Allowance has been made for the reader's increasing algebraic background and sophistication as the text proceeds. Thus, while at the beginning proofs are given in detail even for quite easy results, as the reader proceeds he will find that he is called upon to supply more of the detail. This progression is not continuous, however, as the early part of each chapter proceeds more gradually than the last part of the preceding chapter. Since both the terminology and the concepts of abstract algebra can be expected to be quite new and strange to the reader, many illustrations of definitions and theorems have been included.

The debt the author owes to many previous authors will be apparent. Not so apparent, but certainly no less real, is his debt to both his students and his own teachers and colleagues, all of whom have had an influence on this book, and to whom the author wishes to express his gratitude. Particular thanks are due to Professor William Cunnea for his critical and helpful reading of the manuscript, to the staff of D. C. Heath and Company for their help and consideration, and to the members of the author's family for their encouragement and forbearance during the writing of the book.

WILFRED E. BARNES
Pullman, Washington

Contents

Chapter 1. Some Preliminary Concepts

1. Introduction 1
2. Sets 2
3. Relations 5
4. Functions and Compositions 8
5. The Natural Numbers 11
6. Isomorphism 14

Chapter 2. Groups

1. Introduction 17
2. Definition and Examples of Groups 17
3. Alternative Definitions of a Group 20
4. Cyclic Groups 25
5. Transformation Groups 27
6. Homomorphism and Isomorphism of Groups 33
7. Subgroups 37
8. Normal Subgroups 41
9. Factor Groups 46
10. Groups with Operators 51
11. The Isomorphism Theorems 54
12. Composition Series 58
13. Direct Products of Groups 62
14. Abelian Groups 70
15. The Sylow Theorems 73

Chapter 3. Rings and Ideals

1. Rings 77
2. Ideals, Residue Class Rings 84
3. Homomorphism and Isomorphism of Rings 89
4. Operations on Ideals 93
5. Extensions of Rings 96

6. Polynomial Rings 103
7. Finiteness Conditions 111
8. Factorization of Ring Elements 115
9. Factorization in Polynomial Domains 121
10. Maximal, Prime, and Primary Ideals 124
11. Ideals in Noetherian Rings 130
12. The Characteristic of a Ring 138
13. Modules and Vector Spaces 141

Chapter 4. Fields

1. Prime Fields 149
2. Extensions of Fields 151
3. Finite Extensions 157
4. Splitting Fields 162
5. Separability 164
6. Irreducibility in $F[x]$ 168
7. Finite Fields 174
8. Galois Theory 178
9. The Fundamental Theorem of Algebra 188

Appendix I. The Well-Ordering Axiom 193
Appendix II. Ordered Fields 199

References 209

Index 211

CHAPTER *1*

Some Preliminary Concepts

1. Introduction

If one surveys the subjects of arithmetic and elementary algebra, certain features stand out. One notes that the work deals with some given, or derived, set of objects, usually numbers, and with combinations of these objects. Examples are the sets of natural numbers, of rational numbers, of complex numbers, etc., and the combinations obtained by addition, subtraction, multiplication, and division. Moreover, one finds that there are some properties which these combinations have in common: e.g., one may combine a number with itself and obtain a number in the set except in the case of the natural numbers and subtraction and that of zero and division. Other properties, such as associativity, do not always hold.

It would appear that a fuller understanding of the subject might well result from a systematic study of typical structures, that is, sets with methods of combination obeying a given set of rules. Moreover, such a study ought to have the advantage of economy in that many superficially distinct structures may be found to be basically the same, and hence open to a unified treatment.

Perhaps the most familiar example of this economy is the subject of plane analytic geometry. Here the set of objects may be thought of as the familiar geometric objects of points, lines, etc., and the relations as such things as incidence, parallelism, etc. Equally well, the set of objects may be interpreted as being ordered pairs of numbers, linear equations, etc., and the relations as being consistency, proportionality of coefficients, etc. Results may be obtained either algebraically or geometrically, and may then be at once "translated" into the other "language," instead of requiring separate proof.

Another advantage of such a study, which should not be overlooked, is that it ought to result in developing an appreciation of the esthetic appeal of a well-formulated system. To many mathematicians, this aspect of the subject, which we may call its mathematical beauty, is in itself more than sufficient justification for its study.

This is the approach of so-called modern, or perhaps more accurately abstract, algebra to the material of arithmetic and elementary algebra. Its success with regard to the attainment of deeper understanding, further results, and economy has been outstanding, as has been the growth of the subject. Indeed, literally hundreds of such structures have now been studied and algebra has "invaded" other areas of mathematics to the point where it is often difficult to determine the limits of what may properly be considered algebra.

2. Sets

Before beginning such a systematic study, we shall need some preliminary terms and concepts. First is the notion of a *set* together with some of the elementary properties of sets. We shall not attempt to develop set theory here, but shall merely give a very naive description of those concepts and results which we shall need. We refer the reader to any standard treatment of the subject for a more complete and rigorous development.

By a *set* we mean any collection of entities, concrete or abstract, called the *members of the set.* Notationally, we shall write

$$x \in S \quad \text{or} \quad x \notin S,$$

to mean that x, respectively, is or is not a member of the set S. Similarly,

$$x, y \in S \quad \text{or} \quad x, y \notin S$$

will indicate, respectively, that both x and y are members of S, or that neither x nor y is in S. The symbolism

$$S = \{a, b, c, \ldots\},$$
$$T = \{a, b, c, \ldots, n\}$$

will indicate that a, b, c are some of the elements of S, and that $a, b, c, \ldots, n$ are all of the elements, or members, of T.

Since listing the elements of a set is often awkward or even impossible, and, moreover, every set consists of precisely those elements possessing some particular property (for instance, the property of being members of the set in question), we shall often wish to designate the membership of a set by giving the property which its members possess. Thus we write

$$S = \{x: P(x)\}$$

to signify that S is the set consisting of those elements which possess property P. For example, if R is the set of all real numbers, then $S = \{x: x \in R, |x| < 3\}$ is the set of real numbers of absolute value less than 3. If the overall set being considered, called the *universe set* of the discussion, is clearly understood by the context, we may omit specifying the requirement that x is a member of this set, and, in the above case, simply write $S = \{x: |x| < 3\}$.

We shall say that two sets are *equal,* $S = T$, if every member of one is also a member of the other, and conversely. More general is the notion of *set inclusion.* If every member of S is a member of T, but not necessarily conversely, we shall write

$$S \subseteq T,$$

and say that S is *included in* T or that S is a *subset* of T.

If we wish to say that while every member of S is also a member of T, there is at least one member of T which is not a member of S, then we shall write

$$S \subset T,$$

and say that S is a *proper subset* of T.

Definition. By the *union* of the sets S and T,

$$S \cup T = \{x: x \in S \text{ or } x \in T\},$$

we mean the set of all elements which are in S or in T (or in both S and T).

Definition. By the *intersection* of the sets S and T,

$$S \cap T = \{x: x \in S \text{ and } x \in T\},$$

we mean the set of all elements which are both in S and in T.

The commutativity of union and intersection of sets, respectively

$$S \cup T = T \cup S \quad \text{and} \quad S \cap T = T \cap S,$$

is at once apparent, as is the associativity of these operations on sets, respectively

$$S \cup (T \cup V) = (S \cup T) \cup V \quad \text{and} \quad S \cap (T \cap V) = (S \cap T) \cap V.$$

If we wish to denote the union or intersection of the sets $S_1, S_2, \ldots, S_n$, we shall use the respective notations

$$\bigcup_{i=1}^{n} S_i \quad \text{and} \quad \bigcap_{i=1}^{n} S_i.$$

Similarly,

$$\bigcup_I S_i \quad \text{and} \quad \bigcap_I S_i$$

will respectively denote the union and intersection of all the sets S_i for which i is in the index set I. If the context is such that no confusion can result as to the index set referred to, we may write simply

$$\bigcup S_i \quad \text{and} \quad \bigcap S_i.$$

Since we wish to be able to consider the intersection of any two sets S and T, and it is certainly possible that in some instances they will have no common elements, we must agree to consider the set having no members at all as being just as much a set as any other. This set, called the *empty set* or *null set*, will be designated as the set $\emptyset$.

In case we wish to refer to those elements in the universe of the discussion which are not in the set S, we refer to the elements in the *complement* S' of S,

$$S' = \{x : x \notin S\}.$$

It should be remarked that the universe set of the discussion must always be either explicit or implicit, for to allow the notion of sets of all elements whatever to creep into the picture leads to serious difficulties, including possible contradictions.

Another concept which we need is that of the (Cartesian) *product* of sets S and T,

$$S \times T = \{a : a = (s, t),\ s \in S \text{ and } t \in T\}.$$

Definition. The *product set* $S \times T$ is the set of all *ordered pairs* (s, t) of elements $s \in S$ and $t \in T$.

The order is very important since, in general, the pair (t, s) will not even be a member of $S \times T$. Even if it should be, as, for instance, if $S = T$, still $(s, t) \neq (t, s)$ in general.

Definition. The *ordered pairs* (a, b) and (c, d) are *equal* if and only if both $a = c$ and $b = d$; hence $(s, t) = (t, s)$ only if $s = t$.

The definition of product set has its origin in the notation of analytic geometry, hence the name Cartesian, and can be extended to a product of any (finite or infinite) number of sets. In particular, if n is any positive integer, we may wish to consider the n-fold product of a set S with itself, which we designate by

$$S^n = S \times S \times \cdots \times S \qquad (n \text{ factors } S).$$

Exercises

1. If $S = \{a, b, c\}$, $T = \{b, d\}$, and $V = \{a, c, e\}$, determine each of the sets $S \cap T$, $S \cap V$, $S \cap T \cap V$, $S \cup T$, $T \cup V$, $S \cup T \cup V$, $S \times T$, $T \times S$, $(S \times T) \cap (T \times S)$, and $S \times T \times V$.
2. Let R be the set of all real numbers and

$$S = \{(x, y) : x, y \in R,\ 3x + y = 4\},$$
$$T = \{(x, y) : x, y \in R,\ x - 2y = 2\}.$$

Determine $S \cap T$, and give geometric interpretations of S, T, and $S \cap T$.
3. Let R be the set of all real numbers, and

$$S = \{x : x \in R,\ -1 < x < 3\},$$
$$T = \{y : y \in R,\ y > 2\}.$$

Determine the set $S \times T$ and describe it geometrically.
4. Let m and n be any positive integers and S a set of m elements. How many subsets of S are there, and how many elements in S^n?

3. Relations

We shall often have occasion to consider subsets of a product set. For instance, if we consider a relation in two variables x and y, where x must be a member of S and y a member of T, then the solutions of the relation form a subset of $S \times T$. It is convenient to generalize this idea.

Definition. A general *relation between S and T* is any subset of $S \times T$. In the case that S and T are the same set, $S = T$, we refer simply to a *relation on S*.

For example, "is the father of" is a relation between the set of all males and the set of all people. Notice that not every male will occur as the first element of a pair in the relation, and that, on the other hand, some males will occur as the first elements of several pairs. Other relations of this sort will readily occur to the reader, as well as those of elementary algebra and geometry, such as "is congruent to," as a relation on the set of all plane figures. The notation commonly used for such relations as equality, congruence, less than, etc., is conveniently generalized by writing

$$sRt \qquad \text{to mean} \qquad (s, t) \in R$$

for a relation R between S and T.

The relations we have just defined on a set S are more properly termed *binary relations*, since they are subsets of the two-fold product, $S \times S = S^2$, of S with itself. This concept can be extended to that of *n-ary relations* on S, that is, subsets of the n-fold product S^n of S with itself. As an example of a ternary relation, or subset of S^3, we may mention the relation of betweenness in the set of points in elementary geometry. Since, however, we shall be primarily concerned with binary relations in what follows, the unqualified term *relation* is to be understood to mean *binary relation*, and we shall always specify the type of relation if it is other than binary.

The relation of congruence provides an example of a type of relation which will be of great importance for us.

Definition. A subset R of $S \times S$ is called an *equivalence relation* on S if:

(i) For all $s \in S$, $(s, s) \in R$ (i.e., sRs always holds). [REFLEXIVITY]
(ii) If $(s, t) \in R$, then $(t, s) \in R$ (i.e., sRt implies tRs). [SYMMETRY]
(iii) If (s, t), $(t, u) \in R$, then $(s, u) \in R$ (i.e., sRt and tRu imply sRu). [TRANSITIVITY]

The most obvious example of an equivalence relation is that of equality, and, indeed, equivalence is a generalization of equality. As other examples of equivalence relations, we may mention the property of having the same modulus or absolute value in the set of all complex numbers, or having the same determinant in the set of all nth-order real matrices, or of having the same number of letters in the set of all book titles.

Definition. The members of a class of subsets, any distinct two of which have empty intersection, are called *mutually disjoint.*

Definition. A *partition* of S is a representation of S as the union of nonempty, mutually disjoint subsets of S.

An equivalence relation R on a set S induces a partition of S. For if we let the *equivalence class* of x be

$$\bar{x}_R = \{y: (y, x) \in R\} = \{y: yRx\},$$

then, by (i), no $\bar{x}_R$ is empty, and every element of S is in some $\bar{x}_R$. It remains only to show that the equivalence classes $\bar{x}_R$ and $\bar{y}_R$ are either identical or disjoint for arbitrary x and y in S. Suppose, then, that the intersection is not empty, say $z \in \bar{x}_R \cap \bar{y}_R$. Then zRx and zRy, and, by property (ii), we have also xRz. Now, let t be any element of $\bar{x}_R$, so that tRx. Then, by property (iii), we have, successively, tRz and tRy, so that t is also in $\bar{y}_R$. Hence, $\bar{x}_R \subseteq \bar{y}_R$, and, as the reverse inclusion follows in an entirely similar manner, we conclude that $\bar{x}_R = \bar{y}_R$, and equivalence classes are either disjoint or identical, as asserted.

Conversely, a partition of S defines an equivalence relation R on S if we let xRy if and only if x and y are in the same subset of the partition. Where no confusion can result as to the equivalence relation being referred to, we shall denote $\bar{x}_R$ simply by $\bar{x}$.

We shall frequently be concerned with the collection of equivalence classes

$$\bar{S}_R = \{\bar{x}_R: x \in S\},$$

into which the equivalence relation R decomposes S.

Definition. The set $\bar{S}_R$ of the equivalence classes of S with respect to the relation R is often called the *factor set* of S by, or with respect to, R.

Where the relation R is clearly understood, the factor set of S will be referred to simply by the notation $\bar{S}$. Note that the elements of $\bar{S}$ are subsets of S, not elements of S, so that $\bar{S}$ is not a subset of S.

We may now characterize the relation of *equality* as being that equivalence relation for which each equivalence class (element of the factor set) consists of a single element of S. Thus, by saying that the elements x and y of S are equal, we mean that x is y. (That different symbols, or "names," may be used to designate one and the same entity is, of course, a common practice and offers no difficulty, provided one is careful not to confuse the name of an entity with the entity itself.) With this meaning of equality, actual identity, such rules as the principle of substitution of equals for equals are immediately apparent.

Illustrations of these notions are plentiful. For example, one of the concerns of biologists is the classification of the set of all animals into equivalence classes called phyla. Successively "finer" partitions are obtained by dividing a phylum into classes, a class into orders, an order into families, a family into genera, and a genus into species. That many different equivalence relations, with their respective partitions, may be defined on the same set is well illustrated by the many ways in which equivalence relations are applied to, say, the set of all people in a given country. Thus two people may be called equivalent if they are of the same national origin, or if they have the same religious preference, or if they are of the same age, or are of the same profession, etc.

As another example, consider the set S of elements 1, 2, 3, 4, 5, and 6. We define a partition of S as follows:

$$S = \{1, 2, 3, 4, 5, 6\} = \{1\} \cup \{2, 5, 6\} \cup \{3, 4\}.$$

Of the thirty-six elements in $S \times S$, this partition selects the fourteen-element equivalence relation

$$R = \{(1, 1), (2, 2), (3, 3), (4, 4), (5, 5), (6, 6), (2, 5), (5, 2), (2, 6), (6, 2), (5, 6), (6, 5), (3, 4), (4, 3)\}.$$

To make the properties of reflexivity, symmetry, and transitivity even more apparent in this case, we give the following diagram, where an * indicates that the pair having first member in that row and second member in that column is in R:

	1	2	3	4	5	6
1	*					
2		*			*	*
3			*	*		
4			*	*		
5		*			*	*
6		*			*	*

Exercises

1. Using the notation of plane analytic geometry, give a definition of the ternary relation of betweenness on the set of points in the plane.
2. Which of the following are equivalence relations on the set Z of all integers?
   (a) xRy means x divides y.
   (b) xRy means $x - y$ is an even integer.
   (c) xRy means $x + y$ is an even integer.
   (d) xRy means $x - y$ is an odd integer.
   (e) xRy means $x \leq y$.
   (f) xRy means $x < y$.
3. How many partitions are there of a set of 2 elements? of 3 elements? of 4 elements?
4. Let R be a relation on the set S which is symmetric and transitive and such that, for any $s \in S$, sRs' for some $s' \in S$. Prove that R is an equivalence relation.
5. Show, by examples, that reflexivity, symmetry, and transitivity are independent properties of binary relations; that is, binary relations exist having any given two of these properties without having the other.

4. Functions and Compositions

We now proceed to a somewhat more special situation than that of a general relation between S and T.

Definition. A *mapping*, or *function, from* S *into* T is a subset R of $S \times T$ such that for any $s \in S$, there is exactly one pair in R having s as its first member.

Thus by a mapping, or function, we mean, in effect, just what is usually referred to as a single-valued function. It should be noted that according to our definition, the *domain* of a function is always the entire set S; that is, a function is defined only over its domain. Following customary notation, we shall also denote such a mapping R from S into T by

$$\phi: S \to T \qquad \text{or} \qquad \phi: s \to t,$$

and write

$$\phi(s) = s\phi = s^{\phi} = t \qquad \text{if} \qquad (s, t) \in R.$$

We similarly define for any subset S' of S,

$$S'\phi = \{s\phi: s \in S'\}.$$

The elements s and t are said to *correspond* under the mapping ϕ, and for this reason ϕ is also called a (rule of) *correspondence*. We shall call t the *image* of s under R, and s an (there may be more than one) *antecedent* of t under R. Similarly, $S'\phi$ is called the image of S' under R, and, when convenient, we shall also use ϕ as a "name" for the mapping. If $T = S$, we speak simply of a mapping, or *transformation*, of S.

In the event that each $t \in T$ occurs (at least once) in some pair $(s, t) \in R$, we shall say that R, or ϕ, is a mapping of S *onto* T. This situation is clearly the case if and only if $S\phi = T$. If each $t \in T$ occurs exactly once in a pair $(s, t) \in R$, then R or ϕ is called *one-to-one*, or 1–1.

Definition. If R, or ϕ, is a 1–1 mapping from S to T, then by R^{-1}, or ϕ^{-1}, we mean the *inverse mapping* from T to S defined by

$$(t, s) \in R^{-1} \qquad \text{if and only if} \qquad (s, t) \in R, \text{ or}$$
$$\phi^{-1}(t) = t\phi^{-1} = s \qquad \text{if and only if} \qquad \phi(s) = s\phi = t.$$

Definition. If S and T are two sets between which a 1–1 mapping can be defined, they are called *cardinally equivalent*, since they then have the same cardinal number of elements.

If ϕ is any mapping of S onto T, not necessarily 1–1, we may still wish to consider a sort of inverse to the mapping ϕ. We accomplish this by considering the subsets of S defined by

$$t\phi^{-1} = \{s: s \in S \text{ and } s\phi = t\}.$$

The set $t\phi^{-1}$ is called the *complete inverse image* of t under ϕ. A familiar illustration of this situation is provided by taking S as the set of all real numbers, T as the set of real numbers t such that $-1 \leq t \leq 1$, and letting $s\phi = \sin s$.

We shall also need the notion of a composite, or product, of two mappings.

Definition. If $\phi: A \to B$ and $\sigma: B \to C$ are both mappings, then we define the *composite* or *product mapping*

$$\phi\sigma: A \to C, \text{ by } a(\phi\sigma) = (a\phi)\sigma \text{ for all } a \in A.$$

This definition makes the preference for *right-hand notation* for mappings rather apparent. For $\phi\sigma$ means first ϕ then σ, in the natural order of reading from left to right. If we were to use *left-hand notation*, then we would have

$$(\phi\sigma)(a) = \sigma(\phi(a)),$$

thus reversing the order of writing the symbols indicating the mappings.

The notions of equivalence relation and mapping onto are very closely connected. For if R is an equivalence relation on a set S, then there is a *natural mapping*, or *canonical mapping*, of S onto $\bar{S}_R$ defined by

$$\alpha: S \to \bar{S}_R, \qquad x\alpha = \bar{x}_R.$$

Conversely, suppose that ϕ is a mapping of S onto T. We may then define a relation R on S by xRy if and only if $x\phi = y\phi$. That R is an equivalence relation is easily checked, and we see that

$$\bar{x}_R = (x\phi)\phi^{-1}.$$

Thus every equivalence relation R on S determines, in a natural way, a mapping of S onto the factor set $\bar{S}_R$, and a mapping of S onto T determines an equivalence relation on S.

We may remark that the correspondence between equivalence relations and mappings onto is not perfect, since it is not a 1–1 correspondence. For there may well be many mappings of S onto various sets, all of which determine the same equivalence relation on the set S.

Definition. A mapping from $S \times S$ into S will be called a *binary operation* or *binary composition* on S. Similarly, a mapping from S^n, the n-fold product of S with itself, into S, where n is any positive integer, will be called an *n-ary operation* or *composition* on S.

For example, if Z is the set of all integers, the mapping

$$(a, b)\sigma = a + b \qquad \text{is a binary operation on } Z,$$
$$a\rho = -a \qquad \text{is a unary operation on } Z, \text{ and}$$
$$(a, b, c)\tau = a - b + c \text{ is a ternary operation on } Z.$$

Although we do encounter unary operations such as ρ in ordinary arithmetic and algebra, we are, for the most part, concerned with binary operations. Hence, when we say simply *operation* or *composition*, we shall mean *binary* operation or composition. We may remark that under some definitions of operation, the requirement that the image of (a, b) must be in S is not made. This *closure* property of an operation is automatic for our definition, and we shall have no occasion to use an operation which is not closed.

Besides the notion of operations on a set S just considered, we shall have occasions to consider mappings from a product set $S \times T$ into S. If ϕ is such a mapping, $\phi: S \times T \to S$, we call T a set of *operators* on S, since each element t of T can then be thought of as defining a unary operation on S. That is, if we fix $t \in T$, then the mapping $t: S \to S$ given by $s \to (s, t)\phi = s^t$ is a unary operation on S. To contrast such a mapping $\phi: S \times T \to S$ with our more usual notion of binary operation, $\beta: S \times S \to S$, ϕ is sometimes referred to as a law of *external composition*, and β is then called a law of *internal composition.*

Definition. The law of external composition ϕ with operator set T is said to be *compatible* with the binary operation β on S if, for all $a, b \in S$ and $t \in T$, we have

$$((a, b)\beta, t)\phi = ((a, t)\phi, (b, t)\phi)\beta.$$

For example, if S is the set of all positive real numbers, β is the binary operation of ordinary multiplication, T is the set of all integers, and ϕ is exponentiation, $(a, t)\phi = a^t$, then the fact that ϕ is compatible with β is nothing more than the familiar rule

$$(ab)^t = a^t b^t.$$

Or again, if both S and T are the set of integers, β is ordinary addition and ϕ is ordinary multiplication, then the compatibility of ϕ with β becomes the law of distribution of multiplication over addition:

$$(a + b)t = at + bt.$$

Exercises

1. Let K be the set of all real numbers x. Which of the following mappings of K to K are onto? Which are 1–1?
   (a) $x \to x - 2$. (b) $x \to x^2$. (c) $x \to x^3$.
   (d) $x \to x^2 - x$. (e) $x \to |x| + x$.
2. For the mappings in Exercise 1 which are not 1–1, determine the corresponding equivalence relations and classes.
3. Prove that the relation xRy if and only if $x\phi = y\phi$, where $\phi: S \to T$ is a mapping, is an equivalence relation on S.
4. Let α and β be mappings of S onto T and V, respectively, such that for any $t \in T$, $t\alpha^{-1} \subseteq v\beta^{-1}$ for some $v \in V$. Compare the equivalence relations on S determined by α and β, and show that if γ is defined by $t\gamma = (t\alpha^{-1})\beta$ for all $t \in T$, then γ is a mapping of T onto V. Also, if $\bar{\beta}$ is defined by $\bar{s}\bar{\beta} = s\beta$ for any $s \in \bar{s}$, all $\bar{s} \in \bar{S}_\alpha$, then $\bar{\beta}$ is a mapping of $\bar{S}_\alpha$ onto V. (γ and $\bar{\beta}$ are referred to as the mappings of T and $\bar{S}_\alpha$, respectively, onto V induced by β.)
5. Verify that the composite of two mappings is actually a mapping.

5. The Natural Numbers

Among all the systems of algebra, the most basic is certainly the natural number system, that is, the set $N = \{1, 2, 3, \ldots\}$ together with the customary operations of addition and multiplication. We shall not attempt to carry out a thorough development of this system, but shall, for the most part, merely assume it and its properties as already known. However, a complete axiomatic development of the natural number system can be given, starting, for example, with the postulate system of Peano (here stated in one of the many modified forms currently in use):

The *natural numbers* are a set N, together with a mapping (or unary operation) $\sigma: N \rightarrow N$, called the *successor mapping*, such that:

I. 1 is in N, but 1 is not in $N\sigma$.

II. σ is 1–1; that is, for any x and y in N, if $x\sigma = y\sigma$, then $x = y$.

III. If $T \subseteq N$, $1 \in T$, and $x \in T$ implies $x\sigma \in T$, then $T = N$.

This last postulate is the justification for the method of proof known as *mathematical*, or *finite, induction:* If we have a sequence $P_1, P_2, \ldots, P_n, \ldots$ of propositions which can be indexed by the natural numbers, and we show that P_1 is true and, moreover, that if P_k is true for any natural number k, then P_{k+1} is also true, then it follows that all the P_n are true.

Postulate III can be replaced by other, equivalent, postulates. Among these, the most useful is probably the so-called *second principle of induction.* This states that a set of natural numbers which contains 1 and also contains b if it contains all natural numbers $a < b$ is the set of all natural numbers. Another is the *well-ordered* property of the natural numbers, which states that every nonempty set of natural numbers has a first, or least, member. From each of these postulates we obtain useful modifications of the above method of proof by mathematical induction.

These latter forms of the inductive principle require for their statements the introduction of the notion of order into the system of natural numbers, which in turn requires that we introduce addition. We may define the operation "+" in the set N of natural numbers by:

Definition. For any x and y in N, $x + 1 = x\sigma$, and $x + (y\sigma) = (x + y)\sigma$.

It should be noted with regard to this definition that before it can be used as a definition, one must show two things: (1) an operation with the stated properties actually exists, and (2) such an operation is unique. Proof of these facts will, almost needless to say, make heavy use of Postulate III, the inductive postulate.

Similarly, we define an operation "$\cdot$" in N by:

Definition. For any x and y in N, $x \cdot 1 = x$ and $x \cdot (y\sigma) = (x \cdot y) + x$.

The relation of order, "$>$" (or "$<$"), is defined by:

Definition. For any x and y in N, $x > y$ (or $y < x$) if $x = y + z$ for some z in N.

With these definitions, and, of course, the postulates, particularly the inductive postulate, the *fundamental laws of arithmetic* can be established:

For any x, y, z in N:

$x + (y + z) = (x + y) + z$. [ASSOCIATIVITY OF ADDITION]

$x + y = y + x$. [COMMUTATIVITY OF ADDITION]

$x \cdot (y + z) = (x \cdot y) + (x \cdot z)$. [LEFT, AND RIGHT, DISTRIBUTIVITY

$(x + y) \cdot z = (x \cdot z) + (y \cdot z)$. OF MULTIPLICATION OVER ADDITION]

$x \cdot (y \cdot z) = (x \cdot y) \cdot z$. [ASSOCIATIVITY OF MULTIPLICATION]

$x \cdot y = y \cdot x$. [COMMUTATIVITY OF MULTIPLICATION]

For any x and y in N, exactly one of the following holds:

$x > y$, $x = y$, or $y > x$. [LAW OF TRICHOTOMY]

From these basic properties of the natural number system, one could then proceed to develop all of the commonly used properties of the system. Of these, we shall comment on only two more, namely, the generalized associative laws of addition and multiplication. It is a familiar and extremely useful fact that in the sum or product of any (finite) number of natural numbers, we need not use parentheses to indicate the sequence of applications of the binary operation involved, since the result is the same, regardless of the way in which we associate the numbers involved. We learn to use the principle by observing its validity where the number of terms is not large and then generalize, since to do so seems reasonable. It is perhaps worthwhile to give a proof, based on the inductive postulate of the natural numbers, for one of these results, the other being entirely similar. We shall choose to prove the generalized associative law of multiplication, and, for simplicity, shall agree to write $x \cdot y$ simply as xy.

Theorem. *For any natural number n, the product of the natural numbers x_1, $x_2, \ldots, x_n$, taken in that order, is independent of the manner in which the product is initially associated.*

PROOF. This is true for $n = 1$ or $n = 2$ as there is, then, no choice of associations. It is also true for $n = 3$, since we are now assuming that the associativity of multiplication has been proved as a consequence of the definitions and axioms of the natural numbers. We now assume that for m any natural number less than n, where $n > 3$, it is true that any product of m natural numbers, taken in a fixed order, is independent of the manner of association.

Then if we are given the product of $x_1, x_2, \ldots, x_n$, in that order but arbitrarily associated, it is clear that we may drop all but the "outside" sets of parentheses, thus obtaining, say,

$$(x_1x_2 \cdots x_r)(x_{r+1} \cdots x_n),$$

where r is some natural number less than n. We may then write

$$\begin{aligned}(x_1x_2 \cdots x_r)(x_{r+1} \cdots x_n) &= (x_1 \cdots x_r)((x_{r+1} \cdots x_{n-1})x_n)\\ &= ((x_1 \cdots x_r)(x_{r+1} \cdots x_{n-1}))x_n\\ &= (x_1 \cdots x_rx_{r+1} \cdots x_{n-1})x_n.\end{aligned}$$

(If it should happen that $r + 1 = n$, then the final desired form is obtained at once and the successive re-expressions are unnecessary.) Since an arbitrarily associated product can always be put into this final form, it follows that all such products are equal. Thus, by the second form of the inductive principle, we conclude that the generalized associative law of multiplication is valid in the system of natural numbers.

In elementary mathematics, the system of natural numbers is extended to the system of integers (positive, negative, and zero), and then to the system of rational numbers. While these systems are also of fundamental importance, we shall not go into their development here, but shall assume them and their properties as known when convenient to do so. However, the general methods by which the extensions are made will be treated subsequently.

Exercises

1. Starting with the Peano postulates and the given definitions of addition and multiplication, prove the fundamental laws of arithmetic. (*Suggestion:* Prove them in the order listed, and in proving associativity, use induction on the right member of the triple involved.)
2. Prove the *cancellation law of addition*, i.e., for any natural numbers x, y, and z, if $x + y = x + z$, then $y = z$.
3. Prove that any natural number can be expressed as a sum of 1's.
4. Prove the law of trichotomy.
5. Prove that for any natural numbers x, y, and z, $x > y$ if and only if $xz > yz$.
6. Prove that the relation of order is transitive, i.e., that if $x > y$ and $y > z$, then $x > z$.
7. Prove the *division algorithm for natural numbers:* For given natural numbers x and y exactly one of the following holds:

   (a) $x < y$.
   (b) There is a unique natural number q such that $x = qy$.
   (c) There are unique natural numbers q and r with $r < y$ and $x = qy + r$.
   (*Hint:* If neither (a) nor (b) holds, apply the well-ordering principle to the set of natural numbers of the form $x - py$, where p is a natural number.)

6. Isomorphism

In our first comments on the reasons for the development of a subject like abstract algebra, we noted that one would hope to gain a good deal of economy by simultaneously considering many superficially different systems which are formally the same. It is time we became more precise as to just what we mean by saying that two systems are formally, or abstractly, the same.

By an *algebraic structure*, or *algebraic system*, we mean a set S, together with one or more relations on S (including always the relation of equality, which enables us to tell whether two elements of S are identical or distinct), one or more operations on S, and a set of postulates giving to the elements, relations, and operations their distinctive characteristics. As noted in the last section, giving a law of external composition on S with operator set T may be considered as giving, instead, a set T of unary operations on S. We see that we could, alternatively, define an algebraic structure as a set S, together with relations, operations, and, possibly, one or more laws of external composition, each with its set of operators, and a set of postulates governing the behavior of the elements, relations, operations, and external compositions.

Definition. Two algebraic systems S and T are called *isomorphic* if there is a 1–1 correspondence between the elements, relations, and operations of S and T such that under the correspondence of elements all relations and operations are preserved.

That is, elements of S are in a relation R if and only if the corresponding elements of T are in the corresponding relation R'. If, for example, α is a binary operation in S and α' the corresponding operation in T, a and b elements of S corresponding, respectively, to a' and b' in T, then $(a, b)\alpha$ must correspond *to* $(a', b')\alpha'$. If we designate the correspondence of elements in S and T by the mapping

$$\phi: S \to T, \qquad a\phi = a',$$

this last requirement, in the case of the binary operations above, becomes

$$((a, b)\alpha)' = (a', b')\alpha'.$$

Similar requirements would, of course, hold for the preservation of unary, ternary, and other operations. The preservation of relations may be illustrated by the case of the relation of equality, which we will denote by the symbol "$=$" in both cases. Here we must have

$$a = b \quad \text{if and only if} \quad a' = b'.$$

The mapping $\phi: S \to T$ is called an *isomorphism* of S to T. If S and T are the same system, and the correspondence of relations and operations is the identity correspondence, then the isomorphism is called an *automorphism*.

As a familiar example of an isomorphism of algebraic systems, consider the set S of positive real numbers, expressed as powers of 10, with the binary operation of ordinary multiplication, and the set T of all real numbers with the binary operation of ordinary addition, and in both cases the relation of equality. The mapping $\lambda: S \to T$ defined by $10^x\lambda = x$ is then a 1–1 correspondence of the elements of S and T which preserves the relation of equality. Further, with multiplication in S corresponding to addition in T, we see that operations are also preserved, since

$$(10^x 10^y)\lambda = (10^{x+y})\lambda = x + y = 10^x\lambda + 10^y\lambda.$$

Thus λ is an isomorphism, namely, that isomorphism usually referred to as the (common) logarithm function. It is the fact that the logarithm does define an isomorphism which leads to its algebraic importance. That λ remains an isomorphism if we also consider the usual relation of *greater than* on both S and T is customarily referred to by saying that the logarithm is a *monotonically increasing function.*

It often happens that two algebraic systems are not actually isomorphic, yet retain much of the same structure.

Definition. If we have the structures S and T such that for each relation and operation in S there is a corresponding relation or operation in T (but not necessarily conversely), and we have a mapping α from S into T which preserves the relations and operations of S, then we say that α is a *homomorphism* of S *into* T. If, in addition, the mapping α is *onto* T, then it is called a *homomorphism* of S *onto* T.

Thus an isomorphism is a homomorphism which is 1–1 and onto. If S and T are the same set, then the term *endomorphism* is often used instead of homomorphism.

As an example of a homomorphism, let T be the set of all real numbers, with the customary operations, and let S be the set $T \times T$, with an operation "$*$" defined by

$$(a, b) * (c, d) = (a + c, b + d).$$

Then the mapping π defined by

$$(a, b)\pi = a$$

is a homomorphism of S onto T.

We shall see many more examples of both homomorphisms and isomorphisms throughout the rest of this book. Indeed, establishing homomorphisms and isomorphisms between various systems will be one of our principal concerns. For, from an abstract standpoint, isomorphic systems are indistinguishable, and the isomorphism is really nothing more than a "dictionary" which "translates" expressions from one "language" into another without changing the relationships they express in any way.

With these preliminaries taken care of, we are now ready to proceed with our study of some of the basic formal systems of abstract algebra, particularly those known as groups, rings, and fields. Throughout this study, we shall be interested in discovering alternative descriptions of the same situation, so that we shall often be proving theorems of the type: *Proposition P is true if and only if proposition Q is true.* Since this phrase *if and only if* will occur so frequently, it will be convenient to adopt *iff* as an abbreviation.

Exercises

1. Verify that the above mapping π from $T \times T$ to T is a homomorphism onto.

2. Prove that isomorphism is an equivalence relation on the set of all algebraic systems. Is homomorphism also an equivalence relation on this same set?

CHAPTER 2

Groups

1. Introduction

If we were to begin our study of algebraic systems with the "simplest" such systems, we should perhaps consider a set with the single relation of equality, a single unary operation, and only a very few postulates. Such a system might seem too "poor" in properties to be of much interest. However, a few moments' reflection reveals that the system of natural numbers, that most basic of all algebraic systems, is itself an example of such a system. For the successor mapping is a unary operation, and the list of postulates is certainly not very long. As anyone who has had experience with number theory or even arithmetic is well aware, this system, far from being too "poor" in properties to be of interest, is, indeed, so "rich" in properties that research into its fascinating ramifications has provided the stimulus to a great deal of mathematical development, and study of the natural number system is still an active and growing branch of mathematics.

In the customary approach to elementary arithmetic, however, we are provided at the outset with one or more binary operations, addition and multiplication, which have associativity as one of their most important properties. Of the various possible algebraic systems having a single associative operation, the type known as a *group* has been by far the most extensively studied. Also, the theory of groups is one of the oldest parts of abstract algebra, as well as one particularly rich in applications.

2. Definition and Examples of Groups

Definition. A *group* is a set $G = \{a, b, c, \ldots\}$, together with (besides a relation of equality, which we assume in any algebraic system) a binary operation $(a, b)\phi = a * b$ in G such that:

(1) $*$ is associative, i.e., for any $a, b, c \in G$, $a * (b * c) = (a * b) * c$.

(2) There is an *identity* (or *unity*) element $e \in G$ such that for all $a \in G$, $a * e = e * a = a$.

(3) For each $a \in G$, there exists an *inverse* element $a^{-1} \in G$ such that $a * a^{-1} = a^{-1} * a = e$.

If the group also satisfies:

(4) For all $a, b \in G$, $a * b = b * a$,

then the group is called *Abelian*, or *commutative*.

Definition. If a and b are any two elements of the group for which $a * b = b * a$, then a and b are said to *commute* (with each other).

To be completely precise in denoting a group, we should use some symbolism such as $(G, =, *)$ which specifies the set of elements, the equality relation, and the binary composition. However, it is customary to use the letter designation of the set of elements, in this case G, as a designation of the group, provided there is no danger of confusion as to the notation being used for the binary composition. Again, for purposes of simplicity, we shall frequently use the notation of ordinary multiplication to designate the composition in the group, writing simply ab instead of $a * b$, although it must be emphasized that by doing so we do not assume that the composition actually is ordinary multiplication, which may not even exist in most groups. Also, we shall sometimes use the notation of ordinary addition, $a * b = a + b$, for the composition.

Just as in the case of addition or multiplication in the set of natural numbers, the associative property of a composition leads at once to the generalized associative property of that composition. We shall not need to use parentheses in writing the composite of any finite number of group elements, although we shall do so in many instances for purposes of clarity.

Following familiar procedure, to indicate the composite of an element a of the group with itself n times, where n is any positive integer, we shall write, if using multiplicative notation,

$$a^n = aa \cdots a \quad (n \text{ factors } a),$$

or, if using additive notation,

$$na = a + a + \cdots + a \quad (n \text{ summands } a).$$

It is to be noted that in this latter notation, we do not mean the product n times a, since this will generally not be defined, but rather, the nth *natural multiple* of a.

Similarly, if n is any positive integer,

$$a^{-n} = (a^{-1})^n \quad \text{and} \quad -na = n(-a),$$

where $-a$ is, of course, the inverse of a in the additive notation. Still following customary notation,

$$a^0 = e \qquad \text{and} \qquad 0a = 0,$$

where e and 0 represent the identity element in the multiplicative and additive notations, respectively.

The usual rules of powers and multiples follow at once:

$$a^n a^m = a^{n+m},$$
$$(a^n)^m = a^{nm},$$
$$na + ma = (n + m)a,$$
$$n(ma) = (nm)a.$$

When using additive notation, we shall usually write

$$a + (-b) = a - b.$$

Before deriving any consequences of our definition, we give some examples of groups.

(A) The set of integers with the operation of addition. The ordinary sum of two integers is a unique integer, hence the operation is well-defined, and its associativity is a familiar fact. The identity element is 0 (zero), and the inverse of an integer a is, of course, the integer $-a$. We shall agree to designate this group by the letter Z.

(B) The set of positive rational numbers with the operation of multiplication. Again, since the product of two positive rational numbers is a unique positive rational number, our operation is well-defined, and is known to be associative. In this case, the identity is the number 1, and the inverse of p/q is q/p. (Note that since p/q must be positive, p is not zero and q/p is defined.)

It may be noted that the principal reason for the extension of the system of natural numbers to the system of all integers and the extension of the positive integers to the positive rationals is to secure the group properties for addition and multiplication, respectively.

(C) The set of all integral powers of some fixed, nonzero number, say d, with the operation of ordinary multiplication.

(D) The set of all real numbers with the operation of addition.

(E) The set of all ordered pairs (a, b) of real numbers with the operation $*$ defined by

$$(a, b) * (c, d) = (a + c, b + d).$$

That this operation is *well-defined*, i.e., that the composite is a uniquely determined element of the set, is an immediate consequence of the fact that addition is a well-defined operation on the set of all real numbers. Similarly, the associativity of addition of real numbers implies the associativity of the operation $*$, for we have

$$\begin{aligned} (a, b) * ((c, d) * (e, f)) &= (a, b) * (c + e, d + f) \\ &= (a + (c + e), b + (d + f)) \\ &= ((a + c) + e, (b + d) + f) \\ &= (a + c, b + d) * (e, f) \\ &= ((a, b) * (c, d)) * (e, f). \end{aligned}$$

The identity element is easily seen to be $(0, 0)$, and the inverse of (a, b) is $(-a, -b)$.

(F) The set consisting of a single element, e, with the operation $*$ defined by $e * e = e$.

(G) The set $V = \{e, a, b, c\}$ with a product operation defined by the following table, where the product xy is found at the intersection of the x row and the y column:

	e	a	b	c
e	e	a	b	c
a	a	e	c	b
b	b	c	e	a
c	c	b	a	e

(This tabular method of defining an operation is often useful if the number of elements involved is not large.) We leave to the reader the verification that the group postulates are satisfied. This group is known as the *four group.*

(H) Let G be the set of all ordered pairs of real numbers (a, b) such that $a^2 + b^2 > 0$, with the operation $*$ defined by

$$(a, b) * (c, d) = (ac - bd, ad + bc).$$

Exercises

1. Show that the operation $*$ defined on the set of integers by $a * b = \frac{1}{2}(a + b)$ is nonassociative.
2. Verify that the set and operation in Example (G) above defines a group.
3. Determine all possible groups of two elements, of three elements, of four elements.
4. Do the integers with the operation of subtraction constitute a group?
5. Prove that in the (multiplicative) group G, $(ab)^n = a^n b^n$ for all $a, b \in G$ and all positive integers n if and only if G is Abelian (commutative).
6. In Example (H) above, why is the restriction $a^2 + b^2 > 0$ needed?

3. Alternative Definitions of a Group

We first notice that while in our definition of a group we have not required that either the identity element or the inverse of a given element must be unique, these uniqueness properties are consequences of the definition.

Theorem 2.1. *The identity in a group G is the unique element $e \in G$ such that $e^2 = e$. Also, any element $a \in G$ has a unique inverse a^{-1}, a is the inverse of a^{-1}, and $(ab)^{-1} = b^{-1}a^{-1}$ for all $a, b \in G$.*

PROOF. If e and f are identity elements of G, then

$$e = ef = f,$$

and the identity is unique.

Certainly $e^2 = e$, and if $x^2 = x$ for any $x \in G$, then we have

$$x = xe = x(xx^{-1}) = x^2x^{-1} = xx^{-1} = e,$$

and the first sentence of the theorem is established.

Suppose that b is also an inverse of a, so that $ab = ba = e$. Then

$$a^{-1} = a^{-1}e = a^{-1}(ab) = (a^{-1}a)b = eb = b,$$

and the inverse of a is unique.

Since $aa^{-1} = a^{-1}a = e$, a is *an* inverse of a^{-1}, and, since we have just shown inverses to be unique, it follows that a is *the* inverse of a^{-1}.

Finally, since

$$(ab)(b^{-1}a^{-1}) = a(bb^{-1})a^{-1} = aea^{-1} = aa^{-1} = e,$$

we have that $b^{-1}a^{-1}$ is *an* (hence *the*) inverse of ab.

Definition. The property of being equal to its square (or double, if G is written additively) is thus a characterizing property of the identity element of a group. An element with this property, $x^2 = x$, is said to be *idempotent*.

In our defining axioms for a group, we have not been as economical as we might have been. That is, we have assumed more about the operation than was really necessary in order to obtain all the same results, as may be seen from the following:

Theorem 2.2. *A group may be equivalently defined by replacing properties* (2) *and* (3) *of section* 2 *respectively by:*

(2R) *There is an element $e \in G$ such that, for all $a \in G$, $ae = a$. (e is then called a right identity element.)*

(3R) *For each $a \in G$, there exists an element $a^{-1} \in G$ such that $aa^{-1} = e$. (a^{-1} is then called the right inverse of a.)*

or by:

(2L) *There is an element $e \in G$ such that for all $a \in G$, $ea = a$. (e is then called a left identity element.)*

(3L) *For each $a \in G$, there exists an element $a^{-1} \in G$ such that $a^{-1}a = e$. (a^{-1} is then called the left inverse of a.)*

PROOF. It is clear that (2) and (3) imply either (2R) and (3R) or (2L) and (3L). Assume that (1), (2L), and (3L) are given. Then we have

$$\begin{aligned} aa^{-1} = e(aa^{-1}) &= ((a^{-1})^{-1}a^{-1})(aa^{-1}) = (a^{-1})^{-1}((a^{-1}a)a^{-1}) \\ &= (a^{-1})^{-1}(ea^{-1}) = (a^{-1})^{-1}a^{-1} = e = a^{-1}a, \end{aligned}$$

and (3) is established. Also,

$$a = ea = (aa^{-1})a = a(a^{-1}a) = ae,$$

thus establishing (2).

Clearly, a similar argument shows that (1), (2R), and (3R) also imply (1), (2), and (3), thus completing the proof.

The properties (1), (2L), and (3L) are known as the *left-hand definition of a group*, and the properties (1), (2R), and (3R) as the *right-hand definition*. Incidentally, it can be shown by examples that the combination of properties (1), (2R), and (3L) will not define a group (nor, of course, will (1), (2L), and (3R)). In subsequent work it will usually be convenient to use one or the other of the one-sided definitions when we wish to establish that a given system is a group. Of course, when we are given a group, we shall use the full force of the standard (two-sided) definition in deriving consequences.

Still further definitions of a group are possible, of which we shall give three, in the form of theorems establishing their equivalence with those already given.

Theorem 2.3. *A group may be defined as a set G together with a binary operation, written ab, satisfying* (1) *and:*

(5) *For all $a, b \in G$, $ax = b$ and $ya = b$ have solutions in G.*

PROOF. We first show that (1) and (5) imply (1), (2L), and (3L). Let e be the solution of $ya = a$, so that $ea = a$ for some given $a \in G$. For any $b \in G$, $ax = b$ has a solution $x \in G$. Thus we have

$$eb = e(ax) = (ea)x = ax = b,$$

and e is a left identity element. Also, $ya = e$ has a solution in G, so that a has a left inverse.

Conversely, assume that (1), (2), and (3) hold. Then the equation $ax = b$ has the solution $x = a^{-1}b$, and $ya = b$ has the solution $y = ba^{-1}$, and the proof is complete.

We remark that since the inverse of an element is unique by Theorem 2.2, it follows that the solutions of the equations $ax = b$ and $ya = b$ are also unique, although we did not assume this in condition (5). It is evident that condition (5) will find much application, as the solvability of equations is a question with which algebra is often concerned. Indeed, it is this property with which one is principally concerned when the extension of the natural number system to integers is made (or from positive integers to positive rationals).

The mapping of a group G defined by $a \to a^{-1}$ is a unary operation in G. We may, if we wish, use this unary operation, together with a binary operation, to obtain another definition of a group.

Theorem 2.4. *A group may be defined as a set $G = \{a, b, c, \ldots\}$, together with a binary operation, written ab, and a unary operation, written a^{-1}, such that* (1) *holds and also:*

(6) *For all $a, b \in G$, $a^{-1}(ab) = b = (ba)a^{-1}$.*

PROOF. Clearly (1), (2), and (3) imply (1) and (6), since if (1), (2), and (3) are given, then

$$a^{-1}(ab) = (a^{-1}a)b = eb = b = be = b(aa^{-1}) = (ba)a^{-1}.$$

To show the converse, we assume (1) and (6) from which we have

$$a^{-1}a = ((a^{-1}a)b)b^{-1} = (a^{-1}a)(bb^{-1}) = a^{-1}(a(bb^{-1})) = bb^{-1}.$$

As a special case of this result, we have

$$a^{-1}a = aa^{-1} = bb^{-1} = b^{-1}b, \text{ for all } a, b \in G.$$

Call this common value e, and it remains only to show that e is a left identity element. But this follows from

$$eb = (a^{-1}a)b = a^{-1}(ab) = b, \text{ for all } b \in G.$$

In all the definitions given thus far for a group, the associative property has been explicitly assumed. This is not, or should not be, unexpected, as we have already noted the importance of this property. However, a group can be defined without explicitly assuming associativity. This we now proceed to do. That the notation employed is suggestive of division is no accident, as the operations of ordinary multiplication, division, and inversion are, of course, very closely related. As the next result shows, given either binary operation and suitable axioms, we may define the other binary operation and the unary operation.

Theorem 2.5. *A group may be defined as a set* $G = \{a, b, c, \ldots\}$, *together with a binary operation* a/b *(read, a "slash" b) such that, for all* $a, b, c \in G$*:*

(i) $a/a = b/b$. (ii) $a/(b/b) = a$. (iii) $(a/c)/(b/c) = a/b$.

PROOF. First, assume (i), (ii), and (iii). Write e for the common value of a/a for all $a \in G$, and define a unary operation in G by

$$b^{-1} = e/b, \text{ for all } b \in G.$$

We then have $e^{-1} = e/e = e$, and replacing a by c in (iii), we have

(iv) $e/(b/c) = c/b$.

This last result, together with (ii), yields

$$(b^{-1})^{-1} = e/b^{-1} = e/(e/b) = b/e = b/(b/b) = b.$$

Next, we define a binary operation of product in G by

$$ab = a/b^{-1}, \text{ for all } a, b \in G,$$

and observe that (i), (ii), (iii), and (iv) now read:

(i) $aa^{-1} = e$, (3R). (ii) $ae^{-1} = ae = a$, (2R).
(iii) $(ac^{-1})(bc^{-1})^{-1} = ab^{-1}$. (iv) $(bc^{-1})^{-1} = cb^{-1}$.

Combining (iii) and (iv), we obtain

(v) $(ac^{-1})(cb^{-1}) = ab^{-1}$.

From (ii) and (v), replacing a by x, c by y^{-1}, and b by e, we have

$$x = xe^{-1} = (xy)(y^{-1}e^{-1}) = (xy)y^{-1}.$$

Now in (v) we replace a by xy, b^{-1} by z, and c by y to obtain

(1) $(xy)z = ((xy)y^{-1})(yz) = x(yz)$.

Having established (1), (2R), and (3R), we have completed the first part of the proof.

If, conversely, we are given (1), (2), and (3), we then define a/b to be ab^{-1}, and proceed to verify (i), (ii), and (iii). The details of this verification we leave to the reader.

Before closing our discussion of alternative definitions of a group, we should mention the definitions of structures still simpler than a group, in which only a part of the postulates of a group are assumed. Among these, the simplest is the *groupoid*, which is simply a set, together with a binary operation. If we postulate that the binary operation shall be associative, we have a *semi-group*. If, on the other hand, we do not require associativity, but instead assume that the groupoid is such that the equations $ax = b$ and $ya = b$ have unique solutions for any a and b, we then have what is known as a *quasi-group*. Finally, a quasi-group which has an identity element is a *loop*. Of these structures, semi-groups and loops have both been studied a great deal in recent years, the literature on semi-groups being particularly large and rapidly growing.

Exercises

1. Carry through the argument showing that the left-hand definition of a group is equivalent to the standard definition.
2. Prove that if a group is defined in the usual way, and we let a/b be ab^{-1}, then properties (i), (ii), and (iii) are valid.
3. State and prove Theorem 2.5 using the additive notation for a group. By what "names" are properties (i), (ii), (iii), and (iv) known in an additive group? In a multiplicative group?
4. Show, by example, that (1), (2L), and (3R) do not define a group.
5. (a) Show that the natural numbers are an additive semi-group.
   (b) Show that the integers are a multiplicative semi-group.
   (c) Show that the integers do not form a loop with respect to subtraction.
   (d) Give an example of a quasi-group which is not a loop.
6. Show that a group may be defined either as
   (a) an associative quasi-group, or
   (b) a semi-group with identity and inverses for all elements.

4. Cyclic Groups

Consider the following two examples of groups:

(I) Let G be the set of all complex sixth roots of unity with the operation of ordinary multiplication. G then consists of the complex number $\theta = \frac{1}{2} + i\sqrt{3}/2$ and all its distinct powers, $G = \{\theta, \theta^2, \theta^3, \theta^4, \theta^5, \theta^6 = \theta^0 = 1\}$. Associativity and the existence of an inverse are obvious, and the inverse of θ^i, for $1 \leq i \leq 6$, is θ^{6-i}.

(J) Let G be the set of remainders of all the integers on division by 6, i.e., $G = \{0, 1, 2, 3, 4, 5\}$, and let $a * b$ be the remainder on division by 6 of the ordinary sum of a and b. The existence of an identity element and of inverses is again apparent. In this case, the verification of associativity, while intuitively evident, requires more than a wave of the hand: We first observe that $a * b = d$ is equivalent to $a + b = d + 6k$, where k is an integer (actually, k is either 0 or 1, although we shall not make use of this fact). Thus

$$(a * b) * c = d * c = f$$

is equivalent to

$$\begin{aligned}(a + b) + c = (d + 6k) + c = (d + c) + 6k = (f + 6j) + 6k \\ = f + 6(j + k) = f + 6m,\end{aligned}$$

where j, and hence $m = j + k$, is an integer. Similarly,

$$a * (b * c) = g$$

is equivalent to

$$a + (b + c) = g + 6i$$

for some integer i. Since we know $(a + b) + c = a + (b + c)$, we have

$$f + 6m = g + 6i, \qquad 0 \leq f < 6, \qquad 0 \leq g < 6.$$

Thus the difference of f and g is divisible by 6, and this is possible only if $f - g = 0$, or $f = g$. Hence, the associativity of $*$ is established.

These two groups, each of which can be readily generalized by replacing the integer 6 by any positive integer n, have a most interesting property. In each case, every element of the group is a power of some fixed element of the group. (If the group operation is written as addition, we refer to multiple instead of power of an element.) Groups with this property form an interesting and particularly simple class.

Definition. A (multiplicative) group G is *cyclic* if there is an element $a \in G$ such that for any $b \in G$ there is some integer j (positive, negative, or zero) such that $b = a^j$. Such an element a is called a *generator* of the cyclic group, and we write $G = (a)$.

It follows at once from the definition that every cyclic group is commutative (or Abelian). We also note that a cyclic group may very well have more than one element which is a generator of the group. For instance, in Example (I) above, the elements θ and θ^5 are both generators of the group. Or, again, in the additive group of all the integers, both 1 and -1 are generators. (The reader will find it instructive to develop necessary and sufficient conditions that an element of the cyclic group of nth roots of unity be a generator of this group.)

With regard to the "additive" group of remainders of the integers on division by n, the generalization of the group of Example (J), we find that the type of "addition" used here leads to an equivalence relation on the set of integers.

Definition. For arbitrary integers a, b, and n, we say that *a is congruent to b modulo n*, and write $a \equiv b \pmod{n}$, if the difference $a - b$ is a multiple of n, that is, if $a = b + kn$ for some integer k.

It is easily verified that *congruence modulo n* is an equivalence relation on the set Z of integers. For the relation of congruence modulo n is obviously reflexive and symmetric. The transitivity follows easily also: If $a = b + kn$ and $b = c + jn$ for some integers j and k, then $a = c + (j + k)n$, so that $a \equiv b \pmod{n}$ and $b \equiv c \pmod{n}$ together imply $a \equiv c \pmod{n}$.

Consider now the equivalence classes into which the relation of congruence modulo n divides the set Z, that is, the elements of the factor set $\overline{Z}_n$. These will be the sets

$$\begin{aligned}
\overline{0} &= \{0, n, 2n, \ldots, -n, -2n, \ldots\}, \\
\overline{1} &= \{1, 1 + n, 1 + 2n, \ldots, 1 - n, 1 - 2n, \ldots\}, \\
\overline{2} &= \{2, 2 + n, 2 + 2n, \ldots, 2 - n, 2 - 2n, \ldots\}, \\
&\cdots\cdots\cdots\cdots\cdots\cdots \\
\overline{n - 1} &= \{-1, -1 + n, -1 + 2n, \ldots, -1 - n, -1 - 2n, \ldots\}.
\end{aligned}$$

We may now define on $\overline{Z}_n$ a binary operation (which we shall again write as $+$, although it is certainly not ordinary addition) by

$$\overline{a} + \overline{b} = \overline{a + b},$$

where a and b are any elements of the respective sets $\overline{a}$ and $\overline{b}$ of $\overline{Z}_n$, and the sum on the right, $a + b$, is the ordinary sum of a and b. In order to show that we actually have defined an operation, i.e., that this operation is *well-defined*, we must show that the image element of the pair $(\overline{a}, \overline{b})$ is uniquely determined by $\overline{a}$ and $\overline{b}$ alone, and does not depend in any way upon the "representative" elements a of $\overline{a}$ and b of $\overline{b}$ which we happen to choose. So, suppose that c and

d are also arbitrary elements of the sets $\bar{a}$ and $\bar{b}$, respectively. We then have

$$c = a + jn, \qquad d = b + kn$$

for some integers j and k. Then

$$\begin{aligned} c + d &= (a + jn) + (b + kn) \\ &= (a + b) + (j + k)n \end{aligned}$$

by virtue of the associativity and commutativity of addition, and the distributivity of multiplication over addition for the integers. Thus, we have that

$$\overline{c + d} = \overline{a + b},$$

and our operation is well-defined, independent of the choice of representatives of the respective equivalence classes.

That this operation of *addition modulo n* is associative follows from the associativity of ordinary addition. The identity element is $\bar{0}$ and the inverse of $\bar{a}$ is $\overline{-a}$. (We leave the verification of these facts to the reader.) Thus the elements of $\bar{Z}_n$ form a group, which we call the *group of integers modulo n* and designate simply by Z_n. It should be emphasized that this group Z_n is not the same as the group of remainders on division by n, as each element of Z_n is an infinite set of integers, rather than a single integer.

Exercises

1. Prove that congruence modulo n is an equivalence relation on the set of integers.
2. Prove that the set Z_n with the given operation actually is a group.
3. Find a necessary and sufficient condition that an element of the group of nth roots of unity generates the group.

5. Transformation Groups

Suppose we have a plain square of paper lying on a table. If we were to close our eyes while someone rotated the square through any multiple of 90° (about an axis perpendicular to the plane of the table), or rotated the square through any multiple of 180° about an axis determined by two of its vertices, we would be unable to detect the change unless the vertices had been labeled in some way before the rotations were made. Clearly, if we were to label the vertices so that we could tell them apart, then any of these motions could be described as a transformation of the set of vertices. The particular transformations involved would have the interesting properties of being 1–1 and preserving adjacencies. That is, if any two vertices determine an edge of the square before the transformation, then they also determine an edge after the transformation.

In general, by a *symmetry of the square*, we shall mean any transformation of the set of its vertices which is 1–1 and preserves adjacencies. We recall that the composite of the transformations τ_1 and τ_2 is the transformation $\tau_1\tau_2$, effected by first applying τ_1 and then τ_2. Evidently, this gives a binary operation on the set of symmetries of the square, for which the associative property is almost trivial. To prove it, let τ_1, τ_2, τ_3 be any transformations and v any vertex. Then $v(\tau_1\tau_2)\tau_3 = [(v\tau_1)\tau_2]\tau_3 = v\tau_1(\tau_2\tau_3)$ and, therefore, $(\tau_1\tau_2)\tau_3 = \tau_1(\tau_2\tau_3)$. The identity transformation, or symmetry, is the transformation in which every vertex is left unchanged, and the inverse of a symmetry is clearly also a symmetry. Thus the symmetries form a group, known as the *group of symmetries of the square.* A similar group can be defined for any regular geometric figure. For irregular figures, more restrictions than those given above must be imposed upon the transformations which are to qualify as symmetries. For instance, in the case of a rectangle, only those transformations of the set of vertices which are 1–1, preserve adjacencies, and also replace each side by one of equal length, are considered to be symmetries, thus eliminating rotations by odd multiples of 90° and reflections in diagonals. In all cases, those transformations of the set of vertices of the figure which leave it *visibly unchanged* are the ones considered to be symmetries.

In order to denote a particular transformation, or symmetry, of the square, we may list first the original numbering of the vertices and then write below each vertex number the number of the vertex whose position it is mapped into by the transformation. In this notation,

$$\tau_1 = \begin{pmatrix} 1, 2, 3, 4 \\ 2, 3, 4, 1 \end{pmatrix}$$

means that the square is rotated counterclockwise through 90° by the transformation τ_1:

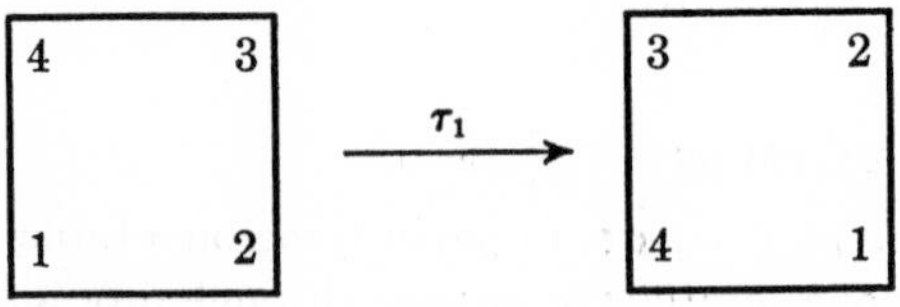

Similarly, the transformation

$$\tau_2 = \begin{pmatrix} 1, 2, 3, 4 \\ 2, 1, 4, 3 \end{pmatrix}$$

would reflect the square about a vertical axis:

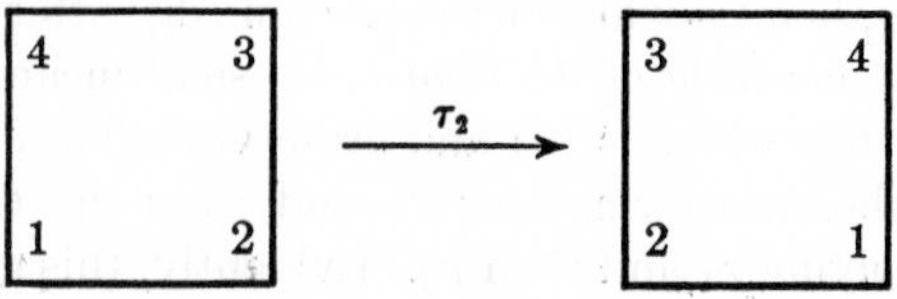

The composite, or product, of these two transformations would then be the transformation

$$\tau_1\tau_2 = \begin{pmatrix}1, 2, 3, 4\\2, 3, 4, 1\end{pmatrix}\begin{pmatrix}1, 2, 3, 4\\2, 1, 4, 3\end{pmatrix} = \begin{pmatrix}1, 2, 3, 4\\1, 4, 3, 2\end{pmatrix},$$

which is the transformation of reflection in the diagonal from lower left to upper right:

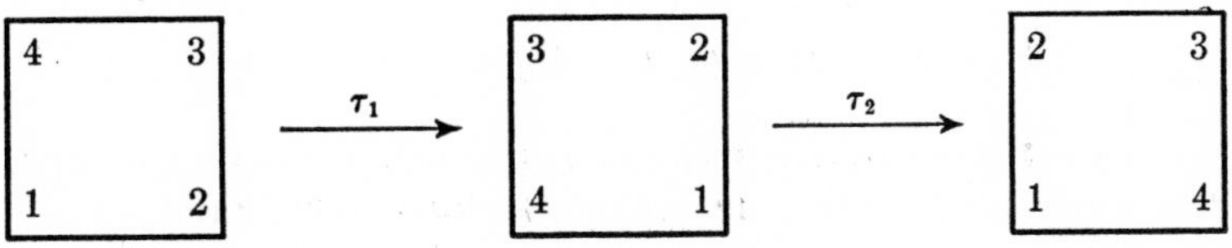

The transformation

$$\tau_2\tau_1 = \begin{pmatrix}1, 2, 3, 4\\2, 1, 4, 3\end{pmatrix}\begin{pmatrix}1, 2, 3, 4\\2, 3, 4, 1\end{pmatrix} = \begin{pmatrix}1, 2, 3, 4\\3, 2, 1, 4\end{pmatrix}$$

is then a reflection in the other diagonal:

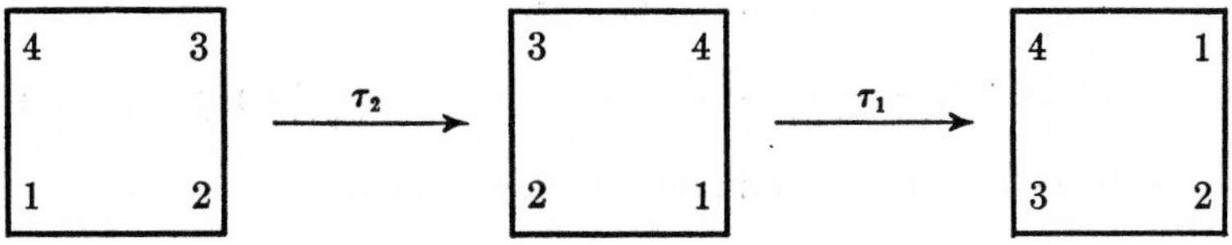

(It is thus apparent that the group of symmetries of the square is not commutative.)

These products can easily be obtained without having to "draw the pictures." For, in the product $\tau_1\tau_2$ we see that under τ_1 the vertex in the "first" position moves into the "second" position, and under τ_2 the vertex in "second" position moves into "first" position, or

$$1(\tau_1\tau_2) = (1\tau_1)\tau_2 = 2\tau_2 = 1,$$

and similarly for the other vertices. Thus we read the product by simply reading the factors successively from left to right, treating each vertex in turn.

The above notation for transformations can be shortened by simply indicating *cycles of replacements*. For example, τ_1 can be read: Vertex 1 replaces vertex 2, which replaces vertex 3, which replaces vertex 4, which replaces vertex 1. This we indicate by writing

$$\tau_1 = (1, 2, 3, 4) = (2, 3, 4, 1) = (3, 4, 1, 2) = (4, 1, 2, 3),$$

since it evidently makes no difference at what point we enter the *cycle*. In like manner, we have

$$\tau_2 = (1, 2)(3, 4) = (2, 1)(3, 4) = (1, 2)(4, 3) = (2, 1)(4, 3),$$

or, equally well,

$$\tau_2 = (3, 4)(1, 2) = (4, 3)(1, 2) = (3, 4)(2, 1) = (4, 3)(2, 1).$$

Those vertices affected by one *factor* of τ_2 are unaffected by the other, and, hence, the order in which they are written is clearly immaterial.

Determining products when the factors are written in this cycle notation is, if anything, even easier than when the factors are in the two-row notation. Again, we take some symbol, determine its image under the first factor, then the image of that under the next factor, and so on, until we have the image under the product. We then take this product image of the first chosen symbol and follow it through the product in the same manner, and so on.

For example, to find the product of

$$\tau_1\tau_2 = (1, 2, 3, 4)(1, 2)(3, 4),$$

we "read" $1 \rightarrow 2 \rightarrow 1$, so that our first cycle is simply (1).

Then, we have $2 \rightarrow 3 \rightarrow 4$ and $4 \rightarrow 1 \rightarrow 2$, so that our second cycle is (2, 4).

Finally, we have $3 \rightarrow 4 \rightarrow 3$, and our final cycle is (3).

Thus, we obtain

$$\tau_1\tau_2 = (1)(2, 4)(3).$$

We may simplify the notation still further if we agree that cycles of length one, such as (1) and (3) in $\tau_1\tau_2$, will be omitted, with the understanding that if a symbol does not appear, then it replaces itself. Thus, we write $\tau_1\tau_2 = (2, 4)$.

The reader is cautioned that notation is not standard in this matter, unfortunately. Some authors replace our word "replaces" in the cycle notation by the phrase "is replaced by." Such a change will result in reversing the procedure in "reading" a product from our left-to-right progression to a right-to-left progression. Beyond this, the notation for a product of two transformations is not standardized either, the notation $\tau_1\tau_2$ being sometimes taken to mean first apply τ_2 and then τ_1. This also results in reversing the progression in "reading" a product of cycles. Since there are, thus, four different possible combinations of notation which may be encountered, much confusion can result unless the reader is careful to ascertain just which notation is being used in any given book or article.

The symmetries of the square will doubtless have been recognized as really being nothing more than a certain set of permutations of the set of vertices. Since we shall wish to consider also permutations of an infinite set of objects, we make the following definition.

Definition. A *permutation*, π, of the set S is a 1–1 mapping of S onto S.

This leads us to another example of a group. Consider the set of all permutations of some given set S. Since permutations are mappings, we have the same meaning for the composite or product of two permutations as for the product of mappings, that is, $\pi_1\pi_2$ means the result of applying first π_1 and then π_2. We assert that, with this binary operation of product, the set of all permutations of S is a group. As before, the associativity of the operation is almost trivial, the identity permutation is the identity mapping, and the inverse of a permutation is the inverse mapping (which always exists, since a permutation is 1–1 and onto). This group is known as the *symmetric group on* S. In the case that S has n elements (where n is some positive integer), the group is also called the *symmetric group on n symbols*, and is denoted by S_n.

If we were to agree to write the first row in the two-row notation for an element of S_n in some standard order, then it could be omitted without loss of meaning. This we shall not do, however, preferring to reserve the single-row notation for indicating cycles, or cyclic permutations.

Definition. A *cycle of length n*, written $(a_1, a_2, \ldots, a_n)$, is a permutation of the form

$$\begin{pmatrix} a_1, a_2, \ldots, a_{n-1}, a_n \\ a_2, a_3, \ldots, a_n, \quad a_1 \end{pmatrix}$$

In order to compute products of permutations conveniently, it will again be desirable to write them in the cycle notation. Then products can be computed exactly as in the case of the symmetries of the square. But in order to do so, we must first prove the theorem tacitly assumed in the discussion of the group of symmetries of the square.

Theorem 2.6. *Any permutation π of a set of n symbols can be expressed as a product of disjoint cycles (i.e., cycles no two of which alter any common symbol).*

PROOF. Consider any symbol, say a_1. Let $a_1\pi = a_2$, $a_2\pi = a_3$, etc., until we first obtain $a_i\pi = a_j$ for some j such that $1 \leq j \leq i \leq n$. We must have $j = 1$ since, otherwise, a_j would be a symbol having two distinct antecedents under π, which is impossible. Hence the effect of π on the symbols $a_1, a_2, \ldots, a_i$ is the cycle $(a_1, a_2, \ldots, a_i)$. Moreover, the remaining $n - i$ symbols must be permuted among themselves by π since, if any of $a_1, a_2, \ldots, a_i$ were to be involved, we would again have a symbol with two distinct antecedents. The proof is now completed by induction on n.

As before, a cycle of length one, (a_1), may be omitted in the representation of π without loss of clarity. Also, it is clear that the order of the disjoint cycles in the representation of π is immaterial, since any pair of disjoint cycles is commutative.

Groups of permutations play a very important role in geometry. For example, consider the set of all translations of the coordinate plane, that is, mappings $\tau: R^2 \to R^2$, where R is the set of all real numbers, defined by

$$(x, y)\tau = (x', y'), \quad x' = x + t_1, \quad y' = y + t_2,$$

where t_1 and t_2 are some fixed real numbers and x, y are arbitrary in R. (The reader should verify that such a mapping τ is a permutation of R^2.)

If σ is the permutation defined by

$$(x', y')\sigma = (x'', y''), \quad x'' = x' + s_1, \quad y'' = y' + s_2$$

then, with the usual definition of the product of permutations,

$$\begin{aligned}(x, y)\tau\sigma &= ((x, y)\tau)\sigma = (x + t_1, y + t_2)\sigma \\ &= ((x + t_1) + s_1, (y + t_2) + s_2) \\ &= (x + (t_1 + s_1), y + (t_2 + s_2)).\end{aligned}$$

Thus, $\tau\sigma$ is that permutation defined by

$$(x, y)\tau\sigma = (x'', y''), \quad x'' = x + (t_1 + s_1), \quad y'' = y + (t_2 + s_2),$$

so that a product of translations is again a translation. The product is known to be associative, and the identity translation and the inverse of a given translation are apparent. Thus, this set of all translations of the coordinate plane is a group. It is also clear that we may characterize τ by the ordered pair (t_1, t_2), and write

$$\begin{aligned}&\tau \leftrightarrow (t_1, t_2), \quad \sigma \leftrightarrow (s_1, s_2), \quad \tau\sigma \leftrightarrow (t_1 + s_1, t_2 + s_2), \\ &\tau^{-1} \leftrightarrow (-t_1, -t_2),\end{aligned}$$

and the identity translation $\epsilon \leftrightarrow (0, 0)$.

The reader will doubtless think of many other groups of permutations of the plane, or of space, which are of geometric interest. Indeed, one approach to geometry is by means of the determination of the geometric properties which remain invariant under a particular group of transformations.

Exercises

1. Determine all the elements of the group of symmetries of the square, and construct its multiplication table.
2. Determine the group of symmetries of the regular pentagon.
3. How many elements are there in the group of symmetries of the regular n-gon?
4. Determine the group of symmetries of the regular tetrahedron.

5. How many elements are there in S_n, the symmetric group on n symbols?
6. Supply the inductive argument referred to in the proof of Theorem 2.6.
7. Verify that the mapping $\tau: R^2 \to R^2$ defined by $(x, y)\tau = (x + t_1, y + t_2)$ in the discussion of this section is a permutation.
8. What geometrical properties remain invariant under the group of translations of the plane?
9. Show that $\alpha^{-1}(1, 2, \ldots, r)\alpha = (1\alpha, 2\alpha, \ldots, r\alpha)$ where α is the permutation $\alpha = \begin{pmatrix} 1, & 2, & \ldots, r, & \ldots \\ 1\alpha, & 2\alpha, & \ldots, r\alpha, & \ldots \end{pmatrix}$.

6. Homomorphism and Isomorphism of Groups

For convenience, we restate our earlier definitions of isomorphism and homomorphism of algebraic systems as they apply to the particular case of groups:

Definition. A mapping $\alpha: G \to H$ of the group G into the group H is called a *homomorphism* of G *into* H if α preserves the operation of G. That is, if $*$ and $\cdot$ are the operations of G and H, respectively, then α preserves the operation of G if, for all $a, b \in G$ it is true that $(a * b)\alpha = (a\alpha) \cdot (b\alpha)$.

Definition. If, in addition, α is onto H, then α is called a *homomorphism onto* H, and H is a *homomorphic image* of G.

Definition. A homomorphism of G into G is an *endomorphism.*

Definition. If α is a 1–1 homomorphism of G onto H, then α is called an *isomorphism*, and we say that G and H are *isomorphic* and write $G \cong H$.†

Definition. An isomorphism of G onto G is called an *automorphism.*

Thus our first example of an isomorphism (section 6, Chapter 1), the common logarithm function, is an example of group isomorphism, namely, an isomorphism of the multiplicative group of positive real numbers onto the additive group of all real numbers.

As another example of the same kind, the group of Example (C) (section 2 of this chapter) is isomorphic to the group of Example (A) under the mapping $d^n \to n$ for every integer n.

Consider the group of Example (E), the group R^2 of all ordered pairs (a, b) of real numbers, with $(a, b) + (c, d) = (a + c, b + d)$, and the group R of real numbers under the operation of ordinary addition. If we define the mapping $\alpha: R^2 \to R$ by $(a, b)\alpha = a$, we may readily verify that α is a homomorphism onto. That α is onto is obvious, and, since

$$[(a, b) + (c, d)]\alpha = (a + c, b + d)\alpha = a + c = (a, b)\alpha + (c, d)\alpha,$$

α preserves the operation of R^2 and, hence, is a homomorphism. If we think

† We earlier noted that isomorphism is an equivalence relation on a set of algebraic systems; hence it is legitimate to say that G and H are isomorphic, instead of saying that G is isomorphic to H.

of R^2 as the group of vectors of the plane, that is, of arrows beginning at the origin of a rectangular coordinate system and ending at the point having coordinates (a, b), with addition performed according to the parallelogram law, we may then interpret the homomorphism α as the projection of points in the plane onto the x-axis. For this reason, such homomorphisms are often spoken of as projections.

As another example of a homomorphism, consider the mapping β of the additive group Z of the integers onto the group of the integers modulo n, Z_n, defined by $a\beta = \bar{a}$, where a is any integer, and $\bar{a}$ is the equivalence class to which a belongs modulo n. Then

$$(a + b)\beta = \overline{a + b} = \bar{a} + \bar{b} = a\beta + b\beta,$$

and β is a homomorphism. Indeed, one of the principal reasons for defining addition in Z_n as we did was to ensure that this mapping would be a homomorphism. We shall subsequently see many more examples of this kind of homomorphism.

Before giving further examples of isomorphisms, it will be convenient to introduce shorter terminology for the phrase *the number of elements in the group G.*

Definition. The *order* of a group G is the number n of elements in the group, if this number is finite. Otherwise, G is said to be of infinite order.

Theorem 2.7. *Any infinite cyclic group is isomorphic to the additive group Z of the integers. Any cyclic group of order n is isomorphic to Z_n.*

PROOF. Let G be a cyclic group with generator a, $G = (a)$. If all the powers of a are distinct, then G is infinite, and the mapping $\alpha: G \to Z$, defined by $a^i\alpha = i$, is an isomorphism. For α is evidently onto, and, since $i \neq j$ implies $a^i \neq a^j$, α is 1–1. Finally, $(a^ia^j)\alpha = (a^{i+j})\alpha = i + j = a^i\alpha + a^j\alpha$, so that α preserves the operation of G.

Suppose, on the other hand, that two different powers of the generator a are equal, say $a^i = a^j$ with $i < j$. Then, we have

$$a^ia^{-i} = a^ja^{-i}, \qquad \text{or} \qquad e = a^{j-i},$$

so that some positive power, $j - i$, of a is the identity element. Since the positive integers are well-ordered, there is a smallest positive integer, say n, such that $a^n = e$.

It then follows that $G = \{e = a^0, a, a^2, a^3, \ldots, a^{n-1}\}$. For, if i and j are now any two distinct nonnegative integers less than n, say $i < j$, then $a^i = a^j$ would imply that $a^{j-i} = e$, contrary to the minimality of n. Thus, the n elements we have listed are all distinct. Further, if k is any integer, then, by the division algorithm of the integers, we have that $k = qn + r$ for integers q and r with $0 \leq r < n$. Then

$$a^k = a^{qn+r} = (a^n)^qa^r = e^qa^r = ea^r = a^r,$$

and every element of G is one of those listed. As in the case where G is infinite, we can then verify that the mapping $\beta: G \to Z_n$, defined by $a^i\beta = \bar{i}$, is an isomorphism. β is clearly 1–1 and onto, and

$$(a^i a^j)\beta = a^{i+j}\beta = \overline{i+j} = \bar{i} + \bar{j} = a^i\beta + a^j\beta,$$

so that β preserves the operation of G.

Thus, to within an isomorphism, every cyclic group is either the additive group of integers, or else the group of integers modulo n, where n is the order of the group. In this abstract sense, we now know all the cyclic groups there are.

Having met with this success in finding a typical way in which to "represent" every possible cyclic group, we may be emboldened to ask if there is some typical form in which a completely arbitrary group can be "represented." That this can indeed be done is one of the classic results of group theory.

Theorem 2.8 (Cayley). *Every group G is isomorphic to a permutation group of its own elements.*

PROOF. For each $g \in G$, define $\theta_g: G \to G$ by $x\theta_g = xg$ for all $x \in G$. The mapping θ_g is onto since, for given $y \in G$, we have

$$(yg^{-1})\theta_g = (yg^{-1})g = y(gg^{-1}) = ye = y.$$

It is also 1–1 since, if $xg = yg$, then $(xg)g^{-1} = (yg)g^{-1}$ and $x = y$. Thus, θ_g is a permutation of the set G.

Now, let

$$G' = \{\theta_g : g \in G\}.$$

With respect to the usual composition of permutations, G' is a group. The operation is associative, θ_e is the identity element of G' since

$$x\theta_g\theta_e = (xg)\theta_e = xge = xg = x\theta_g,$$

so that $\theta_g\theta_e = \theta_g$, and, finally, $\theta_{g^{-1}} = (\theta_g)^{-1}$ since

$$x\theta_g\theta_{g^{-1}} = (xg)\theta_{g^{-1}} = xgg^{-1} = x = x\theta_e$$

for all x and g in G.

It remains to show that G is isomorphic to G', $G \cong G'$. So we define the mapping $\alpha: G \to G'$ by $g\alpha = \theta_g$ for all $g \in G$. Now, for all $x \in G$,

$$x\theta_g\theta_h = (xg)\theta_h = (xg)h = x(gh) = x\theta_{gh}$$

for all $g, h \in G$. Thus,

$$\theta_{gh} = \theta_g\theta_h \text{ and } (gh)\alpha = (g\alpha)(h\alpha).$$

That α is onto is obvious, and α is 1–1, since we have that $\theta_g = \theta_h$ implies $e\theta_g = e\theta_h$, or $g = eg = eh = h$. Thus α is the required isomorphism.

The group G' just constructed is called the *right regular representation* of G (since the elements of G are used as multipliers on the right to effect the permutations of the set G). The group of permutations of G defined by $\pi_g: x \to gx$ is a group sometimes called the *left regular representation* of G. This group is anti-isomorphic to G, that is, the mapping $g \to \pi_g$ is 1–1 and onto, but reverses the order of the operation. (This latter definition, the left regular representation, is not standard, some authors replacing the permutation π_g above by the permutation $\sigma_g: x \to g^{-1}x$ so as to obtain a group isomorphic to G.)

As an example of the right regular representation of a group, we may mention that of the *additive group of the plane*, the group R^2 of all ordered pairs of real numbers with the usual addition $(a, b) + (c, d) = (a + c, b + d)$. Here, the group of translations discussed earlier is precisely the right regular representation of R^2.

Having found a typical form in which to represent any group, namely, as a group of permutations, it might seem that we should now restrict ourselves to a study of such groups. This we shall not do, however. For one of our primary objectives is to obtain apparently different but formally equivalent descriptions of the same situation, both because this increases the applicability of our results, and because of the fact that, in seeking further developments, our intuitive and reasoning skills frequently vary with the context in which a problem is presented.

The automorphisms of a group G, that is, isomorphisms of G onto G, are often of particular interest, partly because they themselves form a group with respect to the usual composition of mappings.

Theorem 2.9. *The set of all automorphisms of a group G is a group.*

PROOF. Clearly the product of two automorphisms of G is, again, an automorphism of G, as is the identity transformation. If α is an automorphism, $x \to x\alpha$, then $\alpha^{-1}: x\alpha \to x$, the inverse mapping, is also an automorphism, as is seen from

$$\begin{aligned}(gh)\alpha^{-1} &= ((g\alpha^{-1}\alpha)(h\alpha^{-1}\alpha))\alpha^{-1} \\ &= ((g\alpha^{-1})(h\alpha^{-1}))\alpha\alpha^{-1} = (g\alpha^{-1})(h\alpha^{-1}).\end{aligned}$$

Exercises

1. Find the right regular representation of each of the following:
   (a) The group of symmetries of the square.
   (b) The symmetric group S_3.
   (c) The cyclic group Z_6.
2. Determine the set of all automorphisms of Z_{12}, and show directly that the set is a group.
3. Show that any homomorphic image of a cyclic group is cyclic.
4. Show that any homomorphic image of an Abelian group is Abelian.
5. Show that homomorphism (onto) is transitive, i.e., if $\alpha: G \to H$ and $\beta: H \to K$ are both homomorphisms (onto), then $\alpha\beta: G \to K$ is also a homomorphism (onto).
6. If G is cyclic of prime order, determine the group of all automorphisms of G.

7. Subgroups

The reader has doubtless observed that certain of the groups we have considered are actually subsets of other groups with the same binary operation. This is a frequent situation and leads to the following definition.

Definition. H is a *subgroup* of the group G if H is a nonempty subset of G which is itself a group with respect to the operation of G. G is then called a *supergroup*, or *overgroup* of H. Subgroups of G other than the trivial subgroups G itself and $E = \{e\}$ are called *proper subgroups* of G.

The groups thus far considered provide many examples of subgroups. For instance, the group of translations of the plane is a subgroup of the group of rigid motions of the plane, as is the group of rotations of the plane, or the group of reflections of the plane in lines passing through some fixed point such as the origin. It is easy to verify these facts by use of either the definition or the theorem next to be proved. Similarly, one may easily demonstrate the fact that the set R' of all ordered pairs $(a, 0)$ is a subgroup of the group R^2 of all ordered pairs of real numbers with coordinate-wise addition considered earlier. The projection homomorphism defined for the group R^2 onto the set of all real numbers can easily be modified to give a homomorphism of R^2 onto its subgroup R'.

The next theorem gives us a very convenient procedure for use in determining whether a given subset of a group is indeed a subgroup, and we shall have many occasions to use it in this way.

Theorem 2.10. *A nonempty subset H of the group G is a subgroup of G iff $ab^{-1} \in H$ for all $a, b \in H$.*

PROOF. If H is a subgroup, then by Theorem 2.1, the identity of H is the identity of G, and the inverse of b in H is the inverse of b in G. Thus if $a, b \in H$, then $b^{-1} \in H$, by group postulate (3), and $ab^{-1} \in H$, since to be a subgroup H must be closed with respect to the operation of G.

Conversely, suppose that $a, b \in H$ implies $ab^{-1} \in H$. Then

$$aa^{-1} = e \in H \text{ for some } a \in H \text{ (since } H \text{ is not empty)},$$
$$eb^{-1} = b^{-1} \in H \text{ for all } b \in H,$$
$$a(b^{-1})^{-1} = ab \in H \text{ for all } a, b \in H,$$

and the associativity of the operation in H is an immediate consequence of its associativity in G. Thus, the group axioms are all satisfied, and H is a subgroup of G.

As an illustration of the use of this theorem in proving that a subset of a group is a subgroup, we give the following theorem. This theorem gives us some basic information concerning homomorphic images of the identity element, inverses, and subgroups.

Theorem 2.11. *Let $\alpha: G \to G'$ be a homomorphism of the group G into the group G'. Then each of the following is true:*

(i) $e\alpha = e'$, *where e and e' are the respective identities of G and G'.*
(ii) $x^{-1}\alpha = (x\alpha)^{-1}$ *for all* $x \in G$.
(iii) *For any subgroup H of G, $H\alpha = \{h\alpha: h \in H\}$ is a subgroup of G'.*
(iv) *For any subgroup H' of G', $H'\alpha^{-1} = \{x: x \in G, x\alpha \in H'\}$ is a subgroup of G.*

PROOF.

(i) $(e\alpha)(e\alpha) = (ee)\alpha = e\alpha$ so that $e\alpha$ is the identity of G'.
(ii) $(x^{-1}\alpha)(x\alpha) = (x^{-1}x)\alpha = e\alpha$ so that $x^{-1}\alpha$ is the inverse of $x\alpha$.
(iii) If $g\alpha, h\alpha \in H\alpha$, then $g, h \in H$, $gh^{-1} \in H$, and, hence, $(gh^{-1})\alpha = (g\alpha)(h^{-1}\alpha) = (g\alpha)(h\alpha)^{-1} \in H\alpha$, and $H\alpha$ is a subgroup of G'.
(iv) If $x, y \in H'\alpha^{-1}$, then $x\alpha, y\alpha \in H'$ and $(xy^{-1})\alpha = (x\alpha)(y^{-1}\alpha) = (x\alpha)(y\alpha)^{-1} \in H'$, so that $xy^{-1} \in H'\alpha^{-1}$, which is, therefore, a subgroup of G.

We note that, while $(H'\alpha^{-1})\alpha = H'$ for all subgroups H' of G', $(H\alpha)\alpha^{-1}$ may properly contain the subgroup H of G. For example, if G is the additive group of integers, H is the subgroup of multiples of 3, $G' = Z_5 = \{\bar{0}, \bar{1}, \bar{2}, \bar{3}, \bar{4}\}$, and $g\alpha = \bar{g}$, then $H\alpha = G'$ while $H\alpha\alpha^{-1} = G \supset H$.

In the group S_n of permutations of a set of n symbols, say of the numbers $1, 2, \ldots, n$, one subgroup is of particular interest. In order to define this subgroup, let us consider the product

$$X = (x_1 - x_2) \cdots (x_1 - x_n)(x_2 - x_3) \cdots (x_2 - x_n) \cdots (x_{n-1} - x_n),$$

which we may write more compactly as

$$X = \Pi(x_i - x_j), \qquad 1 \le i < j \le n.$$

If we apply the permutation $\pi \in S_n$ to the subscripts in the factors of X, the result $X\pi$ will be either X itself or $-X$, since each factor will again appear, possibly in a different order, and possibly with its algebraic sign changed. For X consists of the product of all the (nonzero) differences of the elements $x_1, x_2, \ldots, x_n$, and, clearly, after any permutation of the subscripts, it will still consist of this product, with the possible changes noted.

Definition. If $X\pi = X$, then π is an *even permutation*, and if $X\pi = -X$, then π is an *odd permutation.*

Now, the inverse of an even permutation is evidently even, as is the identity permutation (that permutation which changes none of the subscripts). Also, the product of even permutations is even and, hence, they form a subgroup of S_n.

Definition. The subgroup of S_n consisting of all the even permutations is called the *alternating group* A_n.

Definition. A cycle of length two is a *transposition.*

It may be shown that another characterization of an even permutation of a finite set of symbols is that it can be written as a product of an even number of transpositions, and, similarly, an odd permutation is a product of an odd number of transpositions. We leave the proofs of these facts as an exercise.

Turning our attention once again to an arbitrary group G, we see at once that for any fixed x in G, the set of all powers of x is a subgroup of G.

Definition. The subgroup of G consisting of all powers of the element x of G is called the *subgroup generated by* x and is denoted by (x). This subgroup is necessarily cyclic, and its order is called the *order of the element* x. Thus x is of finite order n if n is the least positive integer such that $x^n = e$. If S is any set of elements of G, $S = \{a, b, c, \ldots\}$, then the subgroup H consisting of all finite products of powers of $a, b, c, \ldots$ is called the *subgroup generated by* S. It is denoted by $H = (S) = (a, b, c, \ldots)$, and S is said to *generate* H or to be a *generating system* for H.

Since a cyclic group is always Abelian, we see that a non-Abelian group will always have Abelian subgroups.

For an arbitrary element n of the additive group Z of the integers, the subgroup (n) generated by n is closely associated with the notion of congruence modulo n. For we have that $a \equiv b \pmod{n}$ iff $a - b \in (n)$. Thus the subgroup (n) defines an equivalence relation on Z, and, also, another group Z_n which is a homomorphic image of Z. As we shall see, this situation is quite general.

Theorem 2.12. *If H is a subgroup of G, then H defines a partition of G (and an equivalence relation on the set G).*

PROOF. Define a relation R on G by aRb iff $a = bh$ for some $h \in H$. Now, $(a, a) \in R$ for all $a \in G$ since $a = ae$ and $e \in H$. (H is a subgroup and, therefore, must contain the unique element e of G for which $e^2 = e$.) If aRb, then $a = bh$ for some $h \in H$, $b = ah^{-1}$ with $h^{-1} \in H$ since H is a group, and hence $(b, a) \in R$. If $(a, b) \in R$ and $(b, c) \in R$, then $a = bh$ and $b = ck$ for some $h, k \in H$ and we have $a = (ck)h = c(kh)$ with $kh \in H$, since H is a group, so that $(a, c) \in R$. We have thus shown that R is reflexive, symmetric, and transitive, and must, therefore, be an equivalence relation on (the set) G. R then induces a decomposition of G into mutually disjoint, nonempty subsets as required for a partition of G.

Definition. The relation R above is called *left congruence modulo* H. The subsets of the decomposition of G obtained in the above theorem are called the *left cosets of* G *modulo* H, and we denote a typical one of them by

$$aH = \{ah : h \in H, a \text{ fixed in } G\}.†$$

Similarly, there is a decomposition of G into *right cosets modulo* H, obtained by defining a relation T on G for which $(a, b) \in T$ iff $a = hb$ for some $h \in H$. T is then called *right congruence modulo* H.

† If G is written additively, we would write $a + H = \{a + h : h \in H, a \text{ fixed in } G\}$.

As an example of the formation of cosets modulo a subgroup, consider our earlier construction of the group Z_n, whose elements actually were the cosets of Z modulo (n), the cyclic subgroup generated by the integer n. Indeed, the notions of congruence modulo a subgroup and of cosets modulo a subgroup are generalizations of these ideas in the group of the integers.

The concept of coset enables us to obtain some interesting results relating the order of a group, the orders of its subgroups, and the orders of its elements.

Theorem 2.13. *If H is a subgroup of order m in a group G of order n, then m divides n, and every coset aH, or Ha, has the same number of elements as H.*

PROOF. Consider the mapping $\alpha: H \to aH$ defined by $h\alpha = ah$ for all $h \in H$. If $ah = ah'$, then $a^{-1}ah = a^{-1}ah'$ and $h = h'$ so that α is 1–1, and that α is onto is obvious. Hence every left coset aH has the same number m of elements as H. A similar argument holds for the right cosets.

Now since the cosets, either left or right, constitute a partition of G, it follows that the order of G must be a multiple of the order of H.

Definition. The number of cosets of the subgroup H in G (including the *identity* coset $eH = He = H$) is the *index* of H in G, written $[G:H]$. (That this number is the same for left and for right cosets follows at once from the above theorem.)

Corollary 2.13.1 (Theorem of Lagrange). *The order of a finite group G is the product of the order of any subgroup H and the index of H in G.*

Corollary 2.13.2 *The order of any element h of the finite group G divides the order of G.*

PROOF. The order of h is the order of the subgroup (h).

In the case of Z and the subgroup (n), since Z is Abelian, we have that, for every $a \in Z$, the left coset for a and the right coset for a are the same, and we are also able to construct a group from the set of cosets. For a non-Abelian group, neither of these results is generally true, except for subgroups of the type called normal.

Exercises

1. Prove that a permutation π of a finite set is even iff π is a product of an even number of transpositions.
2. Prove that every Abelian group of order six is isomorphic to Z_6.
3. Show that any subgroup of a cyclic group is cyclic.
4. Show that every group of prime order is cyclic.
5. Determine (to within an isomorphism) all possible groups of order 4; of order 6.
6. Show that if H and K are subgroups of G, $G \supseteq H \supseteq K$, then the index of K in G is the product of the index of K in H, and the index of H in G, $[G:K] = [G:H][H:K]$.
7. If G is of finite order n and $g \in G$, show that $g^n = e$.
8. Find both the right and left coset decompositions of S_3 determined by $H = ((1, 2))$, i.e., the subgroup H generated by the transposition $(1, 2)$. Do the left cosets of H form a group with respect to the usual multiplication of cosets?

9. Let G be an Abelian group containing elements x and y of order p and q, respectively, with p and q distinct primes. Show that G contains an element of order pq. Also show, by examples, that this result is false if either G is not Abelian or p and q are not distinct.
10. A group G is said to satisfy the *descending chain condition* if every properly descending chain of subgroups $H_1 \supset H_2 \supset H_3 \supset \cdots$ is necessarily finite in length. Show that in such a group every element must have finite order.
11. A set S of elements of the group G which generates G and is such that G is generated by no set having fewer elements than S, is called a minimal generating set for G. Find a minimal generating set for the group of symmetries of the square; for the group S_4.
12. By showing that A_4, of order $4!/2 = 12$, has no subgroup of order 6, show that the converse of Lagrange's Theorem is false.
13. Prove (by induction on n) that every group of order p^n, p a prime, must contain a subgroup of order p.

8. Normal Subgroups

Definition. The subgroup H of G is *normal* in G if $aha^{-1} \in H$ for all $a \in G$ and all $h \in H$ (or, equivalently, if $b^{-1}hb \in H$ for all $b \in G$, $h \in H$). The group G is *simple* if its only normal subgroups are G itself and the identity subgroup $E = (e)$.

Thus every subgroup of an Abelian group is normal, since we then have $aha^{-1} = aa^{-1}h = eh = h$. We shall give some alternative characterizations of the property of normality of a subgroup, but first we prove the following:

Theorem 2.14. *For any subgroup H of G and any element a of G, the set $aHa^{-1} = \{aha^{-1} : h \in H\}$ is a subgroup of G isomorphic to H, $H \cong aHa^{-1}$.*

PROOF. From Theorem 2.10, we know that aHa^{-1} is a subgroup if

$$(aha^{-1})(aka^{-1})^{-1} \in aHa^{-1}$$

for any $h, k \in H$. But this follows at once from

$$(aha^{-1})(aka^{-1})^{-1} = (ah)(a^{-1}a)(k^{-1}a^{-1}) = a(hk^{-1})a^{-1},$$

which is in aHa^{-1}, since hk^{-1} is in the subgroup H. The mapping $h \rightarrow aha^{-1}$ can be readily shown to be 1–1, onto, and product-preserving, and is, thus, the desired isomorphism.

If in the above theorem we take $G = H$, we see that the mapping $g \rightarrow aga^{-1}$, all $g \in G$, and some fixed $a \in G$, defines an automorphism of G.

Definition. For H a subgroup of G and $a \in G$, aHa^{-1} is called a *conjugate subgroup* of H; the isomorphic mapping of H, $h \rightarrow aha^{-1}$, is called *conjugation by a*; and the elements h and aha^{-1} are said to be *conjugate*. Also the automorphism $G \rightarrow G$ given by conjugation by any element $a \in G$ is called an *inner automorphism* of G, and all other automorphisms of G are called *outer*.

We note that the relation xRy iff x is a conjugate of y is an equivalence relation on G, leaving the proof to the reader.

With the aid of these definitions, we may state the following:

Theorem 2.15. *The subgroup H of G is normal iff H is equal to all its conjugates (i.e., H is* self-conjugate) *and iff H is invariant (as a group, not elementwise) under all the inner automorphisms of G. (For this reason, a normal subgroup is often called an* invariant *subgroup.)*

PROOF. The proof is immediate from the above theorem and definitions, and the remark that if aHa^{-1} is contained in H for all $a \in G$, then given $h \in H$ we have $a^{-1}ha \in H$ and $a(a^{-1}ha)a^{-1} = h \in aHa^{-1}$.

Theorem 2.16. *The subgroup H of G is normal in G iff the left coset aH is also the right coset Ha for every $a \in G$.*

PROOF. Consider the left coset $aH = \{ah: h \in H\}$. For any $ah \in aH$ we have

$$ah = (ah)(a^{-1}a) = (aha^{-1})a = ka$$

for some $k \in H$, since H is normal. Thus, any element in the left coset aH is also in the right coset Ha. Similarly, Ha is contained in aH and the desired equality follows.

Conversely, if $aH = Ha$ for all $a \in G$, then $aHa^{-1} = H$ and H is normal in G.

Definition. If H is a normal subgroup of G, $\bar{a}$ will be often used to denote the coset $aH = Ha$, and G/H will denote the *set of all cosets of H*.

We remark that it can be shown that the set of inner automorphisms of a group G is a normal subgroup of the group of all automorphisms of G, the demonstration being left as an exercise.

As an example of the application of Theorem 2.16, we can show that the subgroup K of rotations of the group G of symmetries of the square is normal. For a little calculation shows that G is of order eight and K is of order four. Thus in the partition of G into cosets, either left or right, modulo K, there will be exactly two, one being K itself, and the other all remaining elements of G. Hence each left coset is also a right coset for the same element and K is normal.

The concept of normal subgroup thus enables us to generalize one of the properties of the subgroup (n) of the group Z of the integers, namely that of having the left coset aK also be the right coset Ka. The additional property of having the set of cosets form a group with respect to an operation naturally induced by that of the whole group can also be generalized by the use of normality, as we shall see in the next section. First, however, we wish to consider two ways of combining subgroups to obtain other subgroups.

Definition. If H and K are subgroups of the group G, then the *intersection of H and K*, $H \cap K$, is the intersection of the sets H and K, and the *product of H and K* (in that order) is the set $HK = \{hk: h \in H, k \in K\}$. (If G is written additively, we of course write $H + K$ instead of HK.)

For example, in the group Z of integers, we have $(2) + (3) = Z$ and $(2) \cap (3) = (6)$. Or, in the group S_n of all permutations of a set of n elements, we have, for the subgroups A_n of all even permutations and $((i, j))$, the two-element subgroup generated by the arbitrary transposition (i, j), that $A_n \cap ((i, j)) = (e)$, the identity subgroup, and $A_n((i, j)) = S_n$. (We leave the proof of these statements to the reader.)

Theorem 2.17. *For arbitrary subgroups H and K of G, $H \cap K$ is also a subgroup of G. If H is normal in G, then $H \cap K$ is normal in K (but not necessarily in G). If both H and K are normal in G, so is $H \cap K$.*

PROOF. If $x, y \in H \cap K$, then $x \in H$, $y \in H$, and, similarly, $x \in K$, $y \in K$. Hence, $xy^{-1} \in H$ and $xy^{-1} \in K$, $xy^{-1} \in H \cap K$ and $H \cap K$ is a subgroup.

If H is normal and $x \in H \cap K$, $k \in K$, then we have $kxk^{-1} \in H \cap K$ and $H \cap K$ is normal in K.

Finally, if both H and K are normal, then, for $g \in G$, $x \in H \cap K$, we have $gxg^{-1} \in H$ by the normality of H, and, similarly, $gxg^{-1} \in K$. Thus, $gxg^{-1} \in H \cap K$, which is then normal in G.

We note that an easy extension of the above argument shows that the intersection of any set of subgroups is a subgroup, and leave the proof as an exercise.

Theorem 2.18. *For subgroups H and K of G, the set HK is a subgroup of G iff $HK = KH$. This condition is satisfied if either H or K is normal in G, and if both H and K are normal in G, then so is HK.*

PROOF. To show that HK is a group, we must show that

$$d = (hk)(h'k')^{-1} \in HK$$

for any $h, h' \in H$ and any $k, k' \in K$.

Now, $d = h(kk'^{-1})h'^{-1} = hk_1h'^{-1}$ for some $k_1 \in K$, since K is a group. If $HK = KH$, then $k_1h'^{-1} = h_1k_2$ for some $h_1 \in H$ and some $k_2 \in K$,

$$d = hh_1k_2 = h_2k_2 \qquad \text{for some } h_2 \in H.$$

Thus, $HK = KH$ implies that HK is a subgroup.

Conversely, suppose that HK is a subgroup. Then

$$\begin{aligned} HK &= \{hk: h \in H, k \in K\} \\ &= \{(k^{-1}h^{-1})^{-1}: h \in H, k \in K\}, \text{ since } hk = (k^{-1}h^{-1})^{-1}, \\ &= \{k^{-1}h^{-1}: h \in H, k \in K\}, \text{ since } HK \text{ is a group}, \\ &= \{kh: h \in H, k \in K\} = KH, \text{ since } K \text{ and } H \text{ are groups.} \end{aligned}$$

If H is normal, then $kH = Hk$ for every $k \in K$ (actually, $gH = Hg$ for every $g \in G$) and hence $KH = HK$. Similarly, if K is normal, then $KH = HK$.

If both H and K are normal in G, then, for any $g \in G$, $h \in H$ and $k \in K$, we have $g(hk)g^{-1} = (ghg^{-1})(gkg^{-1}) = h'k'$ for some $h' \in H$ and some $k' \in K$. Thus, HK is invariant under all inner automorphisms of G and is normal in G.

As examples of the content of the last two theorems, consider the group S_4 of all permutations of the set $\{1, 2, 3, 4\}$ and its subgroups A_4 (of all even permutations) and G (of the symmetries of the square). In the latter subgroup, let us use the notation:

$$\begin{aligned} r &= (1, 2, 3, 4), \text{ a rotation (counterclockwise) of } 90°, \\ r^2 &= (1, 3)(2, 4), \quad r^3 = (1, 4, 3, 2), \quad r^4 = e, \\ v &= (1, 2)(3, 4), \text{ a reflection in a vertical axis,} \\ h &= (1, 4)(2, 3), \text{ a reflection in a horizontal axis,} \\ d &= (1, 3), \text{ a reflection in the diagonal from upper left to lower right,} \\ b &= (2, 4), \text{ a reflection in the diagonal from upper right to lower left.} \end{aligned}$$

The elements of G are then e, r, r^2, r^3, v, h, d and b, and we give below the multiplication table for G, where, as usual, the left factor appears in the left-hand column and the right factor in the upper row:

	e	r	r^2	r^3	v	h	d	b
e	e	r	r^2	r^3	v	h	d	b
r	r	r^2	r^3	e	b	d	v	h
r^2	r^2	r^3	e	r	h	v	b	d
r^3	r^3	e	r	r^2	d	b	h	v
v	v	d	h	b	e	r^2	r	r^3
h	h	b	v	d	r^2	e	r^3	r
d	d	h	b	v	r^3	r	e	r^2
b	b	v	d	h	r	r^3	r^2	e

We then find that G has the following subgroups:

$$\begin{aligned} R &= (r) = \{e, r, r^2, r^3\}, \text{ normal in } G, \\ R' &= (r^2, v) = \{e, r^2, v, h\}, \text{ normal in } G, \\ R'' &= (r^2, d) = \{e, r^2, d, b\}, \text{ normal in } G, \\ T &= (r^2) = \{e, r^2\}, \text{ normal in } G, \text{ hence also in } R, R', \text{ and } R'', \\ H &= (h) = \{e, h\}, \text{ normal in } R', \text{ but not in } G, \\ V &= (v) = \{e, v\}, \text{ normal in } R', \text{ but not in } G, \\ D &= (d) = \{e, d\}, \text{ normal in } R'', \text{ but not in } G, \\ B &= (b) = \{e, b\}, \text{ normal in } R'', \text{ but not in } G, \end{aligned}$$

and, of course, the two improper subgroups G and $E = (e)$.

Since we have that A_4 is normal in S_4, we have, by Theorem 2.17, that $A_4 \cap G$ is normal in G. Examining the elements of G, we see that the ones which are even permutations are precisely those of the subgroup R', which is indeed normal in G. Since R is a normal subgroup of G, Theorem 2.18 asserts that HR is a subgroup and $HR = RH$. Actual computation verifies this, since we see that $HR = RH = G$. If we consider the product HB, however, since neither H nor B is normal, even in G, the theorem asserts nothing about the product. And we find that $HB = \{e, h, b, r^3\}$, which is not a subgroup. However, one must not assume it will always be the case that when the theorem fails to assert a result, then the result does not hold, as we may see by considering the product HV. Here neither factor is normal in G, yet we find that $HV = VH = R'$, which is not only a subgroup but normal in G as well.

Exercises

1. Prove that for any group G and subgroup H, if H is of index two, then H is normal.
2. Show that for any group G, the set of all inner automorphisms of G is a normal subgroup of the group of all automorphisms of G.
3. Determine the group of inner automorphisms of the group of symmetries of the square.
4. Let H and K be subgroups of G. Show that $G \supseteq HK \supseteq H \supseteq H \cap K$ and $G \supseteq KH \supseteq H \supseteq H \cap K$.
5. Show, by example, that *is a normal subgroup of* is not a transitive relation on groups, i.e., we may have H a normal subgroup of K and K a normal subgroup of L, and yet H not a normal subgroup of L.
6. If $n \geq 3$, show that every element of A_n is a product of the $n - 2$ three-cycles $(1, 2, 3)$, $(1, 2, 4)$, ..., $(1, 2, n)$ by showing that every even permutation is a product of three-cycles (e.g., $(1, 2)(1, 3) = (1, 2, 3)$ and $(1, 2)(3, 4) = (1, 3, 4)(1, 3, 2)$), and, then, using the result of Exercise 9, section 5.
7. If $n \geq 3$ and K is a normal subgroup of A_n such that K contains a three-cycle, show that $K = A_n$.
8. If $n \geq 5$, show that every normal subgroup of A_n, other than E, must contain a three-cycle, and hence A_n is simple. (*Hint:* If K is such a subgroup, show that the form of a nonidentity element τ of K, leaving fixed as many of $1, 2, \ldots, n$ as possible, must be $\tau = (1, 2, 3, \ldots)(\ldots) \ldots$, $\tau = (1, 2)(3, 4) \ldots$, or $\tau = (1, 2, 3)$. In either of the first two cases, let $\sigma = (3, 4, 5)^{-1}\tau(3, 4, 5)$ and show that $\tau^{-1}\sigma \neq e$ and leaves more of $1, 2, \ldots, n$ fixed than does τ, hence τ must be a three-cycle.)
9. Let H and K be normal subgroups of G such that $H \cap K = (e)$. Show that $hk = kh$ for all $h \in H$, $k \in K$. (*Hint:* Consider the elements of the form $hkh^{-1}k^{-1}$, $h \in H$, $k \in K$.)
10. Show that xRy iff x is conjugate to y is an equivalence relation on a group G, and determine the conjugate classes of S_4.
11. Show that a subgroup N of G is normal iff N is a union of conjugate classes of G, including always the conjugate class $\{e\}$ of the identity.
12. Determine the conjugate classes of A_5 and thus show that A_5 is simple, i.e., has no proper normal subgroups.
13. Show that the intersection H of any set H_i, $i \in I$, of subgroups of G is a subgroup of G.

9. Factor Groups

In general, the set of left cosets of the subgroup H of G is not itself a group. However, in the event that H is normal, which is always the case if G is Abelian, then a binary operation can be introduced into G/H in a natural way, with the result that G/H becomes a group.

Theorem 2.19. *If K is a normal subgroup of G, then G/K is also a group with respect to the operation $(aK)(bK) = (ab)K$.*

PROOF. As in the case of the group Z_n, we must first show that this is, indeed, a well-defined binary operation. To do so, we must prove that if $c \in aK$ and $d \in bK$, then $(aK)(bK) = (cd)K$, so that the product $(aK)(bK)$ is independent of the elements of G chosen as "representatives" of the respective cosets aK and bK. So, suppose that $c = ak$, $d = bh$ for some $k, h \in K$. Then

$$cd = (ak)(bh) = a(bb^{-1})k(bh) = (ab)(b^{-1}kb)h = (ab)(jh)$$

for some $j = b^{-1}kb \in K$, since K is normal. Since K is a group, $jh \in K$ and we have $cd \in (ab)K$, whence $(cd)K = (ab)K$, since distinct cosets are disjoint.

The associativity of the operation on the cosets follows easily from the associativity of the operation in G. The identity element in G/K is $eK = K$, and the inverse of aK is $a^{-1}K$ since

$$(aK)(eK) = (ae)K = aK \qquad \text{and} \qquad (aK)(a^{-1}K) = (aa^{-1})K = eK.$$

Thus G/K is a group, as asserted.

In comparing this argument with that given to show that Z_n is a group, the reader should note the parallel form of the arguments, with the exception that in this more general case the property of normality replaces the more special one of commutativity in Z.

Definition. For K a normal subgroup of G, the group G/K just obtained is called the *factor group* of G modulo K, or, sometimes, the *quotient group* of G modulo K.

In order to become familiar with the content of this last definition, the reader should examine the examples of groups which we have considered thus far, with the object of finding normal subgroups and then determining the resulting factor groups. For example, the set of multiples of 12 is a normal subgroup of the additive group of integers, having as factor group the set of cosets $\overline{0}$, $\overline{1}$, $\overline{2}$, $\overline{3}$, $\overline{4}$, $\overline{5}$, $\overline{6}$, $\overline{7}$, $\overline{8}$, $\overline{9}$, $\overline{10}$, $\overline{11}$, where, of course, $\overline{a} = a + (12)$. The table of addition for these elements can be easily constructed if we observe that the result of removing the overlining and replacing 0 by 12 is nothing more than addition on a clock. Similarly, the additive arithmetic of days of the week is what one obtains if one considers the normal subgroup of multiples of seven in the additive group of the integers. In this latter instance, distinctive "names" for the cosets have already been provided, i.e., $\overline{0}$ = Sunday, $\overline{1}$ = Monday, ..., $\overline{6}$ = Saturday. Other examples in our reckoning of time come readily to mind.

Having seen earlier the close correspondence between subgroups and equivalence relations on the elements of a group, we now turn our attention to normal subgroups. Here, we find that each normal subgroup of a group G determines in a natural way a homomorphism of G, and that every homomorphism of G determines a normal subgroup of G, called the kernel of the homomorphism.

Definition. The *kernel* of the homomorphism $\alpha: G \to H$ of the group G into the group H is the set

$$K = \{g: g \in G, g\alpha = e\alpha = e', \text{the identity of } H\}.$$

Thus the kernel of a homomorphism is the set of elements having the identity element as image.

For example, in the homomorphism of Z onto Z_n given by $a\beta = \bar{a}$, it is evident that the kernel of β is (n), the subgroup of Z generated by n. Thus we have in this case that $Z/(n) = Z\beta$. While we cannot expect such an equality to always hold, the next theorem shows that we do obtain the next best thing, namely, an isomorphism between G/K and the homomorphic image $G\alpha$.

Theorem 2.20 (Fundamental Homomorphism Theorem). *Every homomorphism $\alpha: G \to G\alpha = H$ of a group G onto a group H determines a partition of G for which the equivalence class of the identity is the kernel K of α. K is a normal subgroup of G, and there is a unique isomorphism $\bar{\alpha}$ of G/K onto H. Conversely, if K is any normal subgroup of G, then the mapping β: $G \to G/K$ defined by $a\beta = \bar{a} = aK$ is a homomorphism of G onto G/K. If K is also the kernel of α, then $\alpha = \beta\bar{\alpha}$.*

PROOF. For a given homomorphism α of G onto H with kernel K, we define a relation R on G by $(a, b) \in R$ iff $a\alpha = b\alpha$. R is then an equivalence relation on G, and so determines a partition of G into equivalence classes. The equivalence class of the identity e of G consists of all $a \in G$ such that $a\alpha = e\alpha = e'$, the identity of H. Thus this equivalence class is the kernel K of α. Now, if $a\alpha = b\alpha = e'$, then

$$(ab^{-1})\alpha = (a\alpha)(b^{-1}\alpha) = (a\alpha)(b\alpha)^{-1} = e'e'^{-1} = e',$$

and K is a subgroup of G. Moreover, for any $g \in G$ and $a \in K$,

$$(gag^{-1})\alpha = (g\alpha)(a\alpha)(g^{-1}\alpha) = (g\alpha)e'(g^{-1}\alpha) = (gg^{-1})\alpha = e\alpha,$$

and gag^{-1} is in K so that K is normal, and we may form the factor group G/K of cosets of G modulo K.

Now let $\bar{\alpha}: G/K \to H$ be defined by $\bar{a}\,\bar{\alpha} = a\alpha$, where, of course, $\bar{a} = aK = Ka$. For any $a, b \in \bar{a}$, we have $a = bk$ for some $k \in K$; hence

$$a\alpha = (bk)\alpha = (b\alpha)(k\alpha) = (b\alpha)e' = b\alpha,$$

so that $\bar{\alpha}$ is well-defined. $\bar{\alpha}$ is also onto since, for any $x \in H$, we have $x = a\alpha$ for some $a \in G$ since α is onto; hence $x = \bar{a}\,\bar{\alpha}$. If $\bar{a}\,\bar{\alpha} = \bar{b}\,\bar{\alpha}$, then, for any

$a \in \bar{a}$ and $b \in \bar{b}$, we have $a\alpha = b\alpha$; hence,

$$(b^{-1}a)\alpha = (b^{-1}\alpha)(a\alpha) = (b\alpha)^{-1}(a\alpha) = (a\alpha)^{-1}(a\alpha) = e',$$

whence

$$b^{-1}a \in K \text{ or } a \in bK \text{ and } \bar{a} = \bar{b}.$$

Thus $\bar{\alpha}$ is 1–1. Finally,

$$(\bar{a}\,\bar{b})\bar{\alpha} = (\overline{ab})\bar{\alpha} = (ab)\alpha = (a\alpha)(b\alpha) = (\bar{a}\,\bar{\alpha})(\bar{b}\,\bar{\alpha}),$$

so that $\bar{\alpha}$ is a homomorphism, hence also an isomorphism.

For any normal subgroup K of G, if $\beta\colon G \to G/K$ is given by $a\beta = \bar{a} = aK$, then β is clearly onto, and is a homomorphism, since $(ab)\beta = \overline{ab} = \bar{a}\,\bar{b} = (a\beta)(b\beta)$. It then follows from

$$a\alpha = \bar{a}\,\bar{\alpha} = (aK)\bar{\alpha} = (a\beta)\bar{\alpha} = a(\beta\bar{\alpha})$$

for all $a \in G$ that $\alpha = \beta\bar{\alpha}$. If also $\alpha = \beta\phi$ for some map $\phi\colon G/K \to H$, then

$$a\alpha = a(\beta\phi) = (a\beta)\phi = \bar{a}\phi$$

for all $a \in G$, so that $\phi = \bar{\alpha}$ and $\bar{\alpha}$ is unique.

Definition. The isomorphism $\bar{\alpha}$ constructed in the proof of Theorem 2.20 is called the *natural isomorphism* of G/K onto H. Similarly, the homomorphism β of the same proof is called the *natural homomorphism* of G onto G/K.

As illustrations of this last result, consider again the group G of symmetries of the square, with the notation for the elements of G and its subgroups as given in the last section. In the factor group G/R, we have the cosets

$$\begin{aligned} \{e, r, r^2, r^3\} &= R = eR = rR = r^2R = r^3R \\ &= Re = Rr = Rr^2 = Rr^3, \\ \{v, h, d, b\} &= vR = hR = dR = bR \\ &= Rv = Rh = Rd = Rb, \end{aligned}$$

with multiplication in G/R given by:

	R	vR
R	R	vR
vR	vR	R

As elements of the factor group G/T, we have the cosets

$$\begin{aligned}\{e, r^2\} &= T = eT = r^2T = Te = Tr^2,\\ \{r, r^3\} &= rT = r^3T = Tr = Tr^3,\\ \{v, h\} &= vT = hT = Tv = Th,\\ \{d, b\} &= dT = bT = Td = Tb,\end{aligned}$$

with the multiplication table:

	T	rT	vT	dT
T	T	rT	vT	dT
rT	rT	T	dT	vT
vT	vT	dT	T	rT
dT	dT	vT	rT	T

We observe that G/R has no proper subgroups, while G/T has the proper subgroups $\{T, rT\}$, $\{T, vT\}$, and $\{T, dT\}$, all of which are, of course, normal in G/T. We could then construct the factor groups

$$(G/T)/\{T, rT\}, \qquad (G/T)/\{T, vT\}, \qquad \text{and} \qquad (G/T)/\{T, dT\},$$

each of which would be a group of two elements.

Similarly, we could consider the factor groups G/R', G/R'', R'/T, R'/H, R'/V, R''/T, R''/D and R''/B.

Now, suppose we have a homomorphism α of G onto some group L. Then, one of the following must be the case:

(i) L is isomorphic to G and α has kernel E.

(ii) L is isomorphic to G/T and α has kernel T.

(iii) L is isomorphic to G/R and α has kernel R.

(iii′) L is isomorphic to G/R' and α has kernel R'.

(iii″) L is isomorphic to G/R'' and α has kernel R''.

(iv) L is isomorphic to G/G and α has kernel G.

Cases (iii), (iii′), and (iii″) are equivalent as far as the structure of L is concerned, L being in each case cyclic of order two, yet the cases are different in so far as the kernel of the homomorphism is concerned.

As another example, consider the group R^2 of all ordered pairs of real numbers with the usual addition, and denote the additive group of the real numbers by R. Let $\alpha: R^2 \to R$ be defined by $(a, b)\alpha = a$. Then α is clearly a homomorphism onto. Since $(a, b)\alpha = 0$ iff $a = 0$, we have that $K = \{(0, b) : b \in R\}$ is the kernel of α. The elements of R^2/K are the cosets $\bar{a} = \{(a, b) : a \text{ fixed}, b \text{ arbitrary in } R\}$, since $(a, b)\alpha = (a, c)\alpha = a$ for all $b, c \in R$. We then have that $R^2/K \cong R$ under the mapping $\bar{a} \to a$.

We observe that $H = \{(a, 0): a \in R\}$ is a subgroup of R^2, and is isomorphic to R under the mapping α_H (the mapping α restricted to H). This raises the question as to when a group G with normal subgroup K will contain a subgroup N isomorphic to the factor group G/K. We shall postpone consideration of this question until later, for the present focusing our attention on the above isomorphism of R and H. Since these two groups are isomorphic, they are abstractly identical and in consequence may, if we wish, be identified. In fact, this sort of identification is exactly what we mean when we say that the real numbers are a subset of the complex numbers, for it is easily seen that our group R^2 is isomorphic to the additive group of complex numbers under the correspondence $(a, b) \to a + b\sqrt{-1}$. The reader will doubtless think of other examples of this process of identification of isomorphic structures, and we shall have several occasions to make use of it in what follows.

As a final example, consider the cyclic group G of order six generated by an element x, $G = \{x, x^2, x^3, x^4, x^5, x^6 = e\}$. The subgroups of G are then G itself, $H = \{e, x^2, x^4\} = (x^2)$, $K = (x^3)$ and $E = (e)$, all of which are normal, since G is Abelian. It is clear that G/G is isomorphic to E, G/H to K, G/K to H, and G/E to G. This again raises the question of the preceding paragraph, to which we shall return later on.

Exercises

1. Let G be the group consisting of all finite products of powers of the elements x and y, where x is of order two, y is of order three, and $xy^2 = yx$. Determine the multiplication table of G, all subgroups of G, and all factor groups of G.

2. Let α: $R \to C'$ be the mapping of the group of all real numbers under addition into the group of all nonzero complex numbers under multiplication, defined by $x\alpha = e^{2\pi i x}$. Show that α is a homomorphism, determine the image group $R\alpha$, the kernel K of α, and exhibit the isomorphism of R/K and $R\alpha$.

3. Let Z^2 be the group of all ordered pairs of integers with the usual vector addition, and let H be the cyclic subgroup generated by (1, 1). Determine the cosets of Z^2 modulo H, and show that the factor group Z^2/H is isomorphic to H. Interpret these results geometrically.

4. Let C' be the multiplicative group of nonzero complex numbers, and let K be the set of all complex numbers of modulus 1. Show that K is a normal subgroup of C', determine the cosets of C' modulo K, and exhibit the natural homomorphism of C' onto C'/K. Again, interpret these results geometrically.

5. For any group G, $C = \{x: x \in G, xy = yx \text{ for all } y \in G\}$ is called the *center* of G. Prove that C is a normal subgroup of G, and compute the center of G/C for the case where G is the group of symmetries of the square.

6. For any group G, elements of the form $xyx^{-1}y^{-1}$ are called *commutators*. Prove that the set of all (finite) products of commutators is a normal subgroup K of G, and that G/K is Abelian, i.e., the center of G/K is G/K.

10. Groups with Operators

The results which we have obtained thus far, as well as those we shall subsequently obtain in our study of groups can be considerably extended in their generality by the use of the concept of a group with operators.

Definition. A *group with operator set* is a group G, together with a set $\mathfrak{O}$, called the *set of operators*, and a mapping from the set $G \times \mathfrak{O}$ into G, $(x, m) \to xm$, such that for any $x, y \in G$ and any $m \in \mathfrak{O}$

$$(xy)m = (xm)(ym),$$

or, if G is written in the additive notation,

$$(x + y)m = xm + ym.$$

Instead of *group G with operator set $\mathfrak{O}$*, we shall usually use the expression *$\mathfrak{O}$-group G*.

As a simple example, consider the set R^3 of all triples $v = (a, b, c)$ of real numbers. These form a group, the group of vectors in three-dimensional space, under the addition defined by

$$(a, b, c) + (a', b', c') = (a + a', b + b', c + c').$$

Now, let the set of operators be the set R of all real numbers m and define

$$vm = (a, b, c)m = (am, bm, cm),$$

an operation usually called *scalar multiplication* by m. The rule $(u + v)m = um + vm$ then appears as the customary distributive law, with the exception that the multiplier m is written only on the right.

The reason for writing xm rather than mx becomes apparent when we observe that the mapping $\overline{m}: G \to G$, defined by $g\overline{m} = gm$, is an endomorphism of G (homomorphism of G into itself). For this is precisely what our requirement $(xy)m = (xm)(ym)$ says: multiplication by m preserves the operation of G.

Since it is possible that $xm = xn$ for all x in G, and two distinct elements m and n of the operator set $\mathfrak{O}$, the mapping $m \to \overline{m}$ is a mapping from $\mathfrak{O}$ into the set of all endomorphisms of G, which need not be either 1–1 or onto. For example, if we take the group Z_6 with the operator set Z, where we define the product $\bar{x}m$ to be the remainder of the ordinary product of any representative of the coset $\bar{x} = x + (6)$, it is clear that we have a group with operator set Z, and, moreover, that $\bar{x}3 = \bar{x}9 = \bar{x}15 = \cdots$ for all $\bar{x} \in Z_6$.

Suppose, conversely, that we have a group G and a set $\overline{\mathfrak{O}}$ of endomorphisms of G. Then for any $\overline{m} \in \overline{\mathfrak{O}}$, we may define an operator m by $xm = x\overline{m}$, the image of x under the endomorphism $\overline{m}$, for all $x \in G$. Since $\overline{m}$ is an endomorphism, we have that $(xy)\overline{m} = (x\overline{m})(y\overline{m})$ and, hence, $(xy)m = (xm)(ym)$. Thus a set $\overline{\mathfrak{O}}$ of endomorphisms of a group G determines an $\mathfrak{O}$-group G.

With this alternative formulation of a group with operators in mind, we can at once obtain some useful results. Thus $em = e$, the identity of G, $x^{-1}m = (xm)^{-1}$, and, more generally, $x^k m = (xm)^k$ for any integer k. We may also think of several sets of endomorphisms which would be of interest in this connection, such as the set of all automorphisms of the group in question, or the set of all its inner automorphisms.

Recall one of our descriptions of a normal (invariant) subgroup: The subgroup H of G is invariant if it is invariant under all the inner automorphisms of G, i.e., if $gHg^{-1} = H$ for all $g \in G$. Thus, the normal subgroups, and only those, are singled out of the set of all subgroups of G by the set, I, of inner automorphisms. Since I gives one determination of G as a group with operators, namely as an I-group, we are at once led to the following:

Definition. A subgroup H of the $\mathfrak{O}$-group G is an *$\mathfrak{O}$-subgroup* of G if $hm \in H$ for all $h \in H$ and all $m \in \mathfrak{O}$, i.e., if H is invariant under the endomorphisms of the set $\overline{\mathfrak{O}}$. I-subgroups are thus our familiar normal, or invariant, subgroups. If A is the set of all the automorphisms of G, then an A-subgroup is called a *characteristic* subgroup, while if E is the set of all endomorphisms of G, then an E-subgroup is called *fully invariant.*

One might naturally ask, at this point, if we could not also extend the notion of a factor group, by considering the cosets of an $\mathfrak{O}$-subgroup H of the $\mathfrak{O}$-group G and suitably defining multiplication of cosets by elements of $\mathfrak{O}$. This is indeed possible if H is not only an $\mathfrak{O}$-subgroup but also normal in G. Since, for any $gh \in gH$ and $m \in \mathfrak{O}$, we have

$$(gh)m = (gm)(hm) \in (gm)H,$$

we naturally define

$$(gH)m = (gm)H, \text{ all } g \in G \text{ and } m \in \mathfrak{O}.$$

Thus, the *image of the coset* (under the endomorphism $\overline{m}$) is the *coset of the image.*

This product is well-defined since, if $gH = g'H$, then $g' = gh$ for some $h \in H$ and we have

$$g'm = (gh)m = (gm)(hm) = (gm)h' \text{ for some } h' \in H,$$

since H is an $\mathfrak{O}$-subgroup, and hence $(g'm)H = (gm)H$.

For a normal $\mathfrak{O}$-subgroup H, the factor set $\overline{G} = G/H$ is also an $\mathfrak{O}$-group. For G/H is known to be a group, and we have

$$\begin{aligned}((xH)(yH))m &= (xyH)m = ((xy)m)H = (xm)(ym)H \\ &= ((xm)H)((ym)H) = ((xH)m)((yH)m)\end{aligned}$$

by the above definition, and the usual definition of coset multiplication, so that G/H is an $\mathfrak{O}$-group.

We have already seen the close connection between factor groups, normal subgroups, and homomorphisms of a group G. This connection holds also for operator groups, provided that we now consider only those homomorphisms which not only preserve the group operation, but also preserve the action of the operators.

Definition. A homomorphism α of the Θ-group G into the Θ-group H is an *Θ-homomorphism* if for all $g \in G$ and all $m \in \Theta$ we have $(gm)\alpha = (g\alpha)m$.

Thus, an *Θ-homomorphism commutes* with all the endomorphisms of the set $\bar{\Theta}$. *Θ-isomorphism*, *Θ-endomorphism*, and *Θ-automorphism* are defined similarly.

We now give the extended versions of our basic Theorems 2.11 and 2.20.

Theorem 2.11′. *Let $\alpha: G \to G'$ be an Θ-homomorphism of the Θ-group G into the Θ-group G'. Then, each of the following is true:*

(i) $e\alpha = e'$, *where e and e' are the respective identities of G and G'.*

(ii) $x^{-1}\alpha = (x\alpha)^{-1}$ *for all $x \in G$.*

(iii) *For any Θ-subgroup H of G, $H\alpha = \{h\alpha: h \in H\}$ is an Θ-subgroup of G'.*

(iv) *For any Θ-subgroup H' of G', $H'\alpha^{-1} = \{x: x \in G, x\alpha \in H'\}$ is an Θ-subgroup of G.*

PROOF. The only new aspects of the theorem are the assertions that $H\alpha$ and $H'\alpha^{-1}$ are closed under the operators of the set Θ. The proof of these assertions we leave to the reader.

Theorem 2.20′. *Every Θ-homomorphism $\alpha: G \to G\alpha = H$ of an Θ-group G onto an Θ-group H determines a partition of G such that the equivalence class of the identity e of G is the kernel K of α. K is a normal Θ-subgroup of G, and G/K is Θ-isomorphic to H. Conversely, if K is any normal Θ-subgroup of the Θ-group G, then there is a natural Θ-homomorphism of G onto G/K.*

PROOF. The only modifications of the first part of the theorem are the assertions that K, the kernel of α, is an Θ-group, and that the isomorphism $\bar{\alpha}$ of G/K onto H is an Θ-isomorphism. In the second part of the theorem, the only new statement is that the homomorphism $\beta: G \to G/K$, defined by $a\beta = aK$, is an Θ-homomorphism. The proofs of these added assertions are left as an exercise for the reader.

In a similar manner, Theorems 2.17 and 2.18 concerning intersection and product of subgroups remain valid if we replace the terms group and subgroup throughout by Θ-group and Θ-subgroup, respectively. The slight additional argument needed in each case is again left to the reader.

Exercises

1. Show that *is a characteristic (fully invariant) subgroup of* is a transitive relation on subgroups, i.e., if H is a characteristic (fully invariant) subgroup of K, and K is a characteristic (fully invariant) subgroup of G, then H is a characteristic (fully invariant) subgroup of G.
2. We have seen that every subgroup of an Abelian group is normal. Is every subgroup of an Abelian group a characteristic subgroup? Prove your answer.
3. Carry out the proof of Theorem 2.11′.
4. Carry out the proof of Theorem 2.20′.
5. State and prove the extended versions of Theorems 2.17 and 2.18.
6. Show that the intersection H of any set H_i, $i \in I$, of Θ-subgroups of the Θ-group G is an Θ-subgroup of G.

11. The Isomorphism Theorems

As we have seen, if α is an $\mathcal{O}$-homomorphism of an $\mathcal{O}$-group G onto an $\mathcal{O}$-group G', then every $\mathcal{O}$-subgroup of G' is the image of at least one $\mathcal{O}$-subgroup of G. In fact, if $H\alpha = H'$ and K is the kernel of α, then, for any L such that $H \subseteq L \subseteq HK$, we have $L\alpha = H'$, since $(HK)\alpha = H\alpha K\alpha = H\alpha$. The next theorem will make the correspondence between normal subgroups precise.

Theorem 2.21 (First Isomorphism Theorem for Groups). *Let α be an $\mathcal{O}$-homomorphism of the $\mathcal{O}$-group G onto the $\mathcal{O}$-group G', with kernel K. Then, H' is a normal $\mathcal{O}$-subgroup of G' iff the $\mathcal{O}$-subgroup $H = H'\alpha^{-1}$ of G is normal and $H \supseteq K$. If this is the case, we have $G/H \cong G'/H'$, or, equivalently, $G/H \cong (G/K)/(H/K)$.*

PROOF. Suppose H' is normal in G' and let $\beta\colon G' \to G'/H'$ be the natural homomorphism. Then, $\alpha\beta$ is a homomorphism of G onto G'/H'. Now,

$$g(\alpha\beta) = e(\alpha\beta) \quad \text{iff} \quad (g\alpha)\beta = (e\alpha)\beta \quad \text{iff} \quad g\alpha \in H' \quad \text{iff} \quad g \in H'\alpha^{-1},$$

which clearly contains K, since $K\alpha = e\alpha$. Thus $H = H'\alpha^{-1}$ is the kernel of the homomorphism $\alpha\beta$, H contains K, H is normal in G, and $G/H \cong G'/H'$. Since $G' \cong G/K$ and $H' \cong H/K$, we have that $G/H \cong (G/K)/(H/K)$ also.

On the other hand, if H is a normal $\mathcal{O}$-subgroup of G and $H \supseteq K$, then $H' = H\alpha$ is a subgroup of G', and is normal, since, if $g' \in G'$, $h' \in H'$, then we have $g' = g\alpha$, $h' = h\alpha$ for some $g \in G$, $h \in H$. Hence,

$$g'h'g'^{-1} = (ghg^{-1})\alpha \in H\alpha = H',$$

since H is normal. Moreover, $H'\alpha^{-1} = H$ since,

$$\text{if } g \in H'\alpha^{-1}, \text{ then } g\alpha = h\alpha$$

for some $h \in H$; hence

$$(gh^{-1})\alpha = e\alpha \text{ and } gh^{-1} \in K \subseteq H,\ g \in hH = H.$$

We thus see that the correspondence $H \leftrightarrow H' = H\alpha$ is 1–1 between the normal $\mathcal{O}$-subgroups H of G which contain the kernel K of α, and the normal $\mathcal{O}$-subgroups H' of $G' = G\alpha$.

Definition. A *maximal* subgroup N of the $\mathcal{O}$-group G is a normal $\mathcal{O}$-subgroup of G such that $N \subset G$ and there exists no normal $\mathcal{O}$-subgroup K of G with $N \subset K \subset G$.

Corollary 2.21.1. *N is maximal in G iff G/N is simple.*

PROOF. Immediate from the theorem, with α the natural homomorphism of G onto G/N.

The next theorem further develops the relations between subgroups, their product and their intersection.

Theorem 2.22 (Second Isomorphism Theorem for Groups). *Let H be an $\mathcal{O}$-subgroup, N a normal $\mathcal{O}$-subgroup of G, α the natural homomorphism of G onto $G/N = \overline{G}$, and $\overline{H} = H\alpha$. Then*

$$\overline{H}\alpha^{-1} = HN,\ \overline{H} = HN/N,\ \text{and } HN/N \cong H/(H \cap N).$$

PROOF. If $x \in \overline{H}\alpha^{-1}$, then $x\alpha \in \overline{H}$, or $x\alpha = h\alpha$ for some $h \in H$. But then, $x \in \overline{h} = hN$, so that $x \in HN$. Conversely, if $y \in HN$, say, $y = hn$ for $h \in H$, $n \in N$, then $y\alpha = (h\alpha)(n\alpha) = \overline{h}\overline{n} = \overline{h} \in \overline{H}$, since $\overline{n} = N$ is the identity of G/N. This establishes the first assertion, $\overline{H}\alpha^{-1} = HN$.

Since N is normal in G, N is certainly normal in HN, so that we may form HN/N. We then have $\overline{x} \in \overline{H}$ iff $x \in \overline{H}\alpha^{-1} = HN$ iff $\overline{x} \in HN/N$. The first of these assertions follows from the definition of $\overline{H}\alpha^{-1}$ and the part of the theorem just proved, while the second follows from the fact that if $x \in HN$, say $x = hn$, then $\overline{x} = (hn)N$, an element of HN/N, and conversely. Thus we have $\overline{H} = HN/N$.

Finally, consider the homomorphism of H onto $\overline{H}$ induced by considering the elements of H as elements of G. Now we have both $h \in H$ and $h\alpha = e\alpha$ iff $h \in H \cap N$. Thus $H \cap N$ is the kernel of this homomorphism, and, by the Fundamental Homomorphism Theorem (Theorem 2.20′), we conclude that

$$H/(H \cap N) \cong \overline{H} = HN/N,$$

and the theorem is proved.

Corollary 2.22.1. *If H and K are distinct maximal $\mathcal{O}$-subgroups of the $\mathcal{O}$-group G, then $G/K \cong H/H \cap K$, and $G/H \cong K/H \cap K$. (To be precise, we should write $H/(H \cap K)$ and $K/(H \cap K)$, but we customarily omit the parentheses.)*

PROOF. We need only show that under the given conditions, $G = HK = KH$. Since H and K are both normal, $HK = KH$ is a normal subgroup of G. Clearly, HK contains both $H = He$ and $K = eK$. If HK were equal to either H or K, say $HK = H$, then we would have $H \supseteq K$, which is impossible, since $H \neq K$ and K is maximal. Therefore HK properly contains both H and K, and must be G by the maximality of H and K.

For example, in the additive group Z of integers, if p and q are any distinct primes, then (p) and (q) are distinct maximal subgroups of Z, $Z = (p)(q)$, $(pq) = (p) \cap (q)$, or, to be specific, $Z = (3)(5)$, $(15) = (3) \cap (5)$. We then have $Z/(3) = \{\overline{0}, \overline{1}, \overline{2}\}$ and

$$\begin{aligned}(5)/(15) &= \{\ldots, -10, -5, 0, 5, 10, \ldots\}/\{\ldots, -30, -15, 0, 15, 30, \ldots\}\\ &= \{\overline{\overline{0}}, \overline{\overline{5}}, \overline{\overline{10}}\},\end{aligned}$$

and the isomorphism is obvious.

The next theorem further develops relations between the subgroups of a group. It can be derived as a consequence of the Second Isomorphism Theorem, but we shall obtain it independently of the other isomorphism theorems, though it will depend on the Fundamental Homomorphism Theorem.

Theorem 2.23 (Third Isomorphism Theorem — Zassenhaus). *Let K, L, K', and L' be Θ-subgroups of the Θ-group G, with K' normal in K and L' normal in L. Then,*

$$K'(K \cap L') \text{ is normal in } K'(K \cap L),$$
$$L'(L \cap K') \text{ is normal in } L'(L \cap K),$$
$$(K' \cap L)(K \cap L') \text{ is normal in } K \cap L,$$

and the corresponding factor groups are isomorphic, i.e.,

$$K'(K \cap L)/K'(K \cap L') \cong (K \cap L)/(K' \cap L)(K \cap L') \cong L'(L \cap K)/L'(L \cap K').$$

PROOF. As an aid in keeping track of the various subgroups and their relationships which will be developed in the course of the proof, we include the following diagram, where a line from one subgroup to another indicates that

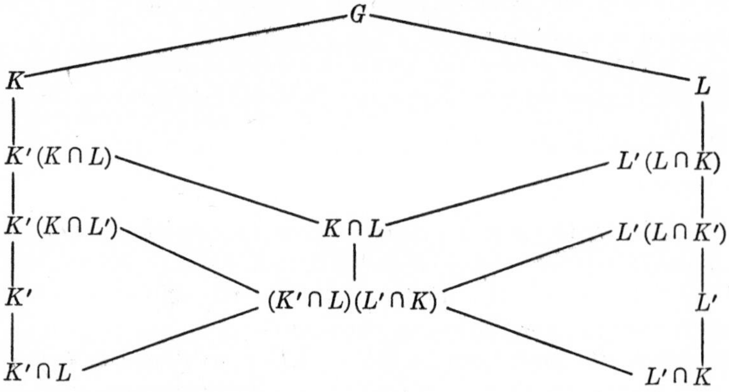

the lower is contained in the upper. Since K' is normal in K, we have (by Theorem 2.17) that $K' \cap L = (K' \cap K) \cap L = K' \cap (K \cap L)$ is normal in the subgroup $K \cap L$ of K. Similarly, $K \cap L'$ is normal in $K \cap L$ (considered as subgroups of L for this application of Theorem 2.17). Then, by Theorem 2.18, the product $(K' \cap L)(K \cap L')$ is a normal subgroup of $K \cap L$ and we may form the factor group $(K \cap L)/(K' \cap L)(K \cap L')$.

Let

$$\alpha\colon K'(K \cap L) \to (K \cap L)/(K' \cap L)(K \cap L')$$

be defined by

$$K'x \to (K' \cap L)(K \cap L')x = \bar{x}$$

for all $x \in K \cap L$. We shall show that α is a well-defined mapping of $K'(K \cap L)$ onto $(K \cap L)/(K' \cap L)(K \cap L')$, and, moreover, is a homomorphism.

Suppose that $ax = by$ for some $a, b \in K'$, and $x, y \in K \cap L$. Then $y = (b^{-1}a)x$, and $b^{-1}a = yx^{-1} \in K' \cap (K \cap L) = K' \cap L \subseteq (K' \cap L)(K \cap L')$. Thus $y \in (K' \cap L)(K \cap L')x$, so that $(ax)\alpha = (by)\alpha$ and α is well-defined. That α is onto $(K \cap L)/(K' \cap L)(K \cap L')$ is obvious.

Since K' is normal in K, we have $K'x = xK'$ for all $x \in K \cap L$. Hence for any $a, b \in K'$ and $x, y \in K \cap L$, $(ax)(by) = a(xb)y = a(b'x)y = (ab')(xy)$ for some $b' \in K'$. Then

$$((ax)(by))\alpha = ((ab')(xy))\alpha = \overline{xy} = \bar{x}\,\bar{y} = (ax)\alpha(by)\alpha,$$

and α is a homomorphism.

Now the kernel of α is

$$\begin{aligned}\{ax\colon a \in K', x \in (K' \cap L)(K \cap L')\} &= K'(K' \cap L)(K \cap L')\\ &= K'(K \cap L'),\end{aligned}$$

and, by the Fundamental Homomorphism Theorem, we have $K'(K \cap L')$ is normal in $K'(K \cap L)$ and

$$K'(K \cap L)/K'(K \cap L') \cong (K \cap L)/(K' \cap L)(K \cap L').$$

In a similar manner, we obtain that $L'(L \cap K')$ is normal in $L'(L \cap K)$ and

$$L'(L \cap K)/L'(L \cap K') \cong (L \cap K)/(L' \cap K)(L \cap K'),$$

from which our desired result follows by the transitivity of isomorphism and the fact that $(L' \cap K)(L \cap K') = (K' \cap L)(K \cap L')$.

Exercises

1. Let G be any group of permutations not all of which are even. Show that the even permutations in G form a normal subgroup of index two.
2. Let G be the group of symmetries of the square. Exhibit the correspondence between normal subgroups $\overline{H}$ of S_4/G and normal subgroups H of S_4, $S_4 \supseteq H \supseteq G$.
3. Obtain the Third Isomorphism Theorem as a consequence of the second. (*Hint:* Show that $K'(K \cap L')$ is a normal subgroup of $K'(K \cap L)$, then apply the Second Isomorphism Theorem with $H = K \cap L$, $N = K'(K \cap L')$ to obtain

$$K'(K \cap L')(K \cap L)/K'(K \cap L') \cong (K \cap L)/(K \cap L) \cap K'(K \cap L').$$

Show that this reduces to

$$K'(K \cap L)/K'(K \cap L') \cong (K \cap L)/(K' \cap L)(K \cap L').)$$

4. Show that the Second Isomorphism Theorem is a consequence of the Third.
5. Let α be an $\mathcal{O}$-homomorphism of the $\mathcal{O}$-group G into the $\mathcal{O}$-group G', L an $\mathcal{O}$-subgroup of G, K a normal $\mathcal{O}$-subgroup of L, and H the kernel of α. Show that KH is normal in LH, $K(L \cap H)$ is normal in L, $K\alpha$ is normal in $L\alpha$, and the corresponding factor groups, LH/KH, $L/K(L \cap H)$, and $L\alpha/K\alpha$ are $\mathcal{O}$-isomorphic.

12. Composition Series

As an important application of the Third Isomorphism Theorem, we shall develop the *Jordan-Hölder Theorem*, which gives much information about the possible structure of the set of subgroups of certain groups.

Definition. The finite chain $G = G_0 \supseteq G_1 \supseteq \cdots \supseteq G_r = E$ of Θ-subgroups of the Θ-group G is a *subinvariant series* of G if each G_i is normal in G_{i-1}, and is a *normal series* of G if each G_i is normal in G, $i = 1, 2, \ldots, r$. The integer r is the *length* of the series, and the factor groups G_{i-1}/G_i are the *factors* of the series.

Definition. A second subinvariant (respectively normal) series of G,

$$G = H_0 \supseteq H_1 \supseteq \cdots \supseteq H_s = E$$

is a *refinement* of the first if every G_i is also an H_j for some j. Two subinvariant (respectively normal) series of G are *isomorphic* if their factors are isomorphic in some order, i.e., if $r = s$ and, for any i, $G_{i-1}/G_i \cong H_{j-1}/H_j$ for some j, and conversely.

Definition. A *composition* (respectively *principal*, or *chief*) *series* of G is a subinvariant (respectively normal) series of G in which no $G_{i-1} = G_i$ and which has only simple factors.

Thus, a principal series of G is necessarily also a composition series, since a normal series is also a subinvariant series. If the operator set Θ contains the set I of inner automorphisms, then, of course, a subinvariant series is also a normal series, since Θ-subgroups are always normal in G.

For example, let G be the group of symmetries of the square with the notation for subgroups as given in Section 8. Then $G \supset R' \supset H \supset E$ is a composition series of G, but not a principal series since H is not normal in G. On the other hand, the series $G \supset T \supset E$ is a normal series, but is not a principal series since G/T is not simple. However, $G \supset R \supset T \supset E$, a proper refinement of $G \supset T \supset E$, is a principal series of G. The series $G \supset T \supset E$ can also be refined to yield either of the series $G \supset R' \supset T \supset E$ or $G \supset R'' \supset T \supset E$, both of which are principal.

Definition. If Θ contains all automorphisms of G, then a composition series is called a *characteristic series*, and if Θ is the set of all endomorphisms of G, then a composition series is called a *fully invariant series*.

Theorem 2.24 (Schreier Refinement Theorem). *Two given subinvariant series of the Θ-group G have refinements which are isomorphic.*

PROOF. We shall prove the theorem by constructing the required refinements. Let the given subinvariant series be

$$G = G_0 \supseteq G_1 \supseteq \cdots \supseteq G_r = E, \text{ and}$$
$$G = H_0 \supseteq H_1 \supseteq \cdots \supseteq H_s = E.$$

Now, let $G_{i,j} = G_i(G_{i-1} \cap H_j)$ and $H_{i,j} = H_j(H_{j-1} \cap G_i)$, for all $i = 1, 2, \ldots, r - 1$, and all $j = 1, 2, \ldots, s - 1$.

Then interpolate the chain

$$G_{i,1} \supseteq G_{i,2} \supseteq \cdots \supseteq G_{i,s-1}$$

between G_{i-1} and G_i, and, likewise, interpolate the chain

$$H_{1,j} \supseteq H_{2,j} \supseteq \cdots \supseteq H_{r-1,j}$$

between H_{j-1} and H_j. Finally let

$$G_{i,0} = G_{i-1} \ (= G_i(G_{i-1} \cap H_0)), \qquad G_{i,s} = G_i \ (= G_i(G_{i-1} \cap H_s)),$$
$$H_{0,j} = H_{j-1} \ (= H_j(H_{j-1} \cap G_0)), \quad H_{r,j} = H_j \ (= H_j(H_{j-1} \cap G_r)).$$

Then, by the Third Isomorphism Theorem, $G_{i,j}$ is normal in $G_{i,j-1}$, $H_{i,j}$ is normal in $H_{i-1,j}$, and, moreover,

$$G_{i,j-1}/G_{i,j} \cong H_{i-1,j}/H_{i,j}, \quad i = 1, \ldots, r; \quad j = 1, \ldots, s.$$

Thus the resulting series, both of length rs, are isomorphic.

To assist in following the relationships and isomorphisms of this result, the following diagram may be helpful.

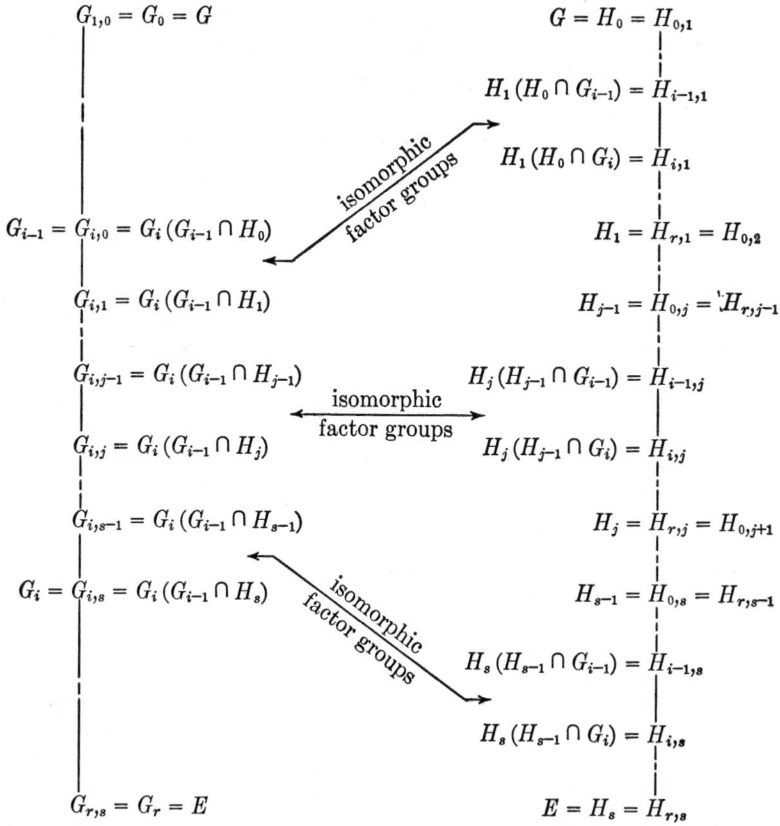

Broken vertical lines indicate inclusion with possible intermediate subgroups, while unbroken vertical lines indicate adjacency in the refined series.

Corollary 2.24.1 (Jordan-Hölder Theorem). *Any two composition series of an $\mathfrak{O}$-group G are isomorphic.*

PROOF. By the theorem, the two composition series have isomorphic refinements. But since the factor groups of a composition series are simple, the only additional factors in a refinement of a composition series must be identity groups. In the pairing of isomorphic factors of the refinements, the identity factors must be paired, and the simple factors of the original series must also be paired. Thus the original series are themselves isomorphic.

Corollary 2.24.2. *If the $\mathfrak{O}$-group G has a composition series, then every subinvariant series can be refined to a composition series, and there is some composition series through any normal $\mathfrak{O}$-subgroup of G.*

PROOF. Immediate from the Schreier Theorem.

We may observe that if, in the statement of the Third Isomorphism Theorem, we had assumed that K, K', L, and L' were all normal subgroups of G, then all groups constructed in the theorem and its proof would, by Theorems 2.17 and 2.18, have also been normal in G. This would have simplified the arguments of the proof, and also would enable us to state the analogues of the Schreier Theorem and its corollaries for principal series: Two given *normal series* of an $\mathfrak{O}$-group G have *isomorphic refinements*; any two *principal series* of G are *isomorphic*; if G has a *principal series*, then every *normal series* can be *refined* to a *principal series* and there is a *principal series* through any *normal* $\mathfrak{O}$-subgroup of G.

As an example of the use of the Schreier Theorem, consider the group Z_{60} of integers modulo 60, and the following subgroups:

$$\begin{aligned} G_1 &= \{0, 2, 4, \ldots, 58\}, & H_1 &= \{0, 3, 6, \ldots, 57\}, \\ G_2 &= \{0, 6, 12, \ldots, 54\}, & H_2 &= \{0, 12, 24, 36, 48\}, \\ G_3 &= \{0, 30\}, & E &= \{0\}. \end{aligned}$$

All these subgroups are normal in Z_{60}, since Z_{60} is Abelian, and

$$Z_{60} \supset G_1 \supset G_2 \supset G_3 \supset E$$

is a principal series, since all of the factor groups are of prime order and hence simple. Now

$$Z_{60} \supset H_1 \supset H_2 \supset E$$

is a normal series, and we know that we may refine it to a principal series. Since we already have

$$Z_{60}/H_1 \cong G_1/G_2 \qquad \text{and} \qquad H_2/E \cong G_2/G_3,$$

it is evident that we need only find the proper subgroup to interpolate between H_1 and H_2. According to the Schreier Theorem, this group will be a group

$H_{i,2} = H_2 + (H_1 \cap G_i)$, $i = 1, 2$. (Note the use of the + sign, since the group Z_{60} is written with additive notation for the group operation.) We have

$$H_{1,2} = \{0, 12, \ldots, 48\} + \{0, 6, \ldots, 54\} = \{0, 6, \ldots, 54\} = G_2,$$

and

$$H_{2,2} = \{0, 12, \ldots, 48\} + \{0, 6, \ldots, 54\} = \{0, 6, \ldots, 54\} = G_2.$$

(We need not compute either $H_{0,2}$ or $H_{3,2}$ as we know these will be H_1 and H_2, respectively.) Since there is no point in refining the H series, and also the G series, to include identity factors, we shall only insert one of $H_{1,2}$ and $H_{2,2}$ into the series. Inserting $H_{1,2} = G_2$, we may verify that

$$Z_{60} \supset H_1 \supset H_{1,2} \supset H_2 \supset E$$

is a principal series, isomorphic to the G series, the additional isomorphic pairs of factors being

$$H_1/H_{1,2} \cong Z_{60}/G_1, \qquad \text{and} \qquad H_{1,2}/H_2 \cong G_3/E.$$

That not every group has a composition series at all is seen by consideration of the infinite cyclic group Z of the integers with respect to addition. For suppose that we have any subinvariant series (hence also a normal series, since Z is Abelian),

$$Z = G_0 \supseteq G_1 \supseteq \cdots \supseteq G_n = E.$$

Now if $G_i \neq E$, then $x \neq 0$ (the identity of Z) is in G_i for some integer x; hence so is $kx = x + x + \cdots + x$ (k summands) for every integer k. Moreover, $kx \neq mx$ if $k \neq m$, since kx and mx are distinct elements of Z. Thus if $G_i \neq E$, G_i is itself infinite cyclic. But then $G_i/E = G_i$ is not simple, since if G_i has generator x, then the subgroup generated by $2x$ is a proper subgroup. Thus no subinvariant series can be a composition series of Z, and Z has no composition series.

Indeed, if an Abelian group has a composition series, it must be a finite group, since all the factors must be simple and the only simple Abelian groups are cyclic of prime order. (The proof of this fact is left as an exercise for the reader.) But if a group is finite, whether Abelian or not, then it always has a composition series.

Theorem 2.25. *Every finite Θ-group G has a composition series.*

PROOF. Being finite, G has only a finite number of normal Θ-subgroups, of which at least one, say H, must be maximal in G, and H is of lower order than G. Similarly, H must have a maximal Θ-subgroup, which is again of lower order than H. This process must terminate with the identity subgroup in a finite number of steps, and the resulting series is a composition series.

A slight modification of this argument shows that the corresponding theorem for *principal series* is also valid, an exercise we leave to the reader.

Exercises

1. Show that if an Abelian group G has a composition series, then G is finite.
2. Show that every finite group has a principal series.
3. Let G be a cyclic group of order n. Determine, to within isomorphism, the factors in any composition series of G.
4. Let G be a group with a composition series, and H a group isomorphic to G. Show that H has a composition series, and the composition factors of H are isomorphic to those of G.
5. Show that the converse to the result of the last exercise is not true, i.e., two non-isomorphic groups can have isomorphic composition factors. (*Hint:* Consider the possible groups of order four.)
6. Show that for any n, the symmetric group S_n has a composition series, and determine the form of the composition series for each value of n. (*Hint:* See Exercise 8, section 8.)
7. Let $D(G)$, the *derived group* of G, be the group generated by all commutators $xyx^{-1}y^{-1}$ of elements of G, and define recursively $D^{k+1}(G) = D(D^k(G))$. Show that $D^k(G)$ is a subgroup of G, invariant under all endomorphisms of G, and that, for H a subgroup of G, $D^k(H) \subseteq D^k(G)$. If H is normal, show that then $D^k(G/H) \cong (HD^k(G))/H$.
8. A group is called *solvable* if it has a composition series for which every factor group is Abelian. Prove that G is solvable if there exists an integer k such that $D^k(G) = e$. Also show that every subgroup and every factor group of a solvable group is solvable.

13. Direct Products of Groups

The composition series and principal series just considered can throw considerable light on the structure of groups, particularly in the case of finite groups. The other principal approach to the structure problem is by considering the possibility of building up a group out of already given groups of simpler structure. To this end, we define the direct product of a set of groups.

Definition. The *direct product* $H = G_1 \otimes G_2 \otimes \cdots \otimes G_n$ of the finite set of $\mathfrak{O}$-groups $G_1, G_2, \ldots, G_n$ is the (Cartesian) product of the sets $G_1, G_2, \ldots, G_n$, i.e., the set $\{(a_1, a_2, \ldots, a_n) : a_i \in G_i\}$, with the binary operation

$$(a_1, a_2, \ldots, a_n)(b_1, b_2, \ldots, b_n) = (a_1b_1, a_2b_2, \ldots, a_nb_n),$$

and for $m \in \mathfrak{O}$,

$$(a_1, a_2, \ldots, a_n)m = (a_1m, a_2m, \ldots, a_nm).$$

G_i is called the ith *component* or *factor* of H, and a_i the ith *component* of $a = (a_1, a_2, \ldots, a_n)$.

Definition. The *direct product* $H = G_1 \otimes G_2 \otimes \cdots$ of an infinite set of $\mathfrak{O}$-groups $G_1, G_2, \ldots$ is similarly defined as the Cartesian product of the sets $G_1, G_2, \ldots$ with the binary operation

$$(a_1, a_2, \ldots)(b_1, b_2, \ldots) = (a_1b_1, a_2b_2, \ldots).$$

Notationally, if I is any set of indices, we shall denote the direct product of the $\mathfrak{O}$-groups G_i, $i \in I$ by $\otimes G_i$, $i \in I$. In case the group operation in the G_i is written additively, we shall, of course, refer to *direct sum* rather than *direct product*, and write

$$H = G_1 \oplus G_2 \oplus \cdots = \oplus G_i,\ i \in I.$$

Theorem 2.26. *The direct product* $H = \otimes G_i$, $i \in I$, *of the* $\mathfrak{O}$*-groups* G_i *is an* $\mathfrak{O}$*-group.*

PROOF. The operation is clearly well-defined, and its associativity follows at once from the associativity of the operations in the component groups G_i. The identity element of H is the element $e = (e_1, e_2, \ldots)$, all of whose components are identity elements of the groups G_i, and the inverse of $a = (a_1, a_2, \ldots)$ is $(a_1^{-1}, a_2^{-1}, \ldots)$. Finally, for any $m \in \mathfrak{O}$, we have

$$\begin{aligned} ((a_1, a_2, \ldots)(b_1, b_2, \ldots))m &= (a_1b_1, a_2b_2, \ldots)m \\ &= ((a_1b_1)m, (a_2b_2)m, \ldots) \\ &= ((a_1m)(b_1m), (a_2m)(b_2m), \ldots) \\ &= (a_1m, a_2m, \ldots)(b_1m, b_2m, \ldots) \\ &= ((a_1, a_2, \ldots)m)((b_1, b_2, \ldots)m). \end{aligned}$$

In the case of a direct product of an infinite set of $\mathfrak{O}$-groups G_i, the subgroup of the direct product consisting of those elements having only a finite number of nonidentity components is known as the *weak direct product* of the G_i.

The most obvious examples of direct product groups are our familiar vector spaces, either of finite or of infinite dimension. In this case, the groups G_i are, of course, all the same group. To be specific, consider the group

$$R^3 = R \otimes R \otimes R,$$

where R is the additive group of real numbers with operator set R, the operator, or external composition being multiplication of real numbers. Then, clearly, R^3 has, among others, the normal subgroups

$$R_1 = \{(a, 0, 0) : a \in R\}, \qquad R_2 = \{(0, b, 0) : b \in R\}, \qquad \text{and}$$
$$R_3 = \{(0, 0, c) : c \in R\}.$$

Moreover, it is fairly evident that R^3 is isomorphic to the direct product $R_1 \otimes R_2 \otimes R_3$ under the mapping $(a, b, c) \to ((a, 0, 0), (0, b, 0), (0, 0, c))$. That this situation is quite general is shown by the next theorem.

Theorem 2.27. Let $H = \bigotimes H_i$, $i \in I$. *Then the subsets*

$$K_i = \{a \in H : a_j = e_j \text{ if } j \neq i\},\ i \in I$$

are normal subgroups of H, $K_i \cong H_i$, *and* $H \cong K = \bigotimes K_i$, $i \in I$.

PROOF. Let $a, b \in K_i$. Then for $j \neq i$, we have

$$(ab^{-1})_j = a_j b_j^{-1} = e_j e_j^{-1} = e_j,$$

hence $ab^{-1} \in K_i$ and K_i is a subgroup.

For any $g \in H$, $a \in K_i$, we have

$$\begin{aligned} gag^{-1} &= (g_1, g_2, \ldots)(a_1, a_2, \ldots)(g_1^{-1}, g_2^{-1}, \ldots) \\ &= (g_1 a_1 g_1^{-1}, g_2 a_2 g_2^{-1}, \ldots). \end{aligned}$$

But, for $j \neq i$, $a_j = e_j$ so that $g_j a_j g_j^{-1} = g_j g_j^{-1} = e_j$, hence $gag^{-1} \in K_i$ and K_i is normal in H.

The mapping $\alpha_i : K_i \to H_i$ defined by $a\alpha_i = a_i$ for all $a \in K_i$ is clearly the required isomorphism of K_i and H_i.

To see that $\bigotimes K_i$, $i \in I$, is isomorphic to H, consider the mapping $\beta : K = \bigotimes K_i \to H$ defined by

$$((a_1, e_2, e_3, \ldots), (e_1, a_2, e_3, \ldots), \ldots)\beta = (a_1, a_2, \ldots).$$

The verification that β is 1–1, onto, and product preserving is an almost obvious computation and will be omitted.

We thus see that a direct product $G = \bigotimes H_i$, $i \in I$, is isomorphic to a direct product of normal subgroups G_i of G. This quite naturally leads us to ask if there are other conditions for which a group will be isomorphic to a direct product of normal subgroups of itself. We are, of course, most interested in conditions which are both necessary and sufficient.

Theorem 2.28. *The following conditions on a group* G *are equivalent.*

(A) $G \cong H = H_1 \otimes H_2 \otimes \cdots \otimes H_n$.

(B) *G has subgroups* $G_1, G_2, \ldots, G_n$ *such that:*

 (i) G_i *is normal in* G.

 (ii) $G = G_1 G_2 \cdots G_n = \prod G_i$, $i = 1, 2, \ldots, n$.

 (iii) $G_i \cap G_i' = e$, *where* $G_i' = G_1 \cdots G_{i-1} G_{i+1} \cdots G_n = \prod G_j$, $j \neq$ i.

(C) *G has subgroups* $G_1, G_2, \ldots, G_n$ *such that:*

 (i′) *For* $g_i \in G_i$, $g_j \in G_j$, $i \neq j$, *we have* $g_i g_j = g_j g_i$.

 (ii′) *For any* $g \in G$, g *is uniquely expressible in the form*

$$g = g_1 g_2 \cdots g_n,\ g_i \in G_i.$$

PROOF. Assume first that (A) holds in G, with $\alpha : G \to H$ the given isomorphism. Let K_i be the normal subgroup of H of the previous theorem, $K_i \cong H_i$, $i = 1, 2, \ldots, n$, and let $G_i = K_i\alpha^{-1}$. It then follows that G_i is normal in G

and, moreover, that $G_i \cong K_i$. Now for any $g \in G$,

$$\begin{aligned} g\alpha &= (h_1, h_2, \ldots, h_n) \\ &= (h_1, e_2, \ldots, e_n)(e_1, h_2, e_3, \ldots, e_n) \ldots (e_1, \ldots, e_{n-1}, h_n). \end{aligned}$$

Thus
$$\begin{aligned} g &= ((h_1, e_2, \ldots, e_n)(e_1, h_2, e_3, \ldots, e_n) \ldots (e_1, \ldots, e_{n-1}, h_n))\alpha^{-1} \\ &= (h_1, e_2, \ldots, e_n)\alpha^{-1}(e_1, h_2, e_3, \ldots, e_n)\alpha^{-1} \ldots (e_1, \ldots, e_{n-1}, h_n)\alpha^{-1} \\ &= g_1 g_2 \cdots g_n \text{ for } g_i \in G_i, \end{aligned}$$

and $G = G_1 G_2 \cdots G_n$. Finally, if $g \in G_i \cap G_i'$, then $g\alpha \in K_i \cap K_i'$, and

$$g\alpha = (e_1, \ldots, e_{i-1}, h_i, e_{i+1}, \ldots, e_n) = (h_1, \ldots, h_{i-1}, e_i, h_{i+1}, \ldots, h_n).$$

Hence, $h_i = e_i$ for all i, $g\alpha = (e_1, e_2, \ldots, e_n)$, $g = (e_1, e_2, \ldots, e_n)\alpha^{-1} = e$, and $G_i \cap G_i' = e$ as required. Thus (A) implies (B).

Assume, next, that (B) holds in G, and let $g_i \in G_i$, $g_j \in G_j$ with $i \neq j$. Then, since G_i and G_j are both normal, we have that

$$(g_i g_j g_i^{-1}) g_j^{-1} = g_i (g_j g_i^{-1} g_j^{-1}) \in G_i \cap G_j \subseteq G_i \cap G_i' = e,$$

hence $g_i g_j g_i^{-1} g_j^{-1} = e$, or $g_i g_j = g_j g_i$, establishing (i′). By condition (ii), if $g \in G$, then $g = g_1 g_2 \cdots g_n$ for $g_i \in G_i$. If also $g = f_1 f_2 \cdots f_n$ for $f_i \in G_i$, then we have

$$f_1^{-1} g_1 = (f_2 \cdots f_n)(g_2 \cdots g_n)^{-1} = f_2 \cdots f_n g_n^{-1} \cdots g_2^{-1}.$$

By (i′) just established, this gives us

$$f_1^{-1} g_1 = (f_2 g_2^{-1})(f_3 g_3^{-1}) \cdots (f_n g_n^{-1}).$$

Thus $f_1^{-1} g_1 \in G_1 \cap G_1'$, and $f_1^{-1} g_1 = e$, $g_1 = f_1$. In a similar manner, we obtain $g_i = f_i$ for $i = 2, \ldots, n$. (Note that, by (i′), we may write $g_1 g_2 \cdots g_n = g_i g_1 g_2 \cdots g_{i-1} g_{i+1} \cdots g_n$.) Thus (B) implies (C).

Finally, suppose that (C) holds in G, and define the mapping $\gamma\colon G \to G_1 \otimes G_2 \otimes \cdots \otimes G_n$ by

$$g\gamma = (g_1 g_2 \cdots g_n)\gamma = (g_1, g_2, \ldots, g_n),$$

where $g = g_1 g_2 \cdots g_n$ is the unique expression of g guaranteed by (ii′). The uniqueness implies that γ is 1–1, and γ is evidently onto since any product $g_1 g_2 \cdots g_n$ is an element of G. Now, let $f = f_1 f_2 \cdots f_n$, $f_i \in G_i$. Then, since the elements of distinct G_i's commute with each other, we have that

$$\begin{aligned} (fg)\gamma &= ((f_1 \cdots f_n)(g_1 \cdots g_n))\gamma = ((f_1 g_1) \cdots (f_n g_n))\gamma \\ &= (f_1 g_1, \ldots, f_n g_n) = (f_1, \ldots, f_n)(g_1, \ldots, g_n) = (f\gamma)(g\gamma), \end{aligned}$$

and γ is the required isomorphism. Thus (C) implies (A).

We have thus shown that (A) implies (B), (B) implies (C), (C) implies (A), and the three conditions are, therefore, equivalent.

It should be observed that the proof that (C) implies (A) actually gives us more than is stated, since we obtain there that G is isomorphic to a direct product of its own subgroups if any of the conditions (A), (B), or (C) hold. This situation is recognized by saying that under these conditions, G is the *interior direct product* of its normal subgroups $G_1, G_2, \ldots, G_n$.

We note also that Theorem 2.28 can be extended to the case of an infinite set of groups H_i, $i \in I$, where I is some set of indices, if we consider, instead of the direct product, the weak direct product of the H_i. In the restatement of conditions (ii) and (iii), it is necessary to define what we mean by $\prod G_i$, $i \in I$. We mean, of course, the set of all elements of the form $g_{i_1}g_{i_2}\cdots g_{i_r}$, where $i_1, i_2, \ldots, i_r$ is any finite subset of I. Likewise, condition (ii′) must be modified to state that any $g \in G$ is uniquely expressible as a product of the form $g_{i_1}g_{i_2}\cdots g_{i_r}$. We leave the details of the modified proof to the reader.

The weak direct product is only one example of a type of subgroup of a direct product known as a subdirect product, defined below.

Definition. Let $G = \bigotimes G_i$, $i \in I$. The mapping $\pi_i : G \to G_i$ defined by $g\pi_i = (\ldots, g_i, \ldots)\pi_i = g_i$, which can be easily shown to be a homomorphism of G onto G_i, is called the *projection* of G on G_i.

Definition. A subgroup H of $G = \bigotimes G_i$, $i \in I$ such that $H\pi_i = G_i$, all $i \in I$, is called a *subdirect product* of the groups G_i, $i \in I$.

For example, in $R^3 = R \oplus R \oplus R$, R the group of all real numbers under addition, the subgroup $L = \{(r, r, r) : r \in R\}$ is a *subdirect sum*, since $L\pi_i = R$, $i = 1, 2, 3$. Interpreted geometrically, L is the line $x = y = z$, whose projection onto any of the x, y, or z axes is indeed the entire axis.

By the use of subdirect sums, we can obtain quite general results, for example:

Theorem 2.29. *Let G be an $\mathfrak{O}$-group with normal $\mathfrak{O}$-subgroups G_i, $i \in I$, such that $\bigcap_{i \in I} G_i = e$. Then G is isomorphic to a subdirect sum of the groups G/G_i.*

PROOF. Let $H = \bigotimes G/G_i$, $i \in I$, and define the mapping $\alpha : G \to H$ by $g\alpha = (gG_1, gG_2, \ldots)$.

Since for $g \neq e$, $g \notin G_i$ for some i, we have gG_i is not the identity in G/G_i, hence $g\alpha$ is not the identity of H and α is 1–1. For $f, g \in G$, we have

$$\begin{aligned}(fg)\alpha = (fgG_1, fgG_2, \ldots) &= ((fG_1)(gG_1), (fG_2)(gG_2), \ldots)\\ &= (fG_1, fG_2, \ldots)(gG_1, gG_2, \ldots)\\ &= (f\alpha)(g\alpha),\end{aligned}$$

and α is a homomorphism. Thus $G \cong G\alpha$. It is clear that $\{gG_i : g \in G\} = G/G_i$ for all i so that $(G\alpha)\pi_i = G/G_i$, and G is isomorphic to the subdirect sum $G\alpha$ of the G/G_i.

We next develop some connections between the notions of direct product and of factor group.

Theorem 2.30. *Let H and K be subgroups of G such that $HK \cong H \otimes K$.* Then $HK/H \cong K$ and $HK/K \cong H$.

PROOF. From Theorem 2.28, we have that H and K are normal subgroups of HK, $HK = KH$ and $H \cap K = e$. Then the Second Isomorphism Theorem yields $HK/K \cong H/(H \cap K) = H$, and $HK/H = KH/H \cong K$.

Corollary 2.30.1. *If H and K are subgroups of G with $G \cong H \otimes K$, then $G/K \cong H$, $G/H \cong K$.*

As a partial converse to the above, we have the following:

Theorem 2.31. *If H and K are normal subgroups of G such that the natural homomorphism α of G onto G/K induces an isomorphism of H onto G/K, then $G \cong H \otimes K$.*

PROOF. If $\alpha: H \to G/K$ is an isomorphism, then $H \cap K = e$, and H and K are given as normal in G. Since $H\alpha = G/K$, we have $(G/K)\alpha^{-1} = HK = G$ and conditions (B) are satisfied, $G \cong H \otimes K$.

While it is not possible to assert that every group is an interior direct product of proper subgroups, such a theorem can be established for Abelian groups. In fact, several theorems of this type, giving various types of decompositions, may be found in more extensive treatments of the theory of groups. Here we shall merely give some typical, and interesting results. We first need the notion of a minimal generating system of a group. We recall that if H is the smallest subgroup of G which contains the elements $a, b, c, \ldots$, then we say H is generated by $a, b, c, \ldots$. (That such a smallest subgroup exists follows from the fact that the intersection of any set of subgroups of G is again a subgroup of G.)

Definition. The subgroup H of G is said to be *finitely generated* if there exists a finite set $\{a_1, a_2, \ldots, a_n\}$ of elements of G such that $H = (a_1, a_2, \ldots, a_n)$. It is clear that if H is finitely generated, then there must exist (at least one) *minimal generating system* for H, that is, a generating system of H of m elements where m is such that H is generated by no set of fewer than m elements.

Thus, for example, the symmetric group S_n is generated by the set of $n - 1$ transpositions $(1, 2), (1, 3), \ldots, (1, n)$, the group $Z^3 = Z \oplus Z \oplus Z$ (Z the additive group of integers) is generated by the three elements $(1, 0, 0)$, $(0, 1, 0)$ and $(0, 0, 1)$, and the group of symmetries of the square is generated by the 90° rotation r and any reflection.

Theorem 2.32. *Let G be a finitely generated Abelian group, having a minimal generating system of n elements. Then, $G \cong G_1 \otimes G_2 \otimes \cdots \otimes G_n$, where each G_i is cyclic, the order of G_i is less than or equal to the order of G_{i+1} and divides it if G_{i+1} is finite.*

PROOF. If G has one minimal generating system of n elements, then every minimal generating system of G will also consist of n elements. We proceed by induction on n, and note that, if $n = 1$, then G is itself cyclic, so that the theorem is trivially true.

Suppose, then, that $n > 1$. If $a_1, a_2, \ldots, a_n$ is a (minimal) generating system for G such that

$$a_1^{f_1} a_2^{f_2} \cdots a_n^{f_n} = e$$

implies that $f_1 = f_2 = \cdots = f_n = 0$, then we assert that

$$G \cong (a_1) \otimes (a_2) \otimes \cdots \otimes (a_n)$$

and that each (a_i) is infinite cyclic. For each (a_i) is normal, since G is Abelian, and $G = \prod(a_i)$. If we have $g \in (a_i) \cap \prod_{j \neq i} (a_j)$, then $g = a_i^{f_i} = \prod_{j \neq i} a_j^{f_j}$. But then $a_i^{-f_i} \prod_{j \neq i} a_j^{f_j} = e$, which, by our assumption, implies that $f_1 = f_2 = \cdots = f_n = 0$, or $g = e$. Finally, each (a_i) must be infinite cyclic, since, otherwise, we would have, for some i, that $a_i^{f_i} = e$ for $f_i \neq 0$, contrary to assumption.

Thus if for any minimal generating system $g_1, g_2, \ldots, g_n$ of G

$$g_1^{f_1} g_2^{f_2} \cdots g_n^{f_n} = e$$

implies that $f_1 = f_2 = \cdots = f_n = 0$, our assertion is valid for n.

Suppose, on the contrary, that for every minimal generating system there exists such a relation for some $f_i \neq 0$. Since $e^{-1} = e$, this is equivalent to assuming that, for every minimal generating system, there exists such a relation with at least one of the exponents $f_i > 0$. The positive integers being well-ordered, there must then exist a minimal generating system $a_1, a_2, \ldots, a_n$ and a relation $a_1^{f_1} a_2^{f_2} \cdots a_n^{f_n} = e$ having a smallest possible positive exponent, say m. That is, there exists no minimal generating system satisfying such a relation involving a smaller positive exponent. Reordering the a_i's, if necessary, we may assume that $m = f_1$, so that

$$e = a_1^m \prod_{i>1} a_i^{f_i}.$$

We now assert that m divides every f_i, $i = 2, \ldots, n$. For, if m does not divide f_j, then $f_j = mq_j + r_j$, with $0 < r_j < m$. For simplicity, suppose $j = 2$. Then we have

$$e = (a_1 a_2^{q_2})^m a_2^{r_2} \prod_{i>2} a_i^{f_i}.$$

Since $a_1 = (a_1 a_2^{q_2}) a_2^{-q_2}$, we have that $(a_1 a_2^{q_2}), a_2, \ldots, a_n$ is also a minimal generating system for G, which contradicts the minimality of m, since $0 < r_2 < m$. Thus m does divide each f_j, say $f_j = mq_j$.

Now let $b = a_1 a_2^{q_2} \cdots a_n^{q_n}$. Then $b, a_2, \ldots, a_n$ is a minimal generating system for G and $b^m = e$, and the minimality of m gives us $b^k \neq e$ for $0 < k < m$. Hence, (b) is cyclic of order m.

Suppose that $g \in (b) \cap (a_2, \ldots, a_n)$. Then

$$g = b^k = a_2^{k_2} \cdots a_n^{k_n}, \text{ for } 0 \leq k < m.$$

This implies that $e = b^k a_2^{-k_2} \cdots a_n^{-k_n}$, which contradicts the minimality of m, unless $k = 0$. Hence $g = b^0 = e$. Clearly, $G = (b)(a_2, \ldots, a_n)$, and again the commutativity of G makes all subgroups normal. Thus

$$G \cong (b) \otimes (a_2, \ldots, a_n).$$

By our inductive assumption, we have that

$$(a_2, \ldots, a_n) \cong (b_2') \otimes (b_3') \otimes \cdots \otimes (b_n'),$$

where the order m_{j-1} of (b_{j-1}') does not exceed the order m_j of (b_j'), and m_{j-1} divides m_j if m_j is finite, $j = 3, \ldots, n$. If $m_2, \ldots, m_n$ are all infinite, we are finished. If they are not, then we must show that m divides m_2. Now we have $m_2 = qm + r$, where $0 \leq r < m$. Then, if b_i, $2 \leq i \leq n$, is the element in G corresponding to b_i' under the above isomorphism, we have

$$e = (bb_2^q)^m b_2^r b_3^0 \cdots b_n^0,$$

which would contradict the minimality of m, unless $r = 0$, since (bb_2^q), $b_2, \ldots, b_n$ is a minimal generating system of G. Hence m does divide m_2 and the proof is complete.

Exercises

1. State and prove the extension of Theorem 2.28 to the case of $G \cong H$, where H is the weak direct product of an arbitrary set of groups H_i.
2. Show that $G_1 \otimes G_2 \otimes \cdots \otimes G_n \cong G_{i_1} \otimes G_{i_2} \otimes \cdots \otimes G_{i_n}$, where $i_1, i_2, \ldots, i_n$ is any permutation of $1, 2, \ldots, n$.
3. Let G_i be a group of finite order m_i, $i = 1, 2, \ldots, n$. Show that $G_1 \otimes G_2 \otimes \cdots \otimes G_n$ has order $m = m_1 m_2 \cdots m_n$.
4. Show that not every group is an interior direct product of proper subgroups of itself by considering the group $G = (s, t)$, where s is of order 3, t is of order 2, and $st = ts^2$.
5. Show that the projections of a direct product onto its components are homomorphisms.
6. Let G be the group of Exercise 4. Is G a subdirect product of groups G/G_i for G_i proper normal subgroups of G?
7. Let G be a finite cyclic group of order $n = p_1^{e_1} \cdots p_r^{e_r}$, where the p_i are distinct primes. Show, by induction on r, that G has a cyclic subgroup G_i of order $p_i^{e_i}$, $i = 1, \ldots, r$ and that $G \cong G_1 \otimes \cdots \otimes G_r$.
8. Show that if G is cyclic of order $n = st$ where $(s, t) = 1$, i.e., s and t are relatively prime, then $G \cong H \otimes K$ where H is of order s and K is of order t.
9. In Z let $\{p_i\}$ be the set of all primes. Exhibit the isomorphism between Z and a subdirect sum of the groups Z_{p_i}.
10. Let G be Abelian and H a subgroup such that G/H is infinite cyclic. Prove that $G \cong H \otimes G/H$. (*Hint:* Consider the subgroup K of G generated by an element of the coset generating G/H.)
11. Show that the words *finitely generated* cannot be deleted from Theorem 2.32 by showing that the additive group of rational numbers is not a direct sum of cyclic groups.

14. Abelian Groups

In a finite group, every element is of finite order, but not conversely. That is, it is possible to have a group in which every element is of finite order and yet the group itself is of infinite order. An example of such a group is the additive group of rational numbers modulo 1, that is, the group R/Z, where R is the additive group of all rational numbers and Z is, as usual, the subgroup of integers. Another such group is that subgroup of the rationals modulo 1 which is generated by the rational numbers of the form $1/p^k$, $k = 1, 2, 3, \ldots$ and p some fixed prime. This latter group is often designated by Z_{p^∞}, and has the property that each element is of order p^k for some nonnegative integer k.

Definition. A group in which every element is of finite order is called a *periodic*, or *torsion group*. If every element of a group except the identity is of infinite order, the group is called *aperiodic*, or *torsion-free*. A torsion group in which the order of every element is a power of the fixed prime p is called a *p-primary* group, or simply a *p-group*.

Perhaps the simplest example of a torsion-free group is that of the additive group of integers. More generally, any infinite cyclic group is clearly torsion-free.

Definition. In an Abelian group G, the subset of elements of finite order is a subgroup, since if $x^m = y^n = e$, then $(xy^{-1})^{mn} = x^{mn}(y^{mn})^{-1} = e$. This subgroup is called the *torsion subgroup* of G.

In contrast, the set of elements of infinite order, together with the identity, do not, in general, constitute a subgroup. For example, in the (Abelian) group of rotations of the plane about some fixed point, the rotations of 1 radian and of $(\pi - 1)$ radians are each of infinite order (why?), yet their product is of order two. We may, however, give the following result.

Theorem 2.33. *If G is a finitely generated Abelian group, then $G \cong T \otimes A$, where T is the torsion subgroup of G and A is torsion-free.*

PROOF. From Theorem 2.32, we have that $G \cong G_1 \otimes G_2 \otimes \cdots \otimes G_n$ where each G_i is cyclic, the order of G_i is less than or equal to the order of G_{i+1}, and divides the latter order if it is finite. Suppose m_k is the order of the largest finite G_i. We let $T = G_1 \otimes \cdots \otimes G_k$ and $A = G_{k+1} \otimes \cdots \otimes G_n$, and have $G \cong T \otimes A$. (If G_1 is infinite, then G is itself torsion-free and $G \cong \{e\} \otimes G$.)

Now T is a torsion group, since all elements of T have order dividing m_k. Moreover, A is torsion-free, since if $x \in A$ were of finite order r, we would have $x^r = (g_{k+1} \cdots g_n)^r = e$ with $g_{k+i} \in G_{k+i}$, or $g_{k+1}^r \cdots g_n^r = e$. In the proof of Theorem 2.32, we would have obtained G_{k+1} of order at most r, contrary to the assumption that G_{k+1} has infinite order. Finally, if $t \in T$ and $a \in A$, $a \neq e$, then $(ta)^r = t^r a^r$, from which it follows that ta is of infinite order, and T is the torsion subgroup of G.

Theorem 2.34. *If G is an Abelian group and T its torsion subgroup, then G/T is torsion-free.*

PROOF. Suppose $\bar{x} \in G/T$ has finite order m. Let $u \in G$ be such that $\bar{u} = \bar{x}$. Then, $\bar{u}^m = \overline{u^m} = \bar{e}$, or $u^m \in T$ whence u^m has finite order, say n. Then $u^{mn} = e$ and $u \in T$, so that $\bar{u} = \bar{x} = \bar{e}$, and the only element of G/T having finite order is the identity.

The next theorem, together with its corollary, while introduced at this point for use in the following theorem, is of considerable interest in its own right for the information it gives on the nature of an element of composite order in an arbitrary group.

Theorem 2.35. *Let G be any group and x any element of G with composite order mn, where m and n are relatively prime. Then, there exist unique elements y of order m and z of order n in G such that $x = yz = zy$. Moreover, both y and z are powers of x.*

PROOF. Since m and n are relatively prime, there exist integers a and b such that $am + bn = 1$. Then, $x = x^{am}x^{bn} = x^{bn}x^{am}$. We let $y = x^{bn}$ and $z = x^{am}$, and must show that y and z have the required orders and are unique.

Now $y^m = x^{bnm} = e^b = e$, and $z^n = x^{amn} = e^a = e$. Thus the orders of y and z must be m' and n', respectively, where m' divides m and n' divides n, and, hence, $m'n'$ divides mn. Now $x^{m'n'} = y^{m'n'}z^{m'n'} = e$, from which it follows that mn divides $m'n'$. This is possible only if $mn = m'n'$. Since m and n are relatively prime, this implies that $m = m'$ and $n = n'$, as required.

If, also, $x = y'z' = z'y'$ with y' and z' of respective orders m and n, then $xy' = y'z'y' = y'x$ and, similarly, $xz' = z'y'z' = z'x$. Thus y' and z' commute with x, hence also with all powers of x, and, in particular, with y and z and their inverses. Let $g = y'^{-1}y$ and from $yz = x = y'z'$, we conclude that $g = z'z^{-1}$. Then $g^m = (y'^{-1}y)^m = (y'^{-1})^m y^m = e$, and $g^n = (z'z^{-1})^n = z'^n(z^{-1})^n = e$. But $g^m = g^n = e$ with m and n relatively prime implies that $g = e$; hence $y = y'$ and $z = z'$.

Corollary 2.35.1. *Let x in any group G have order $n = n_1n_2 \cdots n_r$, with the n_k relatively prime in pairs. Then x has a unique representation $x = x_1x_2 \cdots x_r$ with the x_k commuting with each other and of respective orders n_k. Moreover, each x_k is a power of x.*

PROOF. Induction on r.

Before proceeding further, we give an alternative procedure for the first part of the proof of Theorem 2.35.

PROOF. Let $a = x^m$, $b = x^n$ and we have $ab = ba$, a is of order n and b is of order m. In the set of all elements of the form a^rb^s, there are, then, at most mn distinct elements. If $a^rb^s = a^ub^v$, with $1 \leq r, u \leq n$ and $1 \leq s, v \leq m$, then $a^{r-u} = b^{v-s} = e$, $a^r = a^u$ and $b^s = b^v$. Thus, the mn elements a^rb^s with $1 \leq r \leq n$, $1 \leq s \leq m$ are all distinct, and all are powers of x. Then, for some such r and s, we must have $x = a^rb^s$. We let $y = b^s = x^{ns}$ and $z = a^r = x^{mr}$; hence $x = yz$, $y^m = z^n = e$, and we proceed as before.

The reason for giving this alternative form of the proof is that it avoids use of the result from elementary number theory that, if m and n are relatively prime, then there exist integers a and b such that $am + bn = 1$. Indeed, this number theory result can be obtained from the argument we have just given. For, from $x = yz = x^{mr+ns}$ and the fact that x is of order mn, we can conclude that $mr + ns = 1 + kmn$ for some integer k. Then, $1 - ns = m(r - kn) = mq$, where $q = r - kn$. But this gives $1 = mq + ns$, as desired.

Definition. A *Sylow p-subgroup* of the group G is a subgroup S_p which is a p-group and is not properly contained in any other p-subgroup of G (for the same prime p).

That an Abelian group will have Sylow subgroups for all primes p follows from the fact that, if $x^{p^i} = y^{p^j} = e$, then $(xy^{-1})^{p^k} = e$ for k the maximum of i and j, hence the set of all elements of order some power of p form a subgroup.

Theorem 2.36. *An Abelian torsion group G is isomorphic to the weak direct product of its Sylow p-subgroups.*

PROOF. Since G is Abelian, all subgroups are normal. Clearly, $S_p \cap \prod_{q \neq p} S_q$ is the identity element, since it consists of elements whose order is a power of distinct primes, i.e., elements of order one, and the identity is the only element of order one. If g is an element of G having order $n = n_1 n_2 \cdots n_r$, the unique prime power factorization of n, we have, from the preceding corollary, that $g = g_1 g_2 \cdots g_r$, where each g_i has order a power of a different prime and is, hence, in some S_p. Thus $G = \prod S_p$, the product taken over all primes p, and, by the remark concerning the extension of Theorem 2.28, the theorem is proved.

For finite Abelian groups, we may obtain a stronger result, giving a form of direct product decomposition quite different from that of Theorem 2.32.

Theorem 2.37. *Let G be a finite Abelian group of order $n = p_1^{e_1} p_2^{e_2} \cdots p_r^{e_r}$. Then $G \cong S_{p_1} \otimes S_{p_2} \otimes \cdots \otimes S_{p_r}$, where S_{p_i} is the Sylow p_i-subgroup of G. It is of order $p_i^{e_i}$ and is itself (isomorphic to) the direct product of cyclic groups of orders $p_i^{e_{i1}}, \ldots, p_i^{e_{ik_i}}$, where $e_{i1} + \cdots + e_{ik_i} = e_i$.*

PROOF. Since the order of any element of G must divide n, the only nontrivial Sylow subgroups of G are $S_{p_1}, \ldots, S_{p_r}$, and G is isomorphic to their direct product. By Theorem 2.32, each S_{p_i} is isomorphic to a direct product of cyclic groups whose orders are powers of p_i, and the order of S_{p_i} is the product of these orders, say $p_i^{f_i}$. Then $n = p_1^{e_1} \cdots p_r^{e_r} = p_1^{f_1} \cdots p_r^{f_r}$ and the unique factorization theorem for integers implies that $e_i = f_i$ as required.

Corollary 2.37.1. *If the order of a finite Abelian group G is divisible by a prime p, then G has an element of order p.*

PROOF. The direct factor S_p of G is itself the direct product of cyclic groups whose orders are powers of p. If, in such a cyclic group of order p^e and generator x, we have $e = 1$, then x is the desired element. If $e > 1$, then $x^{p^{e-1}}$ has order p, as required.

Exercises

1. Let G be the additive group of rational numbers modulo 1. Show that G is a torsion group.
2. Show that the group of Exercise 1 is the weak direct product of the groups Z_{p^∞}, where p ranges over all the primes.
3. Let G be the additive group of real numbers modulo 1. What is the torsion subgroup T of G? Is $G \cong T \oplus G/T$?
4. Let G be a finite Abelian p-group. Show that the number of elements x of G such that $x^p = e$ must be a power of p.
5. Show that an Abelian group of order p^2 need not be (isomorphic to) a direct product of groups of order p. What about an Abelian group of order p^k, k an integer greater than 2?

15. The Sylow Theorems

While it is not true, in general, that if n divides the (finite) order of an arbitrary group G, then G has a subgroup of order n (see Exercise 12, section 7), it is true if n is a prime or a power of a prime. This, as well as considerable other information about subgroups of prime power order, is contained in the Sylow Theorems. Before proceeding to their statements and proofs, we need the following.

Definition. Let S be a nonempty subset of the group G, and K a subgroup of G. The *normalizer of S in K* is the set

$$N_K(S) = \{x : x \in K, xSx^{-1} = S\}.$$

If $K = G$, $N_G(S) = N(S)$ is called simply the *normalizer of S*.

Theorem 2.38. *$N_K(S) = K \cap N(S)$ is a subgroup of K and there is a 1–1 correspondence between the cosets of $N_K(S)$ in K and the distinct conjugates xSx^{-1} of S for $x \in K$.*

PROOF. That $N_K(S) = K \cap N(S)$, is immediate from the definition. If $x, y \in N_K(S)$, then y^{-1} and xy are also in $N_K(S)$, so that $N_K(S)$ is a subgroup of K. Now

$$\begin{aligned} xSx^{-1} = ySy^{-1} \text{ iff } S &= x^{-1}ySy^{-1}x = (x^{-1}y)S(x^{-1}y)^{-1}, \\ &\text{iff } x^{-1}y \in N_K(S) \\ &\text{iff } y \in xN_K(S). \end{aligned}$$

Thus conjugates xSx^{-1} of S for $x \in K$ are equal iff they are defined by elements in the same coset of $N_K(S)$ in K, or there is a 1–1 correspondence between the cosets of $N_K(S)$ in K and the distinct conjugates xSx^{-1} of S for $x \in K$.

Definition. For any group G, the *center* of G is the set $C = \{g\colon gh = hg$, all $h \in G\}$. Evidently C is always a normal subgroup of G.

Corollary 2.38.1. *Let the group G have order n and let C, the center of G, be of order c. Then*

$$n = c + \sum n_i,$$

where each n_i is a divisor of n and, moreover, is the number of elements in the conjugate class of some element of G not in C.

PROOF. We need only prove that n_i is a divisor of n. (If $xgx^{-1} = yhy^{-1}$, then $h = (y^{-1}x)g(y^{-1}x)^{-1}$, whence distinct conjugate classes are disjoint.) But n_i is the number of conjugates of some $g \in G$, hence the number of cosets of $N(g)$, and n_i divides n.

Definition. The equation of Corollary 2.38.1 is called the *(conjugate) class equation* of G.

Theorem 2.39 (First Sylow Theorem). *Let G be a finite group of order $n = p^k q$, p a prime not dividing q. Then, G has subgroups H_i of order p^i, $1 \leq i \leq k$, and each subgroup of order p^i is normal in some subgroup of order p^{i+1} for $1 \leq i \leq k$.*

PROOF. The result is trivial if $n = p$. Hence, we shall proceed by induction on the order of G, and assume the theorem for groups of order less than n. Let $C = \{x: xg = gx, \text{ all } g \in G\}$, and C, the center of G, is a normal subgroup of G and, moreover, is Abelian. Let C have order c.

If c is divisible by p, then, by Corollary 2.37.1, we have that C has an element of order p, which generates a cyclic subgroup P of order p. Since the elements of P commute with all elements of G, P is normal in G, and G/P is a group of order $p^{k-1}q$. By the inductive assumption, G/P has subgroups $\overline{H}_i$ of orders p^i, $1 \leq i \leq k-1$, and each such $\overline{H}_i$ is normal in some $\overline{H}_{i+1}$ for $1 \leq i < k-1$. Let α be the natural homomorphism of G onto G/P, and we have $\overline{H}_i\alpha^{-1} = H_{i+1}$ is a subgroup of G, $1 \leq i \leq k-1$, and each such H_i is normal in some H_{i+1}. Now, H_{i+1} consists of the union of p^i disjoint cosets of P, each of which has p elements, and hence H_{i+1} is of order p^{i+1}. We let $H_1 = P$, which being normal in G, is normal in any subgroup of G. Let H be a subgroup of G of order p^i. If $P \subseteq H$, then $H\alpha$ has order p^{i-1} and is normal in some $\overline{H}_i$; hence H is normal in $\overline{H}_i\alpha^{-1}$ of order p^{i+1}. If $P \nsubseteq H$, then $H\alpha$ has order p^i and H is normal in $H\alpha\alpha^{-1}$ since $P \subseteq C$, and $H\alpha\alpha^{-1}$ has order p^{i+1}. Our result follows in the case that c is divisible by p.

If c is not divisible by p, then we divide G into conjugate classes and have

$$n = c + \sum n_i,$$

where $n_i > 1$ is the number of elements in the conjugate class of an element not in C. Not all the n_i can be divisible by p, since, if they all were divisible by p, then c would be also. Let $\{b: b = ghg^{-1}, \text{ some } g \in G\}$, the conjugate class of h, be some conjugate class of n_i elements for which n_i is not divisible by p. The normalizer $N(h)$ of h is then a subgroup of G whose index, n_i, in G, is not divisible by p. Since $n_i > 1$, it follows that $N(h)$ is of order $p^k s < n$. By the inductive assumption, $N(h)$ has subgroups of the required types, which are, of course, also subgroups of G, and the theorem is proved.

Corollary 2.39.1. *If the order of a finite group G is divisible by a prime p, then G contains an element of order p.*

PROOF. Immediate from the theorem.

Corollary 2.39.2. *If the order of a finite group G is $p^k q$, where p is a prime not dividing q, then G contains a Sylow p-subgroup of order p^k and every p-subgroup of G is contained in a Sylow p-subgroup of G.*

PROOF. By Corollary 2.39.1, the order of every p-subgroup of G must be a power of p, since, if the order were divisible by two distinct primes, then the subgroup would contain elements of distinct prime orders and would not be a p-group. Every subgroup of order p^k is, therefore, a Sylow p-subgroup.

Corollary 2.39.3. *Every finite p-group P has order a power of p. If this order is p^k, then every subgroup of P is contained in a maximal subgroup of order p^{k-1}, and every maximal subgroup is normal.*

PROOF. Immediate from the theorem and preceding corollaries.

Corollary 2.39.4. *Every finite p-group has a composition series in which the factor groups are Abelian.*

PROOF. Exercise.

Theorem 2.40 (Second Sylow Theorem). *In a finite group G, the Sylow p-subgroups are all conjugate, and are, in number, the index t of the normalizer of any of them, and t is of the form $1 + mp$.*

PROOF. Let $M = \{S = S_1, S_2, \ldots, S_t\}$ be the set of all conjugates of some fixed Sylow p-subgroup S, $S_i = g_i S g_i^{-1}$ for some $g_i \in G$, and let P be any Sylow p-subgroup of G.

If $P \neq S_i$, then neither can contain the other. Now, for $x_i \in P$, $x_i \notin S_i$ we must have $x_i S_i x_i^{-1} \neq S_i$ since, otherwise, (x_i, S_i) would be a p-group properly containing S_i. Then, $M_i = \{x_i S_i x_i^{-1} : x_i \in P\}$ is a subset of M consisting of t_i conjugates of S, since any conjugate of S_i is also a conjugate of S. Now $t_i > 1$ and is the index of $N_P(S_i)$ in P. Since P has order a power of p, any subgroup of P has index a power of p also. Thus t_i is divisible by p.

For $i \neq j$, the sets M_i and M_j are either equal or disjoint. For, if $xS_ix^{-1} = yS_jy^{-1}$ with $x, y \in P$, then

$$(y^{-1}x)S_i(y^{-1}x)^{-1} = S_j, \quad S_j \in M_i, \quad M_j \subseteq M_i$$

and, similarly, $M_i \subseteq M_j$.

If $P \neq S_i$ for all i, then M is the union of disjoint sets, each of which contains some multiple of p elements, whence t is also a multiple of p. If $P = S_i$ for some i, then M is the union of disjoint sets, all but one of which contain a multiple of p elements, and that one contains a single element, whence, in this case, P is a conjugate of S and $t = 1 + mp$ for some m. But t is the index of $N(S)$, which cannot be divisible by p since then S would also have index divisible by p, which is impossible, and the theorem is proved.

Exercises

1. Let H and K be subgroups of G. Show that H is a normal subgroup of K iff $H \subseteq K \subseteq N_G(H)$.
2. Show that if G has order p^n, p a prime, then the center of G must contain at least p elements.
3. Show that every finite p-group has a composition series whose (simple) factor groups are cyclic (and hence Abelian).
4. Can a simple group have composite order?
5. Determine the Sylow 3-subgroups of the symmetric group S_4 and show that they are all conjugate. Do the same for the symmetric group S_5.

CHAPTER 3

Rings and Ideals

1. Rings

In most of the number systems with which one works in elementary mathematics, there are in simultaneous use two distinct binary operations, generally known as addition and multiplication. This is in contrast to just one operation, as is the case with the groups with which we have thus far been concerned. Modeling our definition on properties common to these number systems, as well as to such structures as the set of all n by n matrices with elements in one of these number systems, or the set of all polynomials with coefficients in, say, the set of all integers, we now define a type of algebraic structure known as a ring.

Definition. A *ring* $(R, *, \circ)$ is a nonempty set R, together with two binary operations (compositions) $*$ and $\circ$, such that R is a commutative group with respect to $*$ and a semi-group with respect to $\circ$, and such that the right and left distributive laws of $\circ$ over $*$ hold, i.e., for any $a, b, c \in R$ we have

$$(b * c) \circ a = (b \circ a) * (c \circ a), \qquad \text{and}$$
$$a \circ (b * c) = (a \circ b) * (a \circ c).$$

We shall usually refer to $*$ as "addition" and to $\circ$ as "multiplication" and use the customary notation for these operations. Also, we shall normally use R as a designation for the ring $(R, *, \circ)$. The additive identity element of R will be denoted by 0, the additive inverse of a by $-a$, and $a + (-b)$ by $a - b$.

Using this latter notation, we see that we may define a ring without reference to either of the notions of group or semi-group as follows:

Definition. A *ring* R is a nonempty set R, together with two binary operations, called addition and multiplication and written $a + b$ and ab, respectively, such that for any $a, b, c \in R$:

(i) $a + (b + c) = (a + b) + c, \qquad \text{and} \qquad a(bc) = (ab)c.$

(ii) There is 0 in R such that $a + 0 = 0 + a$.

(iii) There is $-a$ in R such that $a + (-a) = (-a) + a = 0$.

(iv) $a + b = b + a$.

(v) $(b + c)a = ba + ca, \qquad \text{and} \qquad a(b + c) = ab + ac.$

Of the many examples of rings which come readily to mind from experience with the common systems of elementary mathematics, the most natural is, perhaps, the ring of ordinary integers with the usual addition and multiplication. However, if we examine the properties of the ring of integers, we note that it has properties not enjoyed by rings in general. Among these properties are:

(a) The existence of a multiplicative identity element, which must be unique, called the *unity* element, and which we shall usually designate by the letter e.
(b) The commutativity of multiplication.
(c) The nonexistence of elements x, y, known as *zero-divisors* or *divisors of zero*, such that $xy = 0$ while neither x nor y is itself zero. In this case, x and y are called, respectively, *left* and *right zero-divisors*.

On the other hand, the integers themselves fail to possess a most useful property, namely that:

(d) The set of nonzero elements of the ring constitutes a multiplicative group.

Note that property (d) implies that there exists at least one nonzero element, since a group cannot be an empty set (since it must contain, at least, an identity element). In the event that the element x of a ring R has a multiplicative inverse element, it will be denoted by x^{-1}, as before. These properties lead us to some further definitions.

Definition. If a ring satisfies (a), it is called a *ring with unity.* If it satisfies (b), it is called *commutative* or *Abelian.* If it satisfies (a), (b), and (c), it is an *integral domain.*† If it satisfies (d), it is called a *division ring, sfield, skew-field,* or *quasi-field.*‡ A ring which satisfies (b) and (d), that is, a commutative division ring, is a *field.*

A note of caution here; some authors refer to both sfield and field by the term "field," and then distinguish between commutative and noncommutative "fields."

Definition. In a ring with unity element, an element having a multiplicative inverse is called a *unit.*

Thus the ring of integers is an *integral domain,* whose units are 1 and −1. The subring of even integers, however, is not an integral domain under our definition, since it contains no unity element. We shall see later that the lack of a unity element is never a serious defect in a ring, as it is always possible to "imbed" such a ring in a larger ring, which does have a unity element.

In order to give some indication of the generality of the concept of ring, we turn to some less familiar examples of rings.

(A) The ring of all even integers, or, more generally, the ring of all integers divisible by some fixed integer n, with respect to the usual operations of addition and multiplication.

† Some authors omit (a) from the requirements for an integral domain.
‡ We shall prefer the term *division ring.*

(B) The ring of all real valued functions, continuous on the interval (0, 1), where by $(f + g)(x)$, we mean $f(x) + g(x)$ and by $(fg)(x)$, we mean $f(x)g(x)$. Similarly, the set of all real valued functions differentiable on the interval (0, 1) also form a ring.

(C) The set of all real numbers of the form $a + b\sqrt{2}$, where a and b are rational numbers, with respect to the usual addition and multiplication of real numbers. It may be verified that, in this case, we actually have a field.

In the next four examples, we shall define the addition and multiplication by giving tables similar to those used in the case of the single operation of groups, but this time giving both a table for addition and one for multiplication. In each case, the ring will consist of four elements.

(D) $R = \{a, b, c, d\}$.

+	a	b	c	d
a	a	b	c	d
b	b	a	d	c
c	c	d	a	b
d	d	c	b	a

·	a	b	c	d
a	a	a	a	a
b	a	b	a	b
c	a	a	c	c
d	a	b	c	d

(E) $R = \{a, b, c, d\}$.

+	a	b	c	d
a	a	b	c	d
b	b	a	d	c
c	c	d	a	b
d	d	c	b	a

·	a	b	c	d
a	a	a	a	a
b	a	b	c	d
c	a	c	d	b
d	a	d	b	c

(F) $R = \{a, b, c, d\}$.

+	a	b	c	d
a	a	b	c	d
b	b	c	d	a
c	c	d	a	b
d	d	a	b	c

·	a	b	c	d
a	a	a	a	a
b	a	b	c	d
c	a	c	a	c
d	a	d	c	b

(G) $R = \{a, b, c, d\}$.

+	a	b	c	d
a	a	b	c	d
b	b	a	d	c
c	c	d	a	b
d	d	c	b	a

·	a	b	c	d
a	a	a	a	a
b	a	b	b	a
c	a	c	c	a
d	a	d	d	a

In each of these last four examples, the verification of the ring postulates is essentially a process of detailed enumeration of possible cases of each of the postulates. In the case of commutativity, either of addition or multiplication, we may check by seeing if the operation table is symmetric with respect to the *main diagonal*, that is, the diagonal from upper left to lower right. Thus, addition is commutative, as it must be in a ring, in all four cases, while multiplication is commutative in the first three, but not in the fourth. We also see that in all cases the additive identity, or zero element, is the element a, while d is a unity in (D), b is a unity in (E) and (F), and there is no unity in (G).

(H) Let R be the set of all matrices of order 2 with real numbers as elements, that is, R is the set of all symbols of the form

$$A = \begin{pmatrix} a_{11} & a_{12} \\ a_{21} & a_{22} \end{pmatrix} \quad \text{or} \quad B = \begin{pmatrix} b_{11} & b_{12} \\ b_{21} & b_{22} \end{pmatrix},$$

where a_{ij} and b_{jk} are real numbers, $i, j, k = 1, 2$. We define addition and multiplication by

$$A + B = C, \text{ where } c_{ij} = a_{ij} + b_{ij} \quad \text{(ordinary addition)},$$
$$AB = D, \text{ where } d_{ik} = \textstyle\sum_j a_{ij}b_{jk} \quad \text{(ordinary multiplication)}.$$

Thus, for example, $c_{12} = a_{12} + b_{12}$ and $d_{12} = a_{11}b_{12} + a_{12}b_{22}$. It is almost obvious from the definition that addition is commutative, while the reader can easily convince himself, by means of examples, that multiplication is not commutative. The zero is seen to be the matrix

$$\begin{pmatrix} 0 & 0 \\ 0 & 0 \end{pmatrix},$$

and the additive inverse, or negative of A, is apparently the matrix

$$\begin{pmatrix} -a_{11} & -a_{12} \\ -a_{21} & -a_{22} \end{pmatrix}.$$

The associativity of the two operations and the distributive laws (right and left) can easily be checked, as we shall illustrate in the case of the associativity of addition. Let

$$(A + B) + E = G, \text{ where } A + B = C \text{ and } B + E = F.$$

Then for the typical element g_{ij} of G, we have

$$\begin{aligned} g_{ij} = c_{ij} + e_{ij} &= (a_{ij} + b_{ij}) + e_{ij} \\ &= a_{ij} + (b_{ij} + e_{ij}) \\ &= a_{ij} + f_{ij}, \qquad i, j = 1, 2, \end{aligned}$$

from which it follows that

$$(A + B) + E = A + (B + E).$$

It is not difficult to see that one could replace 2 in all of the above definitions by any positive integer n, and obtain the ring of all real matrices of order n. Further, since in establishing that the above set is a ring with respect to the given definitions of addition and multiplication, we need only use the ring properties of the set of real numbers, we may further extend the definitions to include the ring of matrices of order n with elements taken from any ring R.

(I) The ring of all real quaternions. Here R is the set of all ordered quadruples (a_1, a_2, a_3, a_4) of real numbers. We define addition and multiplication by

$$(a_1, a_2, a_3, a_4) + (b_1, b_2, b_3, b_4) = (a_1 + b_1, a_2 + b_2, a_3 + b_3, a_4 + b_4),$$

$$(a_1, a_2, a_3, a_4)(b_1, b_2, b_3, b_4) = (a_1b_1 - a_2b_2 - a_3b_3 - a_4b_4, a_1b_2 + a_2b_1 + a_3b_4 - a_4b_3, a_1b_3 - a_2b_4 + a_3b_1 + a_4b_2, a_1b_4 + a_2b_3 - a_3b_2 + a_4b_1).$$

With respect to addition, one sees that we have nothing other than the additive group R^4. Checking the properties of a ring regarding multiplication is quite laborious, although straightforward. We may note that $(1, 0, 0, 0)$ is a unity element of this ring, and that the ring of real quaternions is actually a division ring.

(J) The ring of endomorphisms of an additive Abelian group G. Here, we define the product of two endomorphisms as usual, and, if α and β are both endomorphisms of G, then, for $g \in G$, we define

$$g(\alpha + \beta) = g\alpha + g\beta.$$

Since G is Abelian, it follows at once that $\alpha + \beta = \beta + \alpha$. We have that the zero endomorphism, that is, the endomorphism whose kernel is G itself, is the zero of our ring, and for any endomorphism α, $-\alpha$ is defined by

$$g(-\alpha) = -(g\alpha) \text{ for all } g \in G.$$

The associativity of the usual product of mappings assures us that our multiplication is associative, left distributivity follows from,

$$g(\alpha(\beta + \gamma)) = (g\alpha)(\beta + \gamma) = g(\alpha\beta) + g(\alpha\gamma) = g(\alpha\beta + \alpha\gamma),$$

and right distributivity in a similar manner. The identity mapping, which is, of course, an endomorphism, is seen to be a unity element for this ring.

It will be apparent from the foregoing examples that a subset S of a ring R may itself be a ring with respect to the operations of addition and multiplication as defined in the ring R. In such a case, we call S a *subring* of R, and leave it to the reader to verify that a nonempty subset S of the ring R is a subring of R iff, for any $a, b \in S$, both $a - b$ and ab are in S. Alternatively, we could define a subring of R as a subgroup S of the additive group of R such that S is closed with respect to the multiplication of R.

We next obtain a few easy, but important consequences of our definition of a ring.

Theorem 3.1. *For any elements a and b of any ring R, we have*

$$a0 = 0a = 0, \qquad (-a)b = a(-b) = -(ab), \qquad (-a)(-b) = ab.$$

PROOF. $0 + 0 = 0$, since 0 is the additive identity. By left distributivity, we have

$$a0 = a(0 + 0) = a0 + a0.$$

From the associativity of addition and the properties of the additive inverse and identity, we then obtain

$$\begin{aligned} 0 = -a0 + a0 &= -a0 + (a0 + a0) = (-a0 + a0) + a0 \\ &= 0 + a0 = a0. \end{aligned}$$

In a similar manner, we have $0a = 0$.

From

$$0 = (a + (-a))b = ab + (-a)b,$$

we obtain that the inverse of ab is $(-a)b$, or

$$-(ab) = (-a)b,$$

and, similarly,

$$a(-b) = -(ab).$$

In this last statement, we replace a by $-a$ and we have

$$(-a)(-b) = -((-a)b) = -(-(ab)) = ab,$$

as required.

Theorem 3.2. *A division ring contains no divisors of zero.*

PROOF. Let $x \neq 0$ be an element of the ring. Then, by definition of a division ring, x has a multiplicative inverse, x^{-1}, such that $xx^{-1} = x^{-1}x = e$, the unity element. From the previous theorem, we have that if $xy = 0$, then

$$0 = x^{-1}0 = x^{-1}(xy) = (x^{-1}x)y = ey = y.$$

Similarly, if $yx = 0$, then multiplication on the right by x^{-1} leads to the conclusion that $y = 0$, and the ring contains no zero-divisors.

Thus a division ring lacks only the property of commutativity of being an integral domain, or, indeed, a field. As we shall see later in our study of fields, if the division ring is finite, it is a field. For the present, we shall content ourselves with showing that a finite integral domain is a field.

Theorem 3.3. *A finite integral domain is a field.*

PROOF. Let the elements of the integral domain M be $a_1, a_2, \ldots, a_n$. For a fixed nonzero element a of M, consider the set of products $aa_1, aa_2, \ldots, aa_n$. These are all distinct, since if $aa_i = aa_j$, then $a(a_i - a_j) = 0$, and since a is not zero, and thus is not a divisor of zero, we must have $a_i - a_j = 0$ or $a_i = a_j$. Thus each element of M is of the form aa_i, and, in particular, $e = aa_i$, e the unity of M, for some i with $1 \leq i \leq n$. Since M is commutative, we have also that $a_ia = e$, and a_i is the multiplicative inverse of a. Thus the nonzero elements of M form a commutative group, and M is a field.

Theorem 3.4. *Let $a \neq 0$ be an element of a ring without zero-divisors. Then either $ab = ac$ or $ba = ca$ implies that $b = c$.*

PROOF. If $ab = ac$, then $ab - ac = 0$ and, by the left distributive property, we have $a(b - c) = 0$. Since $a \neq 0$ and the ring has no zero-divisors, it must be that $b - c = 0$. Similarly, if $ba = ca$, the right distributive law implies that $b - c = 0$. In either case, we have $b = c$ as asserted.

That the cancellation properties just obtained for rings without zero-divisors do not hold for all rings can be seen by considering the ring of Example (H) on page 80. Here we have

$$\begin{pmatrix} 0 & 1 \\ 0 & 0 \end{pmatrix}\begin{pmatrix} 1 & 0 \\ 0 & 0 \end{pmatrix} = \begin{pmatrix} 0 & 1 \\ 0 & 1 \end{pmatrix}\begin{pmatrix} 1 & 0 \\ 0 & 0 \end{pmatrix} = \begin{pmatrix} 0 & 0 \\ 0 & 0 \end{pmatrix},$$

$\begin{pmatrix} 1 & 0 \\ 0 & 0 \end{pmatrix}$ is not the zero matrix, and yet

$$\begin{pmatrix} 0 & 1 \\ 0 & 0 \end{pmatrix} \neq \begin{pmatrix} 0 & 1 \\ 0 & 1 \end{pmatrix}.$$

While the fact that a ring R is an additive Abelian group provides a very close connection between groups and rings, the connection is, actually, even closer than that fact alone would indicate. For if we define

$$\begin{aligned} M_\rho &= \{\rho_a \colon a \in R,\ b\rho_a = ba \text{ for all } b \in R\}, \\ M_\lambda &= \{\lambda_a \colon a \in R,\ b\lambda_a = ab \text{ for all } b \in R\}, \\ M &= M_\rho \cup M_\lambda, \end{aligned}$$

we may easily verify that ρ_a and λ_a are operators on the additive group of R in consequence of the two distributive properties. We then have that R is an Abelian M-group, a fact that will be of much help in deriving theorems about rings as immediate consequences of corresponding theorems about groups with operators.

Exercises

1. Show that if a ring R has a unity element e, the unity element is unique.
2. Show that if in R^n, the additive group of n-tuples of real numbers, we define $(r_1, \ldots, r_n)(s_1, \ldots, s_n) = (r_1s_1, \ldots, r_ns_n)$, then R^n becomes a commutative ring with unity. Is R^n an integral domain? a division ring?
3. Verify the ring postulates for the "ring" of Example (H).
4. Show that in the ring of real quaternions (Example (I)), if $(a, b, c, d) \neq (0, 0, 0, 0)$, then $(a, b, c, d)^{-1} = (a/N, -b/N, -c/N, -d/N)$, with $N = a^2 + b^2 + c^2 + d^2$.
5. In each of Examples (A) through (J), determine whether the ring in question is commutative, has a unity, is an integral domain or a division ring or a field.
6. Show that $P(S)$, the set of all subsets of the set S, is a commutative ring with unity if we define for $A, B \in P(S)$

$$A + B = A \cup B - A \cap B = \{x \in S : x \in A \text{ or } x \in B, \text{but } x \notin A \cap B\},$$
$$AB = A \cap B.$$

(Example (D) can be considered as a special case of $P(S)$ for S a set of 2 elements.) Is $P(S)$ an integral domain, a division ring?
7. Show that if a, b, c are elements of a ring R and a is not a left zero-divisor, then $ab = ac$ implies $b = c$.
8. If a, b are elements of a division ring D and $a \neq 0$, show that there exist x, y in D such that $ax = b$ and $ya = b$.
9. Show that if R is a finite ring with unity and no zero-divisors, R is a division ring.
10. Let R be a ring with unity and x a unit of R. Show that x has a unique multiplicative inverse in R.
11. Let R be a ring with unity. Show that the set of units of R form a multiplicative group.
12. Show that a nonempty subset S of a ring R is itself a ring with respect to the two compositions of R if and only if a, b in S implies ab and $a - b$ in S.

2. Ideals, Residue Class Rings

In the study of groups, one of our most useful concepts was that of a normal subgroup. We naturally wish to develop a similar notion in the case of rings. Having noted that a ring R may be viewed as an additive M-group, where $M = M_\rho \cup M_\lambda$ with the operators in M_ρ and M_λ, respectively, corresponding to right and left multiplication of all elements of R by some fixed element of R, it is natural to ask if the normal M-subgroups of R are the substructures we want. (We could omit the word "normal" above, since in the additive Abelian group of a ring all subgroups are normal.) As we shall see, these are indeed the analogous structures to the normal subgroups of a group.

Definition. Let R be a ring. An M_ρ-subgroup of R is called a *right ideal* of R, an M_λ-subgroup of R is a *left ideal* of R, and an M-subgroup of R is an *ideal* (or two-sided ideal), of R. A right, left, or two-sided ideal other than R and the zero ideal $0 = \{0\}$ is a *proper* right, left, or two-sided ideal.

We could, equivalently, define a *left ideal* L of R as a subring of R which has the property that, for any $r \in R$ and $a \in L$, $ra \in L$. A *right ideal* K is a subring of R such that for any $r \in R$ and $b \in K$, $br \in K$. An *ideal* is then a subring N of R such that for any $r \in R$ and $n \in N$, we have $rn, nr \in N$.

In the case of a commutative ring, of course, both right and left ideals are two-sided ideals, or simply ideals.

For example, in the ring of all real matrices of order two, the set of all matrices of the form $\begin{pmatrix} a & b \\ 0 & 0 \end{pmatrix}$ constitutes a right ideal, but not a left ideal, while this ring has no proper (two-sided) ideals.

We note that in a division ring there are no proper right (or left) ideals, leaving the verification to the reader.

Theorem 3.5. *The intersection L of any set of left ideals L_i, $i \in I$, of a ring R is a left ideal of R. Similarly, the intersection of any set of right ideals of R is a right ideal of R, and the intersection of any set of ideals of R is an ideal of R.*

PROOF. L is the intersection of a set of M_λ-subgroups of the additive group of R, hence is itself an M_λ-subgroup of R. Similarly in the other two cases.

We may thus speak of the "smallest" ideal containing a given subset S of the ring R, or of the smallest left (right) ideal containing S.

Definition. Let S be a nonempty subset of the ring R. The left, right, or two-sided *ideal generated by* S is the smallest left, right, or two-sided ideal, respectively, containing S, and will be denoted by (S), or, if $S = \{a, b, c, \ldots\}$, by $(a, b, c, \ldots)$. If S consists of a single element a, then (a) is called the *principal* (left, right, or two-sided) ideal generated by a.

Thus the ideal $N = (a, b, c, \ldots)$ generated by the set $\{a, b, c, \ldots\}$ of elements of the ring R is the set of all elements of R expressible as finite sums of terms, each of which is a finite product of elements of R, at least one of which is in the set $\{a, b, c, \ldots\}$. The left ideal generated by the set $\{a, b, c, \ldots\}$ consists of all elements of R expressible as finite sums of terms of the form $rs + ns$, where $r \in R$, $s \in \{a, b, c, \ldots\}$, and ns is the n-fold sum $s + s + \cdots + s$. (If n is negative, say $n = -m$, then $na = -(ma) = -(a + a + \cdots + a)$.) A similar description can be given for the right ideal generated by $\{a, b, c, \ldots\}$.

In the case of the principal left ideal (a), we have that (a) consists of all elements of the form $ra + na$, where na again means the nth *natural multiple*, or n-fold sum of a. If R is a ring with unity element e, then we may interpret na to mean $(ne)a$, so that the principal left ideal (a) then consists of all elements of the form ra, in which case we will sometimes write $(a) = Ra$. Again, similar descriptions of the typical elements of a principal right, or two-sided ideal can be given. For example, the principal (two-sided) ideal (a) is the set;

$$\{na + ra + ar' + \sum_{i,j} r_i a r_j : n \text{ an integer}, r, r', r_i, r_j \in R\},$$

where, in the indicated sum, both i and j can take any finite sets of values. In the case of a commutative ring with unity, we may denote this principal ideal simply by either Ra or aR.

Since ideals are normal subgroups of the additive group of a ring, it follows immediately that an ideal A of the ring R defines a partition of R into disjoint cosets, or *residue classes modulo* A. (The terminology *remainder classes modulo* A is also used.) The residue class of the element x of R modulo the ideal A will be denoted by $\bar{x} = x + A$, since it consists of all elements of R which are of the form $x + a$ for some $a \in A$. The elements $x, y \in R$ are again called congruent modulo A, $x \equiv y \pmod{A}$, if they are in the same residue class modulo A, or, equivalently, if $x - y \in A$.

It may be verified that in all respects except cancellation of common factors, one calculates with congruences modulo A exactly as with equations in ordinary arithmetic. Thus if $x \equiv y \pmod{A}$ and $u \equiv v \pmod{A}$, we have

$$x + u \equiv x + v \equiv y + v \pmod{A},$$
$$xu \equiv xv \equiv yv \pmod{A}, \text{ and}$$
$$nx \equiv ny \pmod{A}, \qquad \text{for any integer } n.$$

Theorem 3.6. *The set of residue classes of a ring R modulo an ideal N form a ring with respect to the operations:*

$$(a + N) + (b + N) = (a + b) + N \textit{ and } (a + N)(b + N) = ab + N.$$

PROOF. Since residue classes modulo the ideal N are also cosets of the additive group of R modulo the normal subgroup N, we have at once that the set of residue classes form an additive Abelian group with respect to the given operation of addition. We must then show that the given multiplication of residue classes is well-defined, associative, and satisfies the two distributive postulates. So let a' and b' be any elements of the respective residue classes $a + N$ and $b + N$. Then we have

$$a' = a + n \text{ and } b' = b + m \text{ for some } n \text{ and } m \text{ in } N,$$

and hence

$$a'b' = (a + n)(b + m) = ab + am + nb + nm = ab + n',$$

where $n' = am + nb + nm$ is an element of N. Thus $a'b' \in ab + N$ and $a'b' + N = ab + N$, and the product of residue classes is independent of the choice of "representatives" of the respective residue classes used to define the product. Since we have

$$\begin{aligned}(a + N)[(b + N)(c + N)] &= (a + N)(bc + N) = a(bc) + N \\ &= (ab)c + N = (ab + N)(c + N) \\ &= [(a + N)(b + N)](c + N),\end{aligned}$$

our multiplication of residue classes is associative.

Also, $(a + N)[(b + N) + (c + N)] = (a + N)[(b + c) + N] = a(b + c) + N$

$$= (ab + ac) + N = (ab + N) + (ac + N)$$
$$= (a + N)(b + N) + (a + N)(c + N).$$

That $[(a + N) + (b + N)](c + N) = (a + N)(c + N) + (b + N)(c + N)$

follows in a similar manner, and the proof is complete.

Definition. The *ring of residue classes* of the ring R modulo the ideal N just constructed is also called the *ring of remainder classes* or the *factor ring* of R modulo N and is denoted by R/N.

The reader will doubtless have observed that, in establishing the associativity and distributivity over addition of the multiplication in the ring of residue classes above, the required expressions were simply combined according to the definitions, then the corresponding property of the ring R appealed to, and the result then decomposed by reversing the steps in the combining procedure previously carried out. Thus the heart of such arguments is much simpler than the computations involved. Many arguments of a similar nature will occur and will generally be left to the reader to supply, which he will be able to do easily, once the general procedure is clearly grasped.

As an example of a residue class ring, consider the ring Z of integers and the principal ideal (n) generated by the positive integer n. We shall denote the residue class ring $Z/(n)$ by Z_n, and, as in the case of groups, the residue class or coset of the integer a by $\bar{a}$, as well as by $a + (n)$. The elements of Z_n are

$$\bar{0} = 0 + (n), \bar{1} = 1 + (n), \ldots, \overline{n-1} = n - 1 + (n).$$

Specifically, suppose $n = 3$. We then have the following tables of addition and multiplication in Z_3:

$+$	$\bar{0}$	$\bar{1}$	$\bar{2}$
$\bar{0}$	$\bar{0}$	$\bar{1}$	$\bar{2}$
$\bar{1}$	$\bar{1}$	$\bar{2}$	$\bar{0}$
$\bar{2}$	$\bar{2}$	$\bar{0}$	$\bar{1}$

$\cdot$	$\bar{0}$	$\bar{1}$	$\bar{2}$
$\bar{0}$	$\bar{0}$	$\bar{0}$	$\bar{0}$
$\bar{1}$	$\bar{0}$	$\bar{1}$	$\bar{2}$
$\bar{2}$	$\bar{0}$	$\bar{2}$	$\bar{1}$

It may be verified that Z_3 is not only an integral domain, as is Z, but Z_3 is actually a field. The reader is cautioned however, not to assume that in the formation of residue class rings all the properties of the original ring will be preserved in all cases. For, while commutativity of multiplication and the existence of a unity element will always be preserved, the lack of zero-divisors, for example, is not always preserved, as may be seen by considering the ring Z_n where n is a composite integer.

Since, in the above example, we saw that Z_3 is a field, we naturally ask if this is the case for all Z_p where p is any prime integer.

Theorem 3.7. *Z_p, the ring of residue classes of the integers modulo the ideal generated by any prime p, is a field.*

PROOF. By Theorem 3.3, it suffices to show that Z_p is an integral domain. Now $\bar{1}$ is a unity element of Z_p, Z_p is commutative, and $\bar{a}\,\bar{b} = \overline{ab} = \bar{0}$ iff $ab = kp$ for some integer k. But since p is a prime, p divides the product ab iff p divides (at least) one of the factors, i.e., iff $\bar{a} = \bar{0}$ or $\bar{b} = \bar{0}$. Thus Z_p contains no divisors of zero and is an integral domain.

From this result, we may easily obtain:

Theorem 3.8 (Fermat's Theorem). *For any integer a and prime p,*

$$a^p \equiv a \pmod{p}.$$

PROOF. The order of the multiplicative group of nonzero elements of Z_p is $p - 1$; hence the order of every element $\bar{x}$ of this group is a divisor of $p - 1$:

$$\overline{x^{p-1}} = (\bar{x})^{p-1} = \bar{1}.$$

Thus if $a \not\equiv 0 \pmod{p}$, we have $a \in \bar{x}$ for some $\bar{x} \neq \bar{0}$ and $a^{p-1} \equiv 1 \pmod{p}$. If, on the other hand, $a \equiv 0 \pmod{p}$, then $a^k \equiv a \pmod{p}$ for any positive integer k. In either case, we have $a^p \equiv a \pmod{p}$.

Exercises

1. Show that the alternative definitions of left, right, and two-sided ideals are equivalent.
2. Show that the set of all matrices of the form $\begin{pmatrix} a & b \\ 0 & 0 \end{pmatrix}$ form a right, but not a two-sided, ideal in the ring R_2 of all real matrices of order two. What are the (two-sided) ideals of R_2?
3. Prove that in a division ring there are no proper ideals.
4. Show that the description given of the typical element of the principal (two-sided) ideal (a) of the ring R is correct.
5. Show that in a commutative ring R with unity, $(a) = Ra = aR$.
6. Let R be a noncommutative ring and L a left, but not two-sided, ideal of R. Is R/L a ring with respect to the usual definitions

   $$(a + L) + (b + L) = (a + b) + L \quad \text{and} \quad (a + L)(b + L) = ab + L?$$
7. Show, by example, that cancellation of nonzero factors is not a permissible operation on congruences. (*Hint:* Consider $15 \equiv 3 \pmod{6}$.)
8. Let A be an ideal of a division ring D. Is D/A a division ring?
9. An element $x \in R$ is called *nilpotent* if $x^n = 0$ for some positive integer n. Show that if R is commutative, then $N = \{x : x \text{ is nilpotent}\}$ is an ideal of R, called the *radical* of R, and that the radical of R/N consists of the zero element only.
10. Prove the Euler extension of the Fermat Theorem, $a^{\phi(m)} \equiv 1 \pmod{m}$, where m is any positive integer, a is a positive integer relatively prime to m, i.e., having no prime factors in common with m, and $\phi(m)$, the Euler ϕ-function, is the number of positive integers less than m and relatively prime to m. (*Hint:* Show that in Z_m the subset $\{\bar{a}: a \text{ relatively prime to } m\}$ is a multiplicative group of order $\phi(m)$.)

3. Homomorphism and Isomorphism of Rings

Having seen the parallel thus far between the roles of normal subgroups in group theory and ideals in ring theory, we naturally wish to see if the parallel extends to the notions of homomorphism and isomorphism.

Definition. Let R and R' be rings. A mapping $\alpha: R \to R'$ of R into R' is called a (ring) *homomorphism* if, for any $x, y \in R$, we have

$$(x + y)\alpha = x\alpha + y\alpha, \qquad (xy)\alpha = (x\alpha)(y\alpha).$$

If, for any $x' \in R'$, we have $x\alpha = x'$ for some $x \in R$, then α is said to be a homomorphism of R *onto* R'. If, also, $x\alpha = y\alpha$ implies that $x = y$, then α is an *isomorphism* of R onto R'. If $R = R'$, then homomorphism and isomorphism are called *endomorphism* and *automorphism*, respectively.

Thus a homomorphism α of the ring R into the ring R' is a mapping which preserves both binary operations of R, and α induces a homomorphism of the additive group of R into the additive group of R'. In view of the fact that a ring R can be interpreted as an additive Abelian group R with operator set $M = M_\rho \cup M_\lambda$, it is worth pointing out that a ring homomorphism of R into R' is not the same as an M-homomorphism of the additive group R. For, in the first place, the operator set M of R is not the same as the operator set M' of R', unless, of course, we have $R = R'$. Even in this latter case of endomorphism, however, the concepts of ring endomorphism and M-endomorphism of the additive group of R do not coincide. For if α is a ring endomorphism and β is an M-endomorphism, we then have

$$(xy)\alpha = (x\alpha)(y\alpha),$$

while

$$(xy)\beta = (x\rho_y)\beta = (x\beta)\rho_y = (x\beta)y = (y\lambda_x)\beta = (y\beta)\lambda_x = x(y\beta).$$

(The reader will find it instructive, in view of these last equations, to determine the M_ρ-endomorphisms of a ring R with unity, viewed as an M_ρ-group, and also the M-endomorphisms of the same ring.)

As illustrations of the notions of homomorphism and isomorphism of rings, consider the following examples:

Let R be any ring and R' the ring of all endomorphisms of the additive group of R (cf. Example (J), Section 3.1). Let α be the mapping of R into R' defined by $x\alpha = \rho_x$. ρ_x is an endomorphism of the additive group of R since

$$(u + v)\rho_x = (u + v)x = ux + vx = u\rho_x + v\rho_x.$$

Now, for any $r, s \in R$, we have

$$(r + s)\alpha = \rho_{r+s} \text{ and } u\rho_{r+s} = u(r + s) = ur + us = u\rho_r + u\rho_s,$$

hence, $(r + s)\alpha = r\alpha + s\alpha$. Similarly, $u\rho_{rs} = u(rs) = (ur)s = (u\rho_r)\rho_s$, so that $(rs)\alpha = (r\alpha)(s\alpha)$, and α is a homomorphism.

Let C be the ring of all complex numbers $a + bi$, and $\alpha: C \to R_2$ the mapping from C into the ring of all real matrices of order two defined by

$$(a + bi)\alpha = \begin{pmatrix} a & b \\ -b & a \end{pmatrix}.$$

We leave it to the reader to verify that α is an isomorphism of C onto a subring of R_2.

Just as in the case of groups, many properties of rings are preserved under homomorphism. For instance, it follows at once that if α is a homomorphism of R into R', then the set $R\alpha$ of images of R under α is a subring of R', since $R\alpha$ is known to be a subgroup of R', and is clearly closed under the multiplication of R', the product of images $(r\alpha)(s\alpha)$ being the image $(rs)\alpha$ of the product. Similarly, if R has a unity element e then $e\alpha$ is the unity of $R\alpha$; if R is commutative so is $R\alpha$; and the image $u\alpha$ of a unit u of R is a unit of $R\alpha$ whose inverse is the image of the inverse of u. Just as with the formation of residue class rings, however, one must not assume that all properties are preserved.

Definition. If α is a homomorphism of the ring R into the ring R', the set $N = \{x \in R: x\alpha = 0\}$ is called the *kernel* of α.

We already know that N is then a (normal) subgroup of the additive group of R, and it is a simple matter to verify that if $x \in N$, $r \in R$, then xr, $rx \in N$, so that the kernel of a homomorphism is an ideal of R.

Just as in the case of groups, the most natural examples of homomorphic mappings of rings are the so-called *natural homomorphisms* of a ring R onto R/N, where N is an ideal of R, defined by $x \to x + N$ for any $x \in R$. That these are homomorphisms and, indeed, are essentially the only homomorphisms of R onto a ring R', follows at once from the next theorem.

Theorem 3.9 (Fundamental Homomorphism Theorem for Rings). *If N is an ideal of the ring R, then the mapping $\alpha: R \to R/N$, defined by $x\alpha = x + N$, is a homomorphism of R onto R/N with kernel N. Conversely, if β is a homomorphism of R onto a ring R', then R' is isomorphic to R/K, where K is the kernel of β.*

PROOF. The mapping α is already known (Theorem 2.20) to be a group homomorphism of the additive group of R onto the additive group of R/N, and clearly α has kernel N. Hence we need only show that α preserves the product operation of R. This follows immediately from

$$(rs)\alpha = rs + N = (r + N)(s + N) = (r\alpha)(s\alpha).$$

Now, suppose that β is a homomorphism of R onto R' with kernel K. Then, K is an ideal of R and we may form the ring R/K. For any $\bar{r} = r + K \in R/K$, we let $\bar{r}\phi = r\beta$. Then, as in the proof of Theorem 2.20, we have that ϕ is well-defined, 1–1, onto, and preserves sums. Also,

$$(\bar{r}\,\bar{s})\phi = (rs + K)\phi = (rs)\beta = (r\beta)(s\beta) = (\bar{r}\phi)(\bar{s}\phi),$$

so that ϕ preserves products and is the required isomorphism of R/K onto R'.

Theorem 3.10 (First Isomorphism Theorem for Rings). *Let α be a homomorphism of the ring R onto the ring R', with N the kernel of α. Then H' is an ideal of R' iff the inverse image $H'\alpha^{-1}$ of H' is an ideal H of R with $H \supseteq N$. If this is the case, then $R/H \cong R'/H'$ or, equivalently, $R/H \cong (R/N)/(H/N)$.*

PROOF. Having proved the corresponding theorem for groups (Theorem 2.21), we need only extend it to the present case, that is, verify the properties of the assertion having to do with the ring multiplication.

Now H' is closed under multiplication by elements of R' (on both right and left) iff $h'r'$ and $r'h'$ are in H' for any $h' \in H'$ and any $r' \in R'$. But this is true iff hr, $rh \in H = H'\alpha^{-1}$ for any $h \in h'\alpha^{-1}$ and $r \in R = R'\alpha^{-1}$. Since $H'\alpha^{-1}$ is the union of all $h'\alpha^{-1}$ for $h' \in H'$, this says that H' is closed under multiplication by elements of R' iff H is closed under multiplication by elements of R, and, hence, H' is an ideal iff H is an ideal.

To complete the argument, we need only show that if β is the natural (ring) homomorphism of R' onto R'/H', then $\alpha\beta$, already known to be a group homomorphism of the additive group of R onto the additive group of R'/H' with kernel H, is also a ring homomorphism. But this follows at once from the fact that, for any r, $s \in R$,

$$(rs)(\alpha\beta) = ((rs)\alpha)\beta = ((r\alpha)(s\alpha))\beta = (r\alpha)\beta(s\alpha)\beta = (r\alpha\beta)(s\alpha\beta).$$

Thus, by the Fundamental Homomorphism Theorem, we have $R/H \cong R'/H'$, and, since also $R' \cong R/N$ and $H' \cong H/N$, we have $R/H \cong (R/N)/(H/N)$, as required.

Thus, just as in the similar situation for groups, we have a 1–1 correspondence between the ideals H of the ring R which contain the kernel of the homomorphism α of R onto R' and the ideals H' of R'.

For example, consider the natural homomorphism α of the ring Z of integers onto the ring $Z_{12} = Z/(12)$ of residue classes of Z modulo the principal ideal generated by the integer 12. The proper ideals of Z which contain (12), the kernel of α, are the ideals (6), (4), (3) and (2) which correspond, respectively, to the ideals $(\bar{6})$, $(\bar{4})$, $(\bar{3})$ and $(\bar{2})$ of $Z_{12} = \{\bar{0}, \bar{1}, \bar{2}, \bar{3}, \bar{4}, \bar{5}, \bar{6}, \bar{7}, \bar{8}, \bar{9}, \overline{10}, \overline{11}\}$. That, for example, $Z/(6)$ is isomorphic to $Z_{12}/(\bar{6})$ is almost obvious. There are, of course, many other ideals of Z whose images under α are ideals of Z_{12} in addition to those containing the kernel (12) of α. For instance, one can easily see that $(9)\alpha$, $(15)\alpha$, $(21)\alpha, \ldots$ are all $(\bar{3})$. (Incidentally, as we shall subsequently prove, it is not an oversight or attempt at simplicity that no ideals of Z other than principal ideals appear in this example, but rather a necessary consequence of the fact that every ideal of Z is a principal ideal.)

We may note that the notation here employed, Z_n, for the ring of residue classes of Z modulo the ideal (n) will be used consistently. No confusion should result from using this notation both for the additive group and the ring, as the context will make clear whether the ring structure or the group structure is being referred to.

We have already noted that the intersection of ideals of R is again an ideal of R. We shall also need the concept for rings, corresponding to that of a product of subgroups of a (multiplicative) group.

Definition. Let M and N be two ideals (or two left ideals, or two right ideals) of the ring R. The *sum* $M + N$ is the set of all sums $m + n$ for $m \in M$, $n \in N$. More generally, if M_i, $i \in I$ (finite or infinite), are all ideals (or all left ideals, or all right ideals) of R, then the sum $\sum_{i \in I} M_i$ is the set of all $\sum_{i \in J} m_i$, where J is any finite subset of I. It follows easily that $\sum_{i \in I} M_i$ is again an ideal (or, respectively, a left ideal or a right ideal) of R.

For example, in the ring R_2 of all real matrices of order two, one may show that L_1, the set of all matrices of the form $\begin{pmatrix} a & 0 \\ b & 0 \end{pmatrix}$, and L_2, the set of all matrices of the form $\begin{pmatrix} 0 & c \\ 0 & d \end{pmatrix}$, where a, b, c, d are any real numbers, are both left ideals whose sum $L_1 + L_2 = R$.

Theorem 3.11 (Second Isomorphism Theorem for Rings). *Let M and N be ideals of the ring R and $\alpha\colon R \to R/N$ the natural homomorphism. Then*

$$M + N = (M\alpha)\alpha^{-1} \quad \textit{and} \quad (M + N)/N \cong M/(M \cap N).$$

PROOF. Again, we need only extend the proof of Theorem 2.22 to the present case by showing that α induces a product preserving map of M onto

$$(M + N)/N = M\alpha.$$

The details of this demonstration we leave to the reader.

As an illustration, again consider the ring Z of integers, and let $M = (9)$, $N = (12)$. Then $M + N$ is all integers which can be expressed in the form $9a + 12b$, a and b in Z, and a little examination shows that $M + N = (3)$. $M \cap N$ is all integers which are multiples of both 9 and 12, that is, $M \cap N = (36)$. We then have, by the theorem, that $(3)/(12) \cong (9)/(36)$. For $(3)/(12) = \{\overline{0}, \overline{3}, \overline{6}, \overline{9}\}$ and $(9)/(36) = \{\overline{0}, \overline{9}, \overline{18}, \overline{27}\}$ and the isomorphic correspondence is apparent.

Exercises

1. Determine the M_ρ-endomorphisms of a ring R with unity, R being viewed as an M_ρ-group, where M_ρ is the set of all right multiplications $r \to ra$ of R. Determine, also, the M-endomorphisms of R, where M is the set of all right and all left multiplications of R.
2. Let C be the ring of complex numbers $a + bi$, a and b real numbers, and R_2 the ring of all real matrices of order two. Show that the mapping $a + bi \to \begin{pmatrix} a & b \\ -b & a \end{pmatrix}$ is an isomorphism of C onto a subring of R_2.

3. Prove that, if α is a homomorphism of the ring R onto the ring R', then:
   (a) If R is commutative, so is R'.
   (b) If R has unity e, then R' has unity $e\alpha$.
   (c) If u is a unit of R, then $u\alpha$ is a unit of R', $(u^{-1})\alpha = (u\alpha)^{-1}$.
4. Can there exist a homomorphism of the ring Z of integers onto the ring of even integers?
5. Prove that the kernel of a ring homomorphism is an ideal of the ring.
6. Prove Theorem 3.9 without the use of Theorem 2.20.
7. Carry out the details of the proof of Theorem 3.11.

4. Operations on Ideals

If we consider the set S of ideals of a ring R, then the mapping $\alpha: S \times S \to S$, defined by $(A, B)\alpha = A \cap B$, is a binary operation on S, and we easily see that α is associative and commutative. Similarly, the mapping $(A, B) \to A + B$ is also a commutative and associative binary operation on the set of ideals of R.

Besides these operations, there are two other binary operations on this set S of ideals in which we shall be interested.

Definition. Let A and B be ideals of a ring R. The *product* AB is the set of all finite sums $\sum_{i=1}^{n} a_i b_i$ with $a_i \in A$, $b_i \in B$.

More generally, if $A_1, A_2, \ldots, A_m$ are any finite set of ideals of R, then the *product* $A_1 A_2 \cdots A_m$ is the set of all finite sums of terms of the form $a_1 a_2 \cdots a_m$ with $a_j \in A_j$.

Definition. Let A and B be ideals of a ring R. The *right* (*left*) *quotient* of A by B, denoted by $A :_r B$ $(A :_l B)$, is the set of all $c \in R$ such that $cB \subseteq A$ $(Bc \subseteq A)$. In particular, if $A = 0$, the right (left) quotient

$$0 :_r B = \{c : cB = 0\}$$

is also called the left (right) *annihilator* or *order* of B. If R is commutative we simply write $A : B$.

For example, in the commutative ring Z of integers, if $A = (15)$ and $B = (12)$, then $AB = (180)$, $A \cap B = (60)$, $A + B = (3)$, $A : B = (5)$ and $B : A = (4)$. (The reader should verify each of these results.) Incidentally, this gives some indication of why the term "ideal" is used. For, while one of the chief "deficiencies" of the ring Z is its lack of divisibility properties, we see that either of the ideals (12) and (15) can be "divided" by the other. Thus, in some sense, ideals might reasonably be expected to be "ideal" for arithmetic purposes. We shall now prove that such "division" of one ideal by another is always possible in any ring, as well as that the product of ideals is an ideal, so that both product and right (or left) quotient are indeed binary operations on the set of ideals of a ring.

Theorem 3.12. *Let A and B be ideals of a ring R. Then AB, $A :_r B$* and *$A :_l B$ are ideals of R.*

PROOF. That AB is an ideal follows from the fact that, if $\sum_{i=1}^{n} a_ib_i$ and $\sum_{j=1}^{m} a_jb_j$ are in AB, $r \in R$, then, clearly, $\sum_{i=1}^{n} a_ib_i - \sum_{j=1}^{m} a_jb_j$ is in AB, $r\sum_{i=1}^{n} a_ib_i = \sum_{i=1}^{n} (ra_i)b_i \in AB$ and, similarly, $(\sum_{i=1}^{n} a_ib_i)\, r \in AB$.

Suppose $c, d \in A :_r B$ and $r \in R$. Then $(c - d)B \subseteq A$, since, for $b \in B$, we have $(c - d)b = cb - db \in A$, and $rdB \subseteq rA \subseteq A$, $crB \subseteq cB \subseteq A$. Thus $A :_r B$ is an ideal of R, and that $A :_l B$ is an ideal follows similarly.

While the operations of intersection and sum are both associative and commutative, the operation of product is associative, but not, in general, commutative unless the ring R is commutative. We see that, for any ideals A and B, we have

$$AB \subseteq A \cap B \subseteq A \text{ (or } B) \subseteq A + B.$$

Further relations between these operations are the subject of the next theorem.

Theorem 3.13. *The following relations hold for ideals in any ring R.*

(i) *If $A \supseteq B$, then $A \cap (B + C) = B + (A \cap C)$*

(Dedekind's Modular Law).

(ii) $A(B + C) = AB + AC$, $(A + B)C = AC + BC$.

(iii) $(\cap A_i) :_r B = \cap(A_i :_r B)$, $i = 1, 2, \ldots, n$.

(iv) $A :_r \sum B_i = \cap(A :_r B_i)$, $i = 1, 2, \ldots, n$.

(v) $A :_r (CB) = (A :_r B) :_r C$.

PROOF.

(i) Suppose $A \supseteq B$. If $x \in B + (A \cap C)$, then, clearly, $x \in B + C$ and $x \in B + A \subseteq A$, whence $x \in A \cap (B + C)$. If, on the other hand, $x \in A \cap (B + C)$, then $x \in B + C$ implies $x = b + c$ for some $b \in B \subseteq A$, $c \in C$. Thus $c = x - b \in A$, since $x \in A$, whence $c \in A \cap C$ and $x = b + c \in B + (A \cap C)$.
Hence $A \cap (B + C) = B + (A \cap C)$.

(ii) Let $x \in A(B + C)$. Then $x = \sum a_i(b_i + c_i)$, $a_i \in A$, $b_i \in B$, $c_i \in C$, $i = 1, 2, \ldots, n$, and, hence, $x = \sum a_ib_i + \sum a_ic_i \in AB + AC$. Conversely, if $x \in AB + AC$, then $x = \sum a_ib_i + \sum a_jc_j$, $i = 1, 2, \ldots, n$, and $j = n + 1, \ldots, m$. Let $b_i = 0$ for $i = n + 1, \ldots, m$, and $c_i = 0$ for $i = 1, \ldots, n$. Then $x = \sum a_ib_i + \sum a_ic_i = \sum a_i(b_i + c_i)$, $i = 1, \ldots, n, \ldots, m$, and $x \in A(B + C)$.
Thus $A(B + C) = AB + AC$. Similarly, $(A + B)C = AC + BC$.

(iii) Here we have
$$(\cap A_i) :_r B = \{c\colon cB \subseteq \cap A_i\} = \cap\{c\colon cB \subseteq A_i\} = \cap(A_i :_r B).$$

(iv) If $c\sum B_i \subseteq A$, then certainly $cB_i \subseteq A$ for $i = 1, \ldots, n$.
Conversely, if $cB_i \subseteq A$ for all i, then $c\sum B_i \subseteq A$.

(v) $A :_r (CB) = \{x\colon xCB \subseteq A\} = \{x\colon xC \subseteq A :_r B\} = (A :_r B) :_r C$.

Similar results will, of course, hold for left quotients, where, instead of (v), we have (v)′ $A :_l (BC) = (A :_l B) :_l C$.

In the event that R is a commutative ring, we shall also be interested in a unary operation on the set of ideals of R. (Such an operation can be defined in the case that R is noncommutative, but for our purposes it will suffice to consider only the much simpler case of commutative rings.)

Definition. Let $A \neq R$ be an ideal of the commutative ring R. The *radical* of A, $\sqrt{A}$, is the set of all $c \in R$, some (positive integral) power of which belongs to A, or alternatively, the set of all elements of R which are *nilpotent modulo* A. The *radical of the ring* R is defined to be $\sqrt{0}$, the set of all nilpotent elements of R.

For example, in the ring Z of integers $\sqrt{0} = 0$, $\sqrt{(4)} = \sqrt{(32)} = (2)$, and $\sqrt{(12)} = (6)$, since 0 is the only nilpotent element of Z, those integers some power of which is divisible by 4 (or by 32) are those integers which are divisible by 2, and some power of an integer is divisible by 12 iff the integer is divisible by 6.

Theorem 3.14. *If A and B are ideals of a commutative ring R, then:*

(i) *$\sqrt{A}$ is an ideal of R containing A.*
(ii) *If $A^k \subseteq B$ for any positive integer k, then $\sqrt{A} \subseteq \sqrt{B}$.*
(iii) $\sqrt{AB} = \sqrt{A \cap B} = \sqrt{A} \cap \sqrt{B}$.
(iv) $\sqrt{A + B} = \sqrt{\sqrt{A} + \sqrt{B}} \supseteq \sqrt{A} + \sqrt{B}$.
(v) $\sqrt{\sqrt{A}} = \sqrt{A}$.

PROOF.

(i) If $c, d \in \sqrt{A}$, then $c^m, d^n \in A$ for some positive integers m and n. Then, since R is commutative, every term in the expansion of $(c - d)^{m+n-1}$ contains either c^m or d^n as a factor, hence, $(c - d)^{m+n-1} \in A$, $m + n - 1$ is a positive integer, and $c - d \in \sqrt{A}$. Moreover, for any $r \in R$, $(rc)^m = r^m c^m \in A$, $rc \in \sqrt{A}$ and, similarly, $cr \in \sqrt{A}$, so that $\sqrt{A}$ is an ideal of R. That $\sqrt{A}$ contains A is trivial.

(ii) If $A^k \subseteq B$ and $c \in \sqrt{A}$, say $c^m \in A$, then $c^{mk} \in A^k \subseteq B$ and $\sqrt{A} \subseteq \sqrt{B}$.

(iii) If $c^m \in AB$, then $c^m \in A \cap B$ and, hence, $c^m \in A$ and $c^m \in B$. Thus $\sqrt{AB} \subseteq \sqrt{A \cap B} \subseteq \sqrt{A} \cap \sqrt{B}$.
But, if $c \in \sqrt{A} \cap \sqrt{B}$, then $c^m \in A$, $c^n \in B$ for some positive integers m and n, hence, $c^{m+n} = c^m c^n \in AB$ and $\sqrt{A} \cap \sqrt{B} \subseteq \sqrt{AB}$, whence the desired equality follows.

(iv) Since $A + B \subseteq \sqrt{A} + \sqrt{B}$, we have $\sqrt{A + B} \subseteq \sqrt{\sqrt{A} + \sqrt{B}}$ by (ii). If $x \in \sqrt{\sqrt{A} + \sqrt{B}}$, then $x^j \in \sqrt{A} + \sqrt{B}$, $x^j = c + d$, where $c^m \in A$, $d^n \in B$ for some positive integers j, m and n. Then, in the expansion of $x^{j(m+n-1)} = (c + d)^{m+n-1}$, each term contains a factor c^m or d^n, whence $x^{j(m+n-1)} \in A + B$ and $\sqrt{\sqrt{A} + \sqrt{B}} \subseteq \sqrt{A + B}$, or $\sqrt{A + B} = \sqrt{\sqrt{A} + \sqrt{B}}$. That $\sqrt{\sqrt{A} + \sqrt{B}} \supseteq \sqrt{A} + \sqrt{B}$ follows from (i).

(v) Clearly, $\sqrt{\sqrt{A}} \supseteq \sqrt{A}$, while, if $c^m \in \sqrt{A}$, then $c^{mn} \in A$ for some n, and the equality follows.

Exercises

1. Show that in the ring Z, if $A = (15)$ and $B = (12)$, then

$$AB = (180), \qquad A \cap B = (60), \qquad A + B = (3),$$
$$A : B = (5), \qquad \text{and} \qquad B : A = (4).$$

2. Let R be a ring with unity, A and B ideals of R. Show that $A :_r B = R$ if and only if $A + B = A$.
3. Let R be a ring with unity, A and B ideals of R and $A :_r B^{k+1} = (A :_r B^k) :_r B$. If $A :_r B^n = R$ for some positive integer n, show that $B \subseteq \sqrt{A}$.
4. Let R be a commutative ring, A, B, and C ideals of R. Show that if $A \supseteq B$, then $A : C \supseteq B : C$ and $C : A \subseteq C : B$.
5. Let α be a homomorphism of the commutative ring R onto R' with kernel N. Show that $(A + B)\alpha = A\alpha + B\alpha$, $(AB)\alpha = (A\alpha)(B\alpha)$, $(A \cap B)\alpha \subseteq A\alpha \cap B\alpha$, with equality if either A or B contains N, $(A : B)\alpha \subseteq A\alpha : B\alpha$, with equality if $A \supseteq N$, and $\sqrt{A}\,\alpha \subseteq \sqrt{A\alpha}$, with equality if $A \supseteq N$.
6. Let A, B, and C be ideals of a ring R such that $B \subseteq C$, $A + B = A + C$, and $A \cap B = A \cap C$. Show that $B = C$.

5. Extensions of Rings

In elementary arithmetic and algebra, the existence of a unity element in the rings of numbers, polynomials, etc., with which one deals is a most useful property. Similarly, the existence of multiplicative inverses of nonzero elements, as, for example, in the field of rational numbers, is a property greatly to be desired in a ring. However, rings, in general, need not have unity elements, nor do multiplicative inverses generally exist. This leads us to ask if, given a ring R, there is some way to remedy these defects. As we shall see, we can always remedy the lack of a unity element. Obtaining multiplicative inverses is rather more difficult, and indeed cannot be done in general, as it would, of course, be impossible for a zero-divisor to have a multiplicative inverse. Thus we shall restrict ourselves to seeking multiplicative inverses of nonzero elements of an integral domain. Before proceeding to the required constructions, however, it will be useful to prove three simple theorems which will serve to simplify many such constructions.

Theorem 3.15. *If N is an ideal of the ring R, and R' is a subring of R such that $R' \cap N = 0$, then R/N contains a subring isomorphic to R'.*

PROOF. The natural homomorphism of R onto R/N induces a homomorphism α of R' into R/N, namely, that homomorphism obtained by restricting the natural homomorphism to the elements of R'. If $a\alpha = b\alpha$ for some a and b in R', then $(a - b)\alpha = a\alpha - b\alpha = 0$. Hence $a - b$ is in both N and R', which have only 0 in common, by assumption, so that $a - b = 0$ or $a = b$. Thus α is a 1–1 map of R' onto the subring $R'\alpha$ of R/N, and a homomorphism which is 1–1 and onto is an isomorphism.

Theorem 3.16. *If R is a ring and β is a 1–1 map of R onto a set T, then addition and multiplication may be defined in T in such a way that β is an isomorphism.*

PROOF. For any t and t' in T, we have

$$t = r\beta,$$
$$t' = r'\beta \qquad \text{for some } r \text{ and } r' \text{ in } R,$$

and, since β is 1–1, we have that r and r' are uniquely determined by t and t', respectively. If we define addition and multiplication in T by

$$t + t' = (r + r')\beta,$$
$$tt' = (rr')\beta,$$

it follows that addition and multiplication are well-defined operations in T. That T is a ring with respect to these definitions and that β is now an isomorphism are trivial consequences of the definitions, the verification of which we leave to the reader.

Theorem 3.17. *If R' and S are disjoint rings such that S contains a subring S', isomorphic to R' under a mapping β', then there exists a ring R, containing R' and isomorphic to S under a mapping β, such that, for all r' in R', we have*

$$r'\beta = r'\beta'.$$

PROOF. Let $R = R' \cup (S - S')$, i.e., the union of R' and the elements of S not in S'. Define β as follows:

$$r\beta = r\beta' \text{ if } r \in R',$$
$$r\beta = r \text{ if } r \in S - S'.$$

β is thus a 1–1 map of R onto $S = S' \cup (S - S')$.

Now, define addition and multiplication as in Theorem 3.16 and the result is immediate.

Definition. If α' is an isomorphism $\alpha'\colon R' \to S'$ of the subrings R' of R and S' of S, then an isomorphism $\alpha\colon R \to S$ will be called an *extension* of α' if $r'\alpha = r'\alpha'$ for all $r' \in R'$.

The utility of the preceding series of theorems is this. If we have succeeded in showing that a ring R' is isomorphic to a subring S' of the ring S, disjoint from R', then we are assured that there exists an *extension* ring R containing R' as a subring and such that the given isomorphism can be extended to an isomorphism of R and S. Since we are assured that the extension can always be carried out, we shall seldom, if ever, actually construct the extension, but, instead, simplify our work by identifying the isomorphic subrings R' and S', and in this sense *imbed* the ring R' in the *extension ring* S.

Theorem 3.18. *Any ring R without unity element can be imbedded in a ring with unity element.*

PROOF. Consider the product set $R \times Z$, Z the ring of integers. For elements (x, m) and (y, n) in $R \times Z$, define sum and product, respectively, by

$$\begin{aligned}(x, m) + (y, n) &= (x + y, m + n),\\ (x, m)(y, n) &= (xy + nx + my, mn),\end{aligned}$$

where the symbol nx means, of course, repeated addition of x (or repeated addition of $-x$, if n is negative). (The reader should note that we are here using the same notation for three different "additions" and three different "multiplications," namely, those of R, of Z, and of $R \times Z$.) This gives well-defined operations of addition and multiplication in $R \times Z$, and the verification of the ring properties in $R \times Z$ is a simple exercise. We see that the identity element is $(0, 0)$ and the unity element is $(0, 1)$ in $R \times Z$.

Consider now, the subset $R \times \{0\}$ of $R \times Z$. Since $(x, 0) - (y, 0) = (x - y, 0)$, and $(x, 0)(y, 0) = (xy, 0)$, and the other ring properties are immediate consequences of the corresponding properties in $R \times Z$, we have that $R \times \{0\}$ is a subring of $R \times Z$. The mapping α, defined by $x\alpha = (x, 0)$, is, evidently, a 1–1 mapping of R onto $R \times \{0\}$ and, moreover,

$$\begin{aligned}(x + y)\alpha &= (x + y, 0) = (x, 0) + (y, 0) = x\alpha + y\alpha,\\ (xy)\alpha &= (xy, 0) = (x, 0)(y, 0) = (x\alpha)(y\alpha),\end{aligned}$$

so that α is an isomorphism. We now apply Theorem 3.17 to construct a ring containing R and isomorphic to $R \times Z$, or, as noted above, simply identify R with $R \times \{0\}$ and thus consider R as imbedded in $R \times Z$.

We note that R is not merely a subring of $R \times Z$, but actually an ideal. For if $r = (r, 0) \in R$ and $a = (x, m) \in R \times Z$, we have $ra = (rx + mr, 0) = rx + mr$, and $ar = (xr + mr, 0) = xr + mr$ are both elements of R.

Having thus found that any ring R without unity can be imbedded in an extension ring R' with unity, it is natural to ask if the properties which characterize R can also be carried over to the ring R'. In the event that R is commutative, it is easy to see that $R' = R \times Z$ is also commutative. The most important other property that R may have is that of having no zero-divisors. While we can not assert that the extension ring $R' = R \times Z$ will also be free of zero-divisors, we can obtain from R' a factor ring which is free of zero-divisors and also contains an isomorphic copy of R. To do so, we may proceed as follows, where we leave some of the details of the argument to the reader.

Let A be the subset of R' such that for any $a \in A$, $aR = 0$. If $a, a' \in A$, $b \in R'$, and $r \in R$, then $(a - a')r = ar - a'r = 0$ and $(ab)r = a(br) = ar' = 0 = b0 = b(ar) = (ba)r$, whence A is an ideal of R'. In R'/A, if $\bar{b}\,\bar{c} = \bar{0}$, then for any $b \in \bar{b}$, $c \in \bar{c}$, we have $bc \in A$; hence $bcR = 0$. Now either $cR = 0$, $c \in A$ and $\bar{c} = \bar{0}$, or else there is some $r \neq 0$ in $cR \subseteq R$ such that $br = 0$. We then have $br = 0 = r(br) = (rb)r$, and, since R is an ideal of R' and contains no zero-divisors, $rb = 0$. For any $s \in R$, we have $r(bs) = (rb)s = 0$; hence, $bs = 0$, $b \in A$, $\bar{b} = \bar{0}$. Thus R'/A has no zero-divisors. Clearly, the unity element $(0, 1) = 1$ of R' is not in A and $\bar{1}$ is the unity of R'/A.

Finally, $R \cap A = 0$, since if $a \in A$ and $a \neq 0$, then $aR = 0$ and $a \notin R$, as R has no zero-divisors. The result then follows by Theorem 3.15.

To begin the attack on the second of our two objectives, that of obtaining multiplicative inverses of the nonzero elements of an integral domain, let us suppose that the integral domain D is contained in some field F, and that the unity of D is not zero. Then if $b \neq 0$ is an element of D, as an element of F b has an inverse, b^{-1}. If we consider the set K of all elements of F of the form ab^{-1}, where a and b are in D and $b \neq 0$, we may easily show that K is a subfield of F. For as a subset of a field, K is certainly commutative and, moreover, if ab^{-1} is any nonzero element of K, that is, if $a \neq 0$, then ba^{-1} is also an element of K and $(ab^{-1})^{-1} = ba^{-1}$. Also, it is almost immediate that K is the smallest subfield of F which contains D.

Definition. If D is a nonzero integral domain contained in a field F, then $K = \{ab^{-1} : a, b \in D, b \neq 0\}$ is the *quotient field* or *field of quotients* of D in F.†

It would be convenient to be able to speak of the quotient field of D, without reference to the field F in which the quotients are taken. That we may do so follows from the next theorem.

Theorem 3.19. *Let D and D' be isomorphic integral domains with isomorphism $\alpha: D \to D'$, contained, respectively, in fields F and F', and let K, K' be the respective quotient fields. Then α can be extended in one and only one way to an isomorphism $\alpha': K \to K'$.*

PROOF. If an extension α' of α exists, then for any $ab^{-1} \in K$ we must have

$$(ab^{-1})\alpha' = (a\alpha')(b^{-1}\alpha') = (a\alpha')(b\alpha')^{-1} = (a\alpha)(b\alpha)^{-1}.$$

Thus α' is unique, if it exists.

We now define $\alpha': K \to K'$ by $(ab^{-1})\alpha' = (a\alpha)(b\alpha)^{-1}$ for arbitrary $ab^{-1} \in K$. Now

$$\begin{aligned}(ab^{-1})\alpha' = (cd^{-1})\alpha' \quad &\text{iff} \quad (a\alpha)(b\alpha)^{-1} = (c\alpha)(d\alpha)^{-1}\\ &\text{iff} \quad (a\alpha)(d\alpha) = (c\alpha)(b\alpha)\\ &\text{iff} \quad (ad)\alpha = (cb)\alpha\\ &\text{iff} \quad ad = cb\\ &\text{iff} \quad ab^{-1} = cd^{-1},\end{aligned}$$

since α is an isomorphism. Thus α' is 1–1.

If xy^{-1} is any element of K', then $x, y \in D'$ and $x = a\alpha$, $y = b\alpha$ for some $a, b \in D$, hence, $(ab^{-1})\alpha' = xy^{-1}$ and α' is onto.

† We do not need to insist that D is nonzero, if we take for K the set $\{0, e\}$, e the unity of F, in this trivial case.

Finally, we have

$$\begin{aligned}(ab^{-1} + cd^{-1})\alpha' &= [(ad + bc)(bd)^{-1}]\alpha' \\ &= [(ad + bc)\alpha][(bd)\alpha]^{-1} \\ &= [(a\alpha)(d\alpha) + (b\alpha)(c\alpha)][(b\alpha)^{-1}(d\alpha)^{-1}] \\ &= (a\alpha)(b\alpha)^{-1} + (c\alpha)(d\alpha)^{-1} \\ &= (ab^{-1})\alpha' + (cd^{-1})\alpha',\end{aligned}$$

and

$$\begin{aligned}[(ab^{-1})(cd^{-1})]\alpha' &= [(ac)(bd)^{-1}]\alpha' \\ &= [(ac)\alpha][(bd)\alpha]^{-1} \\ &= (a\alpha)(c\alpha)(b\alpha)^{-1}(d\alpha)^{-1} \\ &= [(a\alpha)(b\alpha)^{-1}][(c\alpha)(d\alpha)^{-1}] \\ &= (ab^{-1})\alpha'(cd^{-1})\alpha'.\end{aligned}$$

Thus α' preserves both sums and products and is, indeed, an isomorphism. (We leave to the reader the proof that the formulas used for the sum and product of quotients ab^{-1} and cd^{-1} are correct.)

Since α' trivially agrees with α on elements of D, the theorem is proved.

Thus any two quotient fields of an integral domain are isomorphic, and, if we identify these isomorphic extension fields of the integral domain, we may speak of the quotient field, provided, of course, that such a field exists at all. The construction of the next theorem, modelled on the construction of the rational numbers from the integral domain of the integers, shows that an integral domain always has a quotient field.

Theorem 3.20. *Any integral domain D can be imbedded in a field.*

PROOF. Consider the set S of all ordered pairs (a, b), where a and b are elements of D and $b \neq 0$. Let R be a relation on S defined by

$$(a, b)R(c, d) \quad \text{iff} \quad ad = bc.$$

Clearly, R is reflexive and symmetric, since $ab = ba$, and if $ad = bc$ then $cb = da$. If $ad = bc$ and $cy = dx$ with b and d both nonzero, then $ady = bcy$, $ady = bdx$, and, finally, $ayd = bxd$, by the commutativity of D. Since $d \neq 0$, we apply Theorem 3.4 to cancel the factor d and obtain $ay = bx$. It follows that if $(a, b)R(c, d)$ and $(c, d)R(x, y)$, then $(a, b)R(x, y)$ and R is transitive; hence R is an equivalence relation on S. Thus R partitions S into mutually disjoint equivalence classes. Now let a/b denote the equivalence class of (a, b), and define addition and multiplication of these equivalence classes or elements of $S/R = F$ by

$$\begin{aligned}a/b + c/d &= ad + bc/bd, \\ (a/b)(c/d) &= ac/bd.\end{aligned}$$

(Notice that the symbol $ad + bc/bd$ can be interpreted in only one way, since we have, at present, no way whatever of "adding" elements of D to elements of F.) The proof that these definitions of addition and multiplication are independent of the choice of representatives of the equivalence classes is an exercise we leave for the reader, as it is quite analogous to previous such demonstrations.

Now $(a/a)(c/d) = ac/ad$, and $ac/ad = c/d$, since $acd = adc$ by the commutativity of D. Thus $(a/a)(c/d) = (c/d)$, all $c/d \in F$, and a/a is the unity element of F. (Remember that (a, a) is not even an element of S if a is zero.) Clearly, $0/a$ is the additive identity element, or zero of F.

The associativity and commutativity of multiplication and addition, as well as the distributivity of multiplication over addition in F, follow from the corresponding properties in D. We shall illustrate the type of argument involved by showing the distributivity and leave the other demonstrations to the reader.

$$\begin{aligned}(x/y)(a/b + c/d) &= (x/y)(ad + bc/bd)\\ &= x(ad + bc)/ybd\\ &= xad + xbc/ybd\\ &= xad/ybd + xbc/ybd\\ &= xad/ybd + xcb/ydb\\ &= (xa/yb)(d/d) + (xc/yd)(b/b)\\ &= xa/yb + xc/yd\\ &= (x/y)(a/b) + (x/y)(c/d).\end{aligned}$$

We have shown that F is a commutative ring with unity. To show that F is a field, we must show that every nonzero element of F has a multiplicative inverse. So suppose that a/b is such an element; that is, a is not zero (and, of course, b is not zero). Then b/a is an element of F. Since

$$(a/b)(b/a) = ab/ba = ab/ab,$$

the unity of F, b/a is the inverse of a/b, or

$$(a/b)^{-1} = b/a.$$

Consider now the subset D' of F consisting of all elements of F of the form $a/1$, for $a \in D$, with 1 the unity element of D. It can be readily verified that this subset is a subring of F and, indeed, is a commutative integral domain with unity. Since, clearly, $a/1 = b/1$ iff $a = b$, it follows that the mapping $\alpha: D \to D'$, defined by $a\alpha = a/1$ is 1–1 and onto. Now

$$\begin{aligned}(a + b)\alpha &= a + b/1 = a/1 + b/1 = a\alpha + b\alpha,\\ (ab)\alpha &= ab/1 = (a/1)(b/1) = (a\alpha)(b\alpha),\end{aligned}$$

so that α is an isomorphism of D onto D'. An application of our imbedding theorem, Theorem 3.17, completes the proof.

Again, we do not ordinarily make the construction of Theorem 3.17 but, rather, identify the isomorphic integral domains D and D' and, in this sense, imbed D in its quotient field F.

If we wish to make particular application of this construction to the case of the integral domain of the integers, and the resulting field of rationals, we notice that the set S of all ordered pairs of integers whose second elements are not zero may be identified with the set of all common fractions. The resulting equivalence classes are, of course, the rational numbers. Thus when we write a/a for the unity of the field of rationals, it is the *same element* as b/b, since (a, a) and (b, b) are in the same equivalence class for any nonzero integers a and b. In other words, while one may well and properly wish to distinguish between the *fractions* $\frac{2}{4}$ and $\frac{3}{6}$, for example, if one considers $\frac{2}{4}$ and $\frac{3}{6}$ as *rational numbers*, then they are precisely the same number, merely being denoted by two different names.

We note also that, just as with other such imbedding situations, we shall customarily use the simpler notation of elements of D to denote the corresponding elements of the isomorphic subring D' of the quotient field F. Thus, instead of writing $a/1$, we shall write a to indicate this element of F. With this convention in use, we shall no longer be able to write such an expression as $ab + cd/bd$ without the use of parentheses, since it could now mean either $(ab + cd)/bd$, as before, or else $ab + (cd/bd)$, where $ab = ab/1$. We shall, however, in accord with usual practice, agree that in the expression $ab + cd/bd$, the grouping $ab + (cd/bd)$ is meant when no parentheses are used.

One of the most important types of ring extension is the notion of a ring of polynomials with coefficients in a given ring, which will occupy our attention in the next section.

Exercises

1. Show that if β is a homomorphism of the ring R onto R' and S is a subring of R, then the mapping $\alpha\colon S \to R'$, defined by $s\alpha = s\beta$ for all s in S, is a homomorphism.
2. Verify that the ring $R \times Z$, as defined in the proof of Theorem 3.18, actually is a ring.
3. Let E be the ring of even integers. Carry out the construction of $E \times Z$ and, thus, show that this ring E without unity may be imbedded in a ring with unity in more than one way.
4. Show that zero-divisors do exist in the ring $E \times Z$ of the previous exercise, despite the fact that there are none in either E or Z.
5. Construct the zero-divisor-free ring $(E \times Z)/A$, where
$$A = \{a \in E \times Z\colon a(E \times \{0\}) = 0\}$$
and compare this ring with Z.
6. Show that if a, b, c, d are elements of a field F, b and d nonzero, then
$$ab^{-1} + cd^{-1} = (ad + bc)(bd)^{-1}, \qquad (ab^{-1})(cd^{-1}) = (ac)(bd)^{-1},$$
and
$$(ab^{-1})(cd^{-1})^{-1} = (ad)(bc)^{-1}$$
if also $c \neq 0$.

7. In the proof of Theorem 3.20, carry out the demonstrations of the associativity and commutativity of addition and multiplication in F.
8. Let the set N of nonzero-divisors of the commutative ring R be nonempty. Show that N is multiplicatively closed, i.e., a and b in N implies ab in N, and, also, show that R can be imbedded in an extension ring R' in which every nonzero-divisor of R has a multiplicative inverse.
9. Show that any commutative semi-group with cancellation, $ab = ac$ implies $b = c$, can be imbedded in a commutative group.

6. Polynomial Rings

Just as the study of polynomials is one of the most important portions of elementary algebra, so we find that the generalization of these ideas to the case of polynomials with coefficients in an arbitrary ring forms a most interesting and important part of abstract algebra.

If we recall our place value system of notation in ordinary arithmetic, for example $432 = 2(10^0) + 3(10^1) + 4(10^2)$, we note that for these "polynomials in the number 10 with coefficients in Z_{10}" we do not write the powers of 10 at all, but merely the sequence of coefficients. Thus elements of Z can be written in this notation as n-tuples of elements of Z_{10}. Extending this notion, we give the following definition.

Definition. For an arbitrary ring R, the set of *polynomials over* R is that subset of the infinite Cartesian product of R with itself consisting of those elements having only a finite number of nonzero entries, that is, the set

$$\{(a_0, a_1, \ldots, a_n, 0, 0, \ldots) : a_i \in R, i = 0, 1, \ldots, n; n = 0, 1, \ldots\},$$

where we note that a_n is not required to be nonzero.

In order to obtain more familiar notation for polynomials with coefficients in R, we may replace

$$(a_0, a_1, \ldots, a_n, 0, 0, \ldots) \quad \text{by} \quad a_0x^0 + a_1x^1 + \cdots + a_nx^n,$$

where we must understand that the entire symbol x^i is, at present, merely an index corresponding to the subscript i and the $+$ signs are merely replacements for the commas, and no multiplication nor addition is thereby signified. Moreover, since a_n was not required to be nonzero, the new symbol is not uniquely determined. For example, $0x^0$, $0x^0 + 0x^1$, etc., all represent the polynomial $(0, 0, 0, \ldots)$. With these agreements, we may say that

$$R[x] = \{a_0x^0 + a_1x^1 + \cdots + a_nx^n : a_i \in R, i = 0, 1, \ldots, n; n = 0, 1, \ldots\}$$

is the set of *polynomials in the indeterminate x with coefficients in R.* We emphasize that x is, here, simply a symbol totally unrelated to the ring R or its elements, and that two polynomials in x are equal iff they have exactly the same ordered sequence of coefficients.

In order to make $R[x]$ into a ring, we must define addition and multiplication for elements $f(x)$ and $g(x)$ of $R[x]$. If

$$f(x) = a_0x^0 + a_1x^1 + \cdots + a_nx^n \leftrightarrow f = (a_0, a_1, \ldots, a_n, 0, 0, \ldots),$$
$$g(x) = b_0x^0 + b_1x^1 + \cdots + b_mx^m \leftrightarrow g = (b_0, b_1, \ldots, b_m, 0, 0, \ldots),$$

we then define

$$\begin{aligned} f(x) + g(x) &= (a_0 + b_0)x^0 + (a_1 + b_1)x^1 + \cdots \\ &\leftrightarrow f + g = (a_0 + b_0, a_1 + b_1, \ldots), \\ f(x)g(x) &= a_0b_0x^0 + (a_1b_0 + a_0b_1)x^1 + (a_2b_0 + a_1b_1 + a_0b_2)x^2 + \cdots \\ &= c_0x^0 + c_1x^1 + \cdots + c_{n+m}x^{n+m}, \\ &\leftrightarrow fg = (c_0, c_1, \ldots, c_{n+m}, 0, 0, \ldots), \end{aligned}$$

where

$$c_k = \sum_{i+j=k} a_ib_j = \sum_{i=0}^{k} a_ib_{k-i}.$$

We leave to the reader the verification that, with these definitions, $R[x]$ is a ring, as well as that $R[x]$ is commutative iff R is commutative.

By means of the correspondence

$$a_0 \leftrightarrow a_0x^0,$$

we readily see that $R[x]$ contains a subring isomorphic to R. We could, therefore, construct a ring isomorphic to $R[x]$ and containing R, but following our customary procedure, we shall identify R with this isomorphic subring and imbed R in $R[x]$. Thus we write

$$f(x) = a_0 + a_1x + a_2x^2 + \cdots + a_nx^n,$$

where we are also identifying x with x^1, in accordance with the familiar usage. Similarly, if R has a unity element 1, we shall agree to denote the element $1x^n$ simply by x^n.

Definition. If the element $f(x)$ above has $a_n \neq 0$, we say that $f(x)$ has *degree n*, *leading coefficient* a_n, and *leading term* a_nx^n. If we do not know whether a_n is zero or not, then we call n the *virtual degree*, a_n the *virtual leading coefficient*, and a_nx^n the *virtual leading term* of $f(x)$. The zero polynomial, that is the polynomial all of whose coefficients are zero, has no degree. If $f(x) \in R[x]$, R a ring with unity, has unity as leading coefficient, then $f(x)$ is called a *monic* polynomial.

It follows immediately that for $f(x)$ and $g(x)$ as above, the *virtual leading term* of $f(x)g(x)$ is

$$a_nb_mx^{n+m},$$

the *virtual leading coefficient* is a_nb_m, and the *virtual degree* is $n + m$, while if $a_nb_m \neq 0$, then the word *virtual* can be omitted.

Similarly, it follows that the degree of $f(x) + g(x)$ is, at most, the maximum of the degrees of $f(x)$ and $g(x)$, being equal to this maximum if $f(x)$ and $g(x)$ have different degrees, and, possibly, being less if $f(x)$ and $g(x)$ have the same degree.

Having defined these notions, most of which are certainly familiar, we may proceed to draw some conclusions. Just as the division algorithm is of fundamental importance in ordinary arithmetic, its analogue is of fundamental importance in the theory of polynomial rings.

Theorem 3.21. *Let R be any ring with unity element, $f(x)$ and $g(x)$ be as above with $a_n \neq 0$ and b_m a unit element in R. Then there exist unique elements $q(x)$, $p(x)$, $r(x)$, and $s(x)$ in $R[x]$, such that $r(x)$ and $s(x)$ are zero or of degree less than m, $q(x)$ and $p(x)$ are zero or of degree $n - m$, and*

$$f(x) = q(x)g(x) + r(x) = g(x)p(x) + s(x).$$

PROOF. We shall carry out the arguments only for $q(x)$ and $r(x)$, those for $p(x)$ and $s(x)$ being entirely similar.

To show the existence of $q(x)$ and $r(x)$, we proceed by induction on the degree n of $f(x)$. If $n < m$, the result is trivial, as we may then take $q(x) = 0$ and $r(x) = f(x)$. So, suppose the result valid for any $f_1(x)$ of degree less than n, where we may now assume $n \geq m$. Consider the polynomial

$$f_1(x) = f(x) - a_n b_m^{-1} x^{n-m} g(x),$$

which is certainly of degree at most n. But, since the coefficient of x^n in $f_1(x)$ is

$$a_n - a_n b_m^{-1} b_m = 0,$$

it follows that the degree of $f_1(x)$ is at most $n - 1$. Hence, by the inductive assumption, there exist polynomials $q_1(x)$ and $r(x)$, with $q_1(x)$ zero or of degree at most $n - m - 1$ and $r(x)$ zero or of degree less than m, such that

$$f_1(x) = q_1(x)g(x) + r(x) = f(x) - a_n b_m^{-1} x^{n-m} g(x).$$

Hence

$$f(x) = (q_1(x) + a_n b_m^{-1} x^{n-m})g(x) + r(x) = q(x)g(x) + r(x), \quad \text{and}$$
$$q(x) = q_1(x) + a_n b_m^{-1} x^{n-m}$$

is of degree $n - m$. (Since b_m^{-1} is a unit and $a_n \neq 0$, $a_n b_m^{-1} \neq 0$.)

If, also, $f(x) = q'(x)g(x) + r'(x)$ with $q'(x)$ of degree $n - m$ and $r'(x)$ zero or of degree less than m, then

$$(q(x) - q'(x))g(x) = r'(x) - r(x).$$

Now, $r'(x) - r(x)$ is zero or of degree less than m. On the other hand, since the leading coefficient of $g(x)$ is a unit, the degree of $(q(x) - q'(x))g(x)$ will be at least m, which is impossible, unless the leading coefficient of $q(x) - q'(x)$ is 0. But this means that $q(x) - q'(x) = 0 = r'(x) - r(x)$, and the uniqueness is established, thus completing the proof.

The polynomials $q(x)$ and $r(x)$ are called, respectively, the *right quotient* and *right remainder* of $f(x)$ on division by $g(x)$. Similarly, $p(x)$ and $s(x)$ are the *left quotient* and *left remainder* of $f(x)$ on division by $g(x)$. Of course, in the event that R is commutative, then it may be easily shown that $R[x]$ is also, and we need not distinguish between left and right.

We may remark that if R is commutative, then even if b_m is not a unit of R, there will still exist $q(x)$ and $r(x)$ with degrees as above, but no longer necessarily unique, such that if $k =$ maximum $(n - m + 1, 0)$, then $b_m^k f(x) = q(x)g(x) + r(x)$. Since the proof is but a slight modification of that in the theorem above, we leave it to the reader.

As an easy consequence of the division algorithm, we may obtain the remainder theorem, but first we need the following definition.

Definition. Let R be a ring with unity and c an element of a ring S containing R. Then, if

$$f(x) = a_0 + a_1x + a_2x^2 + \cdots + a_nx^n \in R[x],$$

we define

$$f_R(c) = a_0 + a_1c + a_2c^2 + \cdots + a_nc^n,$$

and $$f_L(c) = a_0 + ca_1 + c^2a_2 + \cdots + c^na_n.$$

If S is commutative, then $f_R(c) = f_L(c) = f(c)$.

With regard to this definition, we note that the addition and multiplication indicated in $f_R(c)$ and $f_L(c)$ are, of course, the addition and multiplication of the ring S. If S is commutative, it may be readily shown that $R[c]$, the set of all $f(c)$ for $f(x)$ in $R[x]$, is a subring of S and is called the ring of polynomials in the element c with coefficients in R. Contrary to the situation in $R[x]$, in $R[c]$ it is perfectly possible for a polynomial to be zero without all the coefficients being zero. For example, if S is the field of complex numbers and $c = \sqrt{-1}$, then $f(c) = 1 + c^2 = 0$. If S is commutative, $S \supseteq R$, then the mapping from $R[x]$ onto $R[c]$, defined by

$$f(x) = a_0 + a_1x + \cdots + a_nx^n \to f(c) = a_0 + a_1c + \cdots + a_nc^n$$

can be shown to be a homomorphism and will be of much importance in our later study of fields.

Theorem 3.22 (Remainder Theorem). *Let R be a ring with unity, $c \in R$. The right remainder $r(x)$ of $f(x)$ on division by $x - c$ is $f_R(c)$ and the left remainder $s(x)$ is $f_L(c)$.*

PROOF. (Note that $x - c$ is not an element of $R[x]$ unless R has a unity.) We have $f(x) = q(x)(x - c) + r$, where r must be an element of R since the remainder $r(x)$ is zero or of degree less than one, and $q(x)$ is a polynomial of degree $n - 1$. Let

$$q(x) = q_0 + q_1x + \cdots + q_{n-1}x^{n-1}.$$

We have that

$$f(x) = -q_0c + (q_0 - q_1c)x + \cdots + (q_{n-2} - q_{n-1}c)x^{n-1} + q_{n-1}x^n + r.$$

Hence

$$\begin{aligned} f_R(c) &= -q_0c + (q_0 - q_1c)c + \cdots + (q_{n-2} - q_{n-1}c)c^{n-1} + q_{n-1}c^n + r \\ &= r. \end{aligned}$$

In similar fashion we deduce that $f_L(c) = s$.

Definition. If in $R[x]$ we have $f(x) = g(x)h(x)$, then $g(x)$ is a *left factor* or *divisor* of $f(x)$, and $h(x)$ is a *right factor* or *divisor* of $f(x)$.

Corollary 3.22.1. *Let $f(x)$ be in $R[x]$, R a ring with unity. Then $f(x)$ has $x - c$ as a right factor iff $f_R(c) = 0$, and has $x - c$ as a left factor iff $f_L(c) = 0$.*

PROOF. Immediate from the theorem.

Definition. If R, and hence also $R[x]$, is commutative an element c of a ring S containing R is called a *root* or *zero* of $f(x)$ if $f(c) = 0$.†

Theorem 3.23. *If $c_1, c_2, \ldots, c_k \in R$ are distinct zeros of $f(x)$ in $R[x]$ and R is an integral domain, then $f(x)$ is divisible by the product*

$$(x - c_1)(x - c_2) \cdots (x - c_k).$$

PROOF. The result is known for $k = 1$ by the corollary above; so we proceed by induction on k, and assume the result for $k = i - 1$, $i > 1$, so that

$$f(x) = (x - c_1)(x - c_2) \cdots (x - c_{i-1})g(x).$$

Then, since R is commutative, we have

$$f(c_i) = (c_i - c_1)(c_i - c_2) \cdots (c_i - c_{i-1})g(c_i) = 0.$$

Since the c_j are all distinct and R has no zero-divisors, it follows that $g(c_i) = 0$, and, hence, that

$$g(x) = (x - c_i)h(x).$$

Thus

$$f(x) = (x - c_1)(x - c_2) \cdots (x - c_{i-1})(x - c_i)h(x),$$

completing the proof by induction.

Corollary 3.23.1. *If R is an integral domain, then $f(x)$ of degree n in $R[x]$ has at most n distinct zeros in R.*

PROOF. Immediate from the theorem.

† It would, perhaps, be more desirable to designate such an element c as a zero of $f(x)$ and a root of the equation $f(x) = 0$, but common usage has made the terms *root* and *zero* essentially synonymous.

If R is not commutative, the previous theorem and its corollary need not be valid. For, in the proof of Theorem 3.23, we made essential use of the fact that if R is an integral domain, then

$$f(x) = (x - c_1)(x - c_2) \cdots (x - c_{i-1})g(x)$$

implies

$$f(c_i) = (c_i - c_1)(c_i - c_2) \cdots (c_i - c_{i-1})g(c_i).$$

But if R were not commutative, this would not follow. For if we let

$$f(x) = (x - a)(x - b) = x^2 - (a + b)x + ab,$$

we then have

$$\begin{aligned} f_L(c) &= c^2 - ca - cb + ab, \\ f_R(c) &= c^2 - ac - bc + ab, \\ (c - a)(c - b) &= c^2 - ac - cb + ab, \end{aligned}$$

and all of these three expressions may well be distinct if R is not commutative. Thus we could have either or both of $f_L(c)$ and $f_R(c)$ equal to zero, and yet $(c - a)(c - b) \neq 0$.

For example, let D be the ring of real quaternions (a, b, c, d), as defined in Example (I), Section 1, of this chapter. Then the polynomial

$$f(x) = x^2 + (1, 0, 0, 0) = x^2 + 1 \text{ in } D[x]$$

has six distinct zeros in D; i, $-i$, j, $-j$, k, and $-k$, where

$$i = (0, 1, 0, 0), j = (0, 0, 1, 0), \text{ and } k = (0, 0, 0, 1).$$

In particular, we have

$$\begin{aligned} &x^2 + 1 = (x + i)(x - i) \text{ and } f_R(j) = f_L(j) = j^2 + 1 = 0, \text{ yet} \\ &(j + i)(j - i) = 2k \neq 0, \end{aligned}$$

and the argument of Theorem 3.23 would not apply.

Returning now to the case of a ring of polynomials over an integral domain, we have the following theorem.

Theorem 3.24. *If $f(x)$ and $g(x)$ are nonzero elements of $R[x]$, R an integral domain, then the degree of $f(x)g(x)$ is the sum of the degrees of $f(x)$ and $g(x)$.*

PROOF. Since neither $f(x)$ nor $g(x)$ is zero, both have degrees and nonzero leading coefficients, say a_n and b_m. The virtual leading coefficient of the product is the product a_nb_m of these leading coefficients, and, since an integral domain has no divisors of zero, $a_nb_m \neq 0$, a_nb_m is the actual leading coefficient of $f(x)g(x)$, and the result follows.

In elementary algebra and analysis, we frequently have occasion to consider polynomials in two or more indeterminates.

Definition. For any ring R, we define recursively

$$R[x_1, x_2, \ldots, x_n] = R[x_1, x_2, \ldots, x_{n-1}][x_n],$$

and, similarly, if $c_1, c_2, \ldots, c_n$ are elements of a ring containing R,

$$R[c_1, c_2, \ldots, c_n] = R[c_1, c_2, \ldots, c_{n-1}][c_n].$$

Notice that in any products of indeterminates, this definition implies that an indeterminate of lower index will occur to the left of an indeterminate with higher index.

Thus each element of $R[x_1, x_2, \ldots, x_n]$ is a finite sum of *monomials*, terms of the form $rx_1^{e_1}x_2^{e_2} \cdots x_n^{e_n}$. The degree of a (nonzero) monomial is

$$e_1 + e_2 + \cdots + e_n,$$

and the degree of a sum $m_1 + m_2 + \cdots + m_k$ of monomials is at most the maximum of the degrees of $m_1, m_2, \ldots, m_k$.

If R is a ring with unity 1, then for any $r \in R$, we have

$$xr = (1x)(rx^0) = (1r)(xx^0) = rx,$$

so that x commutes, in $R[x]$, with any element of the ring R. Similarly, if R has a unity, then so does $R[x]$ and, hence, in $R[x, y] = R[x][y]$ we have

$$yx = (1y)(xy^0) = (1x)(yy^0) = xy.$$

But then, clearly, $R[x][y] = R[y][x]$ or $R[x, y] = R[y, x]$. By repeated application of this argument, we see that in forming $R[x_1, x_2, \ldots, x_n]$, the order in which the x_i are "adjoined" is immaterial. Since, moreover, we know that any ring R without a unity can be imbedded isomorphically in a ring S with unity, in $S[x_1, x_2, \ldots, x_n]$ the order of adjoining the x_i is immaterial and $R[x_1, x_2, \ldots, x_n]$ is a subring of $S[x_1, x_2, \ldots, x_n]$, it follows that the order of adjunction is also immaterial in $R[x_1, x_2, \ldots, x_n]$. It should be observed, however, that if R does not have a unity, it is meaningless to consider the "product" xr in so far as the definitions of multiplication which we are using are concerned, since in this case "x" is not an element of $R[x]$.

Theorem 3.25. *If R is an integral domain, then so is $R[x]$.*

PROOF. We have already noted that if R is commutative with unity, then so is $R[x]$. When R has no divisors of zero, then neither does $R[x]$, as follows at once from Theorem 3.24. If neither $f(x)$ nor $g(x)$ is zero in $R[x]$, then their product is not zero.

Corollary 3.25.1. *If R is an integral domain, then so is $R[x_1, x_2, \ldots, x_n]$.*

PROOF. Induction on n.

Since any integral domain may be imbedded in its quotient field, we may give the following definition.

Definition. Let D be an integral domain, and $D[x]$ the integral domain of polynomials in an indeterminate x with coefficients in D. The quotient field of $D[x]$ is called the *field of rational functions* in x with coefficients in D and is denoted by $D(x)$.

Theorem 3.26. *If R is an infinite integral domain and $f(x_1, x_2, \ldots, x_n)$ is a nonzero element of $R[x_1, x_2, \ldots, x_n]$, then there exist infinitely many $a_i \in R$ for each of* $i = 1, 2, \ldots, n$, such that $f(a_1, a_2, \ldots, a_n) \neq 0$.

PROOF. We proceed by induction on n. If $n = 1$, the result follows at once from the corollary to Theorem 3.23. So suppose that the result holds for k, and suppose, further, that $f(x_1, \ldots, x_k, x_{k+1})$ is of degree $m > 0$ in x_{k+1}, that is, as an element of $R[x_1, \ldots, x_k][x_{k+1}]$. (If not, then the result holds trivially for $k + 1$, since then $f(x_1, x_2, \ldots, x_k, x_{k+1})$ is an element of $R[x_1, \ldots, x_k]$.) Then we have

$$f(x_1, \ldots, x_k, x_{k+1}) = g_0 + g_1x_{k+1} + \cdots + g_mx_{k+1}^m,$$

where $g_j \in R[x_1, \ldots, x_k]$ and g_m is not the zero polynomial. By the inductive assumption, there are infinitely many $a_i \in R$ for each of $i = 1, 2, \ldots, k$, such that $g_m(a_1, \ldots, a_k) = c_m \neq 0$ in R. For any of these choices of $a_1, \ldots, a_k$, we have $g_j(a_1, \ldots, a_k) = c_j \in R$, $j = 1, \ldots, m$, and

$$f(a_1, \ldots, a_k, x_{k+1}) = c_0 + c_1x_{k+1} + \cdots + c_mx_{k+1}^m,$$

with $c_m \neq 0$. Corollary 3.23.1 now assures us that there are infinitely many $a_{k+1} \in R$, such that

$$f(a_1, \ldots, a_k, a_{k+1}) \neq 0,$$

and the inductive argument is complete.

That the assumption of an infinite number of elements in the integral domain R is essential to the proof is seen if we consider the case of the polynomial $x^p - x$ in the polynomial ring $Z_p[x]$, where, as usual, Z_p is the residue class ring of the integers modulo p, and we take p to be a prime. Then the Fermat Theorem, Theorem 3.8, says precisely that all elements of Z_p are zeros of $x^p - x$, and yet $x^p - x$ is certainly not the zero polynomial. Thus if the integral domain is finite, it is possible for a nonzero polynomial in $R[x]$ to "vanish identically," in direct opposition to the familiar situation in elementary analysis.

In the above example, we have a case of a polynomial of degree n over an integral domain of n elements which has every element of the integral domain as a zero. That this is a "best possible" example is seen from the fact that Theorem 3.23 and its corollary imply that any polynomial of virtual degree n over an integral domain of $n + 1$ elements which has every element of the integral domain as a zero must indeed be the zero polynomial, a result more in keeping with the customary situation.

Exercises

1. Verify that $R[x]$, as defined in this section, actually is a ring.
2. Show that $R[x]$ is commutative if R is and has a unity if R does.
3. Show that if R is a commutative ring with unity, $f(x) = a_0 + a_1x + \cdots + a_nx^n$, $g(x) = b_0 + b_1x + \cdots + b_mx^m$, a_n and b_m not zero, are elements of $R[x]$, and $k = \text{maximum } (n - m + 1, 0)$, then there exist polynomials $q(x)$ and $r(x)$ in $R[x]$ such that $b_m^k f(x) = g(x)q(x) + r(x)$ is zero or of degree less than m.
4. Let R_2 be the ring of real matrices of order two,
$$f(x) = \begin{pmatrix} 1 & 1 \\ 0 & 1 \end{pmatrix} + \begin{pmatrix} 2 & 0 \\ 2 & 0 \end{pmatrix}x^2,\ g(x) = \begin{pmatrix} 1 & 2 \\ -2 & 1 \end{pmatrix} + \begin{pmatrix} 1 & 0 \\ 0 & 1 \end{pmatrix}x \quad \text{in } R_2[x].$$
Find the $q(x)$, $p(x)$, $r(x)$ and $s(x)$ of Theorem 3.21 in this case.
5. Show that if R is commutative with unity, $f(x) = (x - a_1) \cdots (x - a_n)$ is in $R[x]$ and $c \in R$, then $f_R(c) = f_L(c) = (c - a_1) \cdots (c - a_n)$.
6. Let R be the ring Z^2 of Exercise 2, Section 3.1. Show that the polynomial $(1, 0)x$ in $Z^2[x]$ has infinitely many zeros in Z^2. Also, find all the zeros in Z^2 of $(-2, -6) + (-1, 1)x + (1, 1)x^2$.
7. Show that if S is a commutative ring containing R and c, then the mapping $R[x] \to R[c]$, $a_0 + a_1x + \cdots + a_nx^n \to a_0 + a_1c + \cdots + a_nc^n$ is a homomorphism of $R[x]$ onto $R[c]$.
8. Show that Theorem 3.24 is no longer valid if the polynomials $f(x)$ and $g(x)$ are not restricted to be both nonzero.
9. Let $f(x_1, x_2, \ldots, x_k)$ in $R[x_1, x_2, \ldots, x_k]$, R an integral domain, have degree d_i in x_i, $i = 1, 2, \ldots, k$. How many elements must R have to assure that
$$f(a_1, a_2, \ldots, a_n) \neq 0$$
for some $a_1, a_2, \ldots, a_n$ in R?

7. Finiteness Conditions

In the ring Z of integers, many of the most useful properties, for the purposes of ordinary arithmetic, stem from the unique factorization of any integer into a product of units (1's and -1's) and primes. This property, in turn, is a consequence of the inductive property of the natural numbers, which essentially assures us that given any natural number, there are only a finite number of smaller natural numbers. Since we shall wish to investigate the possibilities of extending the Fundamental Theorem of Arithmetic, or some analogue thereof, to more general rings, it will be well to consider first the various properties which a ring may have which are in some way similar to the inductive property of the natural numbers, or positive integers.

In the examples which we have used thus far, all ideals of the ring Z which have occurred have been principal ideals, that is, ideals generated by a single element. This leads to the hypothesis that every ideal of Z is a principal ideal. More generally, we may wish to consider the following type of ring.

Definition. A *principal ideal ring* (abbreviation: PIR) is a commutative ring with unity in which every ideal is principal. A *principal ideal domain* (PID) is an integral domain in which every ideal is principal.

Theorem 3.27. *The ring Z of integers is a principal ideal domain.*

PROOF. Having already observed that Z is an integral domain, we need only show that every ideal of Z is principal. The zero ideal is clearly principal, so let A be any nonzero ideal of Z. Since A is itself a ring, it is an additive group and thus must contain some positive integer. The set of positive integers in A is thus not empty, and must contain a least integer, by the well-ordered property of the positive integers. Let this integer be d, the least positive integer in A.

Now if n is any integer in A, then there exist integers q and r such that $n = qd + r$, with $0 \leq r < d$. But then $r = n - qd = n + (-qd)$ is an element of A, and the minimality of d implies that $r = 0$. Thus $n = qd$ for some integer q and $n \in (d)$. Hence $A \subseteq (d)$, and the reverse inclusion is obvious from the definition of an ideal.

Therefore, $A = (d)$, a principal ideal.

It is apparent that every nonnegative integer determines an ideal of Z, and the above result shows that the converse is true, every ideal of Z determines a unique nonnegative integer, its generator. This means that any statement about the nonnegative elements of Z should be translatable into the language of ideals of Z. The fact that this is so provides us with a useful tool in generalizing the properties of the ring of integers to more general rings.

In the natural numbers, the inductive principle is equivalent to the well-ordering principle, that is, any nonempty set of natural numbers contains a least natural number, or, equally well, in any nonempty set of nonnegative integers there is a least nonnegative integer. Also, if we recall many of the arguments concerning the nonnegative integers, we find that they are based on the notion of "finite descent," that is, that given any positive integer, there are only a finite number of smaller positive integers. Let us see what form these notions take when translated into the language of ideals of Z.

Since every ideal of Z is principal, if we have two ideals, A and B, such that A is contained properly in B, $A = (a) \subset (b) = B$, then we see that a must be divisible by b, since only elements divisible by b are in (b). Moreover, if we require that both a and b be nonnegative, as we may do without loss of generality, we see that b is less than a. Conversely, if a and b are nonnegative integers such that b is less than a and b divides a (written $b|a$), then it follows that $(a) \subset (b)$. Thus the "finite descent" property of the nonnegative integers is equivalent to the property of Z that we cannot have a "properly ascending chain" of ideals of more than finite length. Correspondingly, the well-ordered property of the positive integers becomes, in Z, the property that in any nonempty set of ideals there must be an ideal maximal in the sense that it is not properly contained in any ideal of the set. For rings in general, these notions take the form of the following definitions.

Definition. Let A and B be ideals of a ring R. If $A \subseteq B$, then B is a *divisor* of A, and A is a *multiple* of B. If $A \subset B$, then B is a *proper divisor* of A, and A is a *proper multiple* of B.

Definition. A ring R is said to satisfy the *ascending chain condition* (*for ideals*) (ACC) if each sequence of ideals $A_1, A_2, \ldots$ of R such that $A_1 \subset A_2 \subset \cdots$ has only a finite number of terms. Similarly, R satisfies the *descending chain condition* (*for ideals*) (DCC) if every descending chain $A_1 \supset A_2 \supset \cdots$ has only a finite number of terms. Corresponding definitions would, of course, hold for ACC on left (right) ideals, or DCC on left (right) ideals.

It is clear that the ACC is equivalent to the statement that, in each sequence $A_1 \subseteq A_2 \subseteq \cdots \subseteq A_n \subseteq \cdots$, the equality must hold beyond some finite index n. The corresponding restatement of the DCC is obvious.

Definition. A ring R is said to satisfy the *maximal condition* (*for ideals*) (MC) if, in any nonempty set of ideals of R, there must exist some ideal which is maximal in the set, i.e., is not properly contained in any other ideal of the set. R satisfies the *minimal condition* (*for ideals*) (mC) if, in any nonempty set of ideals of R, there must exist some ideal which is minimal in the set. Similar definitions would hold for conditions on sets of left (right) ideals.

More general than a principal ideal is an ideal having a finite basis.

Definition. Let the ideal A in the ring R be generated by the set S. If A is not generated by any proper subset of S, then S is a *basis* of A. The ring R is said to satisfy the *finite basis condition* (*for ideals*) (FBC) if every ideal in R has a finite basis. Again, similar definitions would hold for finite basis conditions for left or for right ideals.

The ring Z of integers thus satisfies the ACC, FBC, and MC, but not the DCC nor the mC. That we cannot give examples of rings satisfying some but not all of the ACC, FBC, and MC is the content of the next theorem.

Theorem 3.28. *For any ring R, the ACC, MC, and FBC are equivalent.*

PROOF.

(i) ACC implies MC. Let M be any nonempty set of ideals of R, A_1 an ideal in the set M. Either A_1 is maximal in M and we are through, or else there is an A_2 in M such that $A_1 \subset A_2$. If A_2 is maximal in M we are through, and, if not, then there is an A_3 in M such that

$$A_1 \subset A_2 \subset A_3.$$

By the ACC, this process must terminate after a finite number, say n, of steps with an ideal A_n, which is maximal in the set M.

(ii) MC implies FBC. If there exists an ideal B of R which does not have a finite basis, then there is an infinite set of elements $a_i \in B$, $i = 1, 2, \ldots, n, \ldots$ such that,

$$\text{if } A_i = (a_1, a_2, \ldots, a_i) \text{ then } A_i \subset A_{i+1}.$$

The set $M = \{A_i : i = 1, 2, \ldots\}$ is then a nonempty set of ideals, none of which is maximal in the set M. Hence the MC implies the FBC.

(iii) FBC implies ACC. Let

$$A_1 \subseteq A_2 \subseteq \cdots \subseteq A_n \subseteq \cdots$$

be an ascending chain of ideals and let

$$A = \cup A_i,\ i = 1, 2, \ldots, n, \ldots .$$

Then, by an easy argument which we leave as an exercise, it follows that A is an ideal. By the FBC, we have that A is finitely generated, say $A = (a_1, a_2, \ldots, a_n)$. By the definition of A, we have $a_j \in A_{i_j}$ for some A_{i_j}, $j = 1, 2, \ldots, n$. Let k be the maximum of $i_1, i_2, \ldots, i_n$, and it follows, at once, that $A \subseteq A_k$. But $A_k \subseteq A$, by the definition of A, hence $A = A_k$ and we have

$$A_1 \subseteq A_2 \subseteq \cdots \subseteq A_k = A_{k+1} = A_{k+2} = \cdots.$$

Corollary 3.28.1. *A principal ideal ring satisfies the ACC and MC.*

PROOF. In a PIR every ideal has a one element basis.

Corollary 3.28.2. *If A is an ideal in a commutative ring with ACC, then A contains $(\sqrt{A})^n$ for some positive integer n.*

PROOF. $\sqrt{A}$ has a finite basis, say $\sqrt{A} = (b_1, b_2, \ldots, b_k)$. Now, $b_i^{ni} \in A$ for some n_i, whence, if $n = n_1 + n_2 + \cdots + n_k - k + 1$, we have $(\sqrt{A})^n \subseteq A$, since, for $b \in \sqrt{A}$, we must have b_i^{ni} for some i in every term of the expansion of b^n.

The equivalence of the DCC and the mC for arbitrary rings may be shown by similar arguments.

Having established these equivalences among the finiteness conditions on a ring, in particular the various ways in which the inductive property of the natural numbers may be generalized, we turn, in the next section, to the problem of generalizing the unique factorization property of the integers.

Exercises

1. Show that the ring Z of integers does not satisfy the descending chain condition.
2. Show that the (set theoretic) union of any ascending chain of ideals of R is an ideal of R.
3. Prove the equivalence of the descending chain condition and the minimal condition for any ring.
4. Let A be an ideal of the ring R such that the ACC holds both in A (as a ring) and in R/A. Show that the ACC holds in R. (*Hint:* If $\{B_i\}$ is an ascending sequence of ideals of R, show that both the ascending sequences $\{A + B_i\}$ and $\{A \cap B_i\}$ must be constant beyond some finite index. Then, use the result of Exercise 6, Section 3.4 to show that the sequence $\{B_i\}$ must do likewise.)
5. Show that if the ACC holds in the ring R, then the ACC also holds in R/A for any ideal A of R. Also show that if R is a PIR, then so is R/A.
6. Show that if R is an integral domain with DCC on ideals, then R is a field. (*Hint:* Consider, for $a \neq 0$ in R, the sequence of ideals $(a) = Ra, Ra^2, \ldots$.)

8. Factorization of Ring Elements

We turn now to consideration of the Fundamental Theorem of Arithmetic and some of its generalizations, in which the notion of a principal ideal ring will play a central role. In the course of these developments, we will obtain theorems justifying the results regarding divisibility and greatest common divisors in the ring of integers, which results we have been freely using up to now without proof, assuming them known from more elementary mathematics.

Definition. If, for elements a, b, and c in a ring R, we have $ab = c$, then we call a a *left factor* or *left divisor* of c. If d is a left divisor of both b and c, then d is a *common left divisor* of b and c. If, also, every common left divisor of b and c is a left divisor of d, then d is a *greatest common left divisor* of b and c. Similar definitions, of course, hold for right divisors. If d is both a *greatest common left divisor* and a *greatest common right divisor* of b and c, then d is a *greatest common divisor*, or g.c.d., of a and b. Similar definitions hold for *common divisors* and g.c.d.'s of any finite number of elements of R.

Definition. If, for ideals A, B, and C of R, we have $A \subseteq C$ and $B \subseteq C$, then C is a *common divisor* of A and B. If, in addition, $A \subseteq D$ and $B \subseteq D$ imply $C \subseteq D$, then C is the *greatest common divisor* (g.c.d.) of A and B.

We may notice that the g.c.d. of two ideals A and B always exists and, moreover, is unique, being the ideal generated by the union of the elements of A and of B. Thus we may denote the g.c.d. of A and B by (A, B).

In the case of two elements of a ring, however, not only may they fail to have a common divisor, but even if a g.c.d. exists, it may fail to be unique. Thus in the ring of even integers, the elements 2 and 4 have no common divisors, and, indeed, 2 itself has no divisors at all.

In the ring Z_{10} of the integers modulo 10, we have $\bar{4} = \bar{4}\,\bar{6}$ and $\bar{6} = \bar{1}\,\bar{6} = \bar{4}\,\bar{4}$, so that $\bar{4}$ and $\bar{6}$ are both common divisors of $\bar{4}$ and $\bar{6}$, from which it follows, at once, that $\bar{4}$ and $\bar{6}$ are both g.c.d.'s of $\bar{4}$ and $\bar{6}$.

At the other extreme from the situation in the ring of even integers is that which exists in a field. Here the notion of g.c.d. becomes useless since any nonzero element of the field is a g.c.d. of any pair of elements of the field.

Theorem 3.29. *Let R be a PIR, $a, b \in R$. Then there exist $d, r, s \in R$ such that d is a g.c.d. of a and b, and $d = ar + bs$.*

PROOF. R is commutative by definition; hence we need not distinguish between left and right divisors. Since R is a PIR, the ideal (a, b) must be a principal ideal (d) for some $d \in R$. Then $a = gd$ and $b = hd$ for some g and h in R and d is a common divisor of a and b. Since d is in (a, b), we have $d = ar + bs$ for some r and s in R. Now if d' is any common divisor of a and b, then $a = g'd'$ and $b = h'd'$ for some $g', h' \in R$. We then have

$$d = g'd'r + h'd's = d'(g'r + h's),$$

by the commutativity and distributivity of R, and, hence, d' divides d. Thus d is a g.c.d. of a and b, as asserted.

Corollary 3.29.1. *If d' is any g.c.d. of a and b in a PIR, then there exist r' and s' in the ring such that*

$$d' = ar' + bs'.$$

PROOF. Exercise.

Corollary 3.29.2. *Let R be a PIR and $a_1, a_2, \ldots, a_n \in R$. Then, there exists d in R such that d is a g.c.d. of $a_1, a_2, \ldots, a_n$.*

PROOF. Exercise.

Definition. Let R be a ring with unity. We recall that an element of R having a multiplicative inverse is called a unit of R. Two elements of R are called *associates* if one is a unit times the other.

Multiplication by the inverse of the unit shows that the relation of being associate is symmetric; in fact it is an equivalence relation.

Definition. An element of R which is not a unit and has only units and associates as divisors is called *irreducible.*

Definition. Let R be a commutative ring with unity. An element p of R is *prime* if whenever p divides a product ab of elements of R, then p divides at least one of a and b.

It follows, by an easy induction argument, that if a prime divides any product, it must divide at least one of the factors.

Definition. Two elements of R are *relatively prime* if their only common divisors are units.

Thus in the ring $Z[x, y]$, the units are 1 and -1, the polynomials x and y are both irreducible and prime, as is any polynomial in $Z[x, y]$ of degree one, and the polynomials x^2 and y^2, while not irreducible nor prime, are relatively prime. Further, although 0 is prime in this ring, it is reducible; for example, $0 = 0 \cdot 2$ and 2 is neither a unit nor an associate of 0. More generally, if R is any integral domain containing a nonunit $r \neq 0$, then 0 is prime but reducible. Thus our definition of prime element is not quite the same as the familiar number theoretic definition of primes in the ring Z. The reader may also find it instructive to determine the units of the ring of second-order matrices with integer elements, as well as to determine the irreducible elements and primes of this ring.

In the case of a PIR or a PID, these notions are particularly useful, as may be seen from the next few theorems.

Theorem 3.30. *If R is a PIR with unity e and $a, b \in R$ are relatively prime, then there exist $r, s \in R$ such that $e = ar + bs$.*

PROOF. e is a common divisor of a and b, and since only units are common divisors of a and b and every unit divides e, clearly, e is a g.c.d. of a and b. The result then follows from Corollary 3.29.1.

Theorem 3.31. *An irreducible element p of a PIR R is prime.*

PROOF. Suppose p divides ab. Then, $(p, b) = (d)$ for some d in R, hence $p = rd$ for some r in R. Since p is irreducible, either r or d must be a unit.

If d is a unit, then $dd^{-1} = e$ is in $(d) = (p, b)$ and, hence, $e = ps + bt$ for some s, t in R. Then

$$a = ae = aps + abt = pas + abt,$$

and since p divides ab, $ab = px$ for some x in R,

$$a = pas + pxt = p(as + xt),$$

so that p divides a.

If, on the other hand, r is a unit, then r has an inverse r^{-1} and $d = r^{-1}p$ is in (p), whence $(d) = (p)$, and we have $b \in (p)$. Then p divides b.

Thus if the irreducible element p divides the product ab, p must divide one of the factors, and p is prime.

Corollary 3.31.1. *Any nonzero element p of a PID R is prime iff it is irreducible.*

PROOF. That p irreducible implies p prime has just been established. Suppose, conversely, that p is prime and that $p = ab$ for some a, b in R. Then p divides at least one of a and b, say $a = pd$, and we have

$$p = pdb$$

or

$$p(e - db) = 0.$$

Since $p \neq 0$ and R is an integral domain, we conclude that

$$e - db = 0$$

and b is a unit. Similarly, if p divides b, then a must be a unit and p is irreducible.

Theorem 3.32. *If R is a PID, then every nonzero element of R can be expressed as a product of prime elements. This factorization is unique, apart from unit factors and the order of the factors.*

PROOF. Suppose the theorem false, and consider the set of principal ideals whose nonzero generators can not be so expressed. This set is nonempty, by assumption, and has a maximal element, say (r), by the MC, which holds in any PIR, in particular, in a PID. Now r is certainly not itself a prime, and, hence, $r = st$ for some nonunits s and t of R. Thus $(r) \subseteq (s)$ and $(r) \subseteq (t)$.

If $(r) = (s)$, then s is in (r), $s = ra$ for some a in R, and $r = rat$. This implies that $r(e - at) = 0$, and, since r is not zero and R is an integral domain, we must have $e - at = 0$, t is a unit, contrary to assumption. Hence we must have $(r) \subset (s)$, and, similarly, $(r) \subset (t)$.

Now the maximality of (r) implies that both s and t have prime factorizations; hence their product r does also. But this is a contradiction; hence our assumption is false, and the existence part of the theorem is established.

Now suppose that

$$r = p_1p_2 \cdots p_m = q_1q_2 \cdots q_n$$

are two such prime factorizations of an arbitrary nonzero element r. Then p_1 must divide some q_i and, since R is commutative, we may assume that p_1 divides q_1, $q_1 = p_1\epsilon_1$. Since q_1 is prime, ϵ_1 is a unit. Thus we have

$$p_1p_2 \cdots p_m = p_1\epsilon_1q_2 \cdots q_n,$$

and, since p_1 is nonzero in an integral domain, we conclude that

$$p_2 \cdots p_m = \epsilon_1q_2 \cdots q_n.$$

Continuing this process, we finally obtain $m = n$, since, otherwise, we would have a product of one or more primes equal to a product of units. Moreover, each p_i is a unit times some q_j, and conversely. Thus the factorization is unique, apart from unit factors and the order of the factors.

Definition. An integral domain in which a unique factorization theorem holds, i.e., in which every nonzero element is expressible uniquely (apart from unit factors and the order of factors) as a product of prime elements, is a *unique factorization domain*, or UFD.

That any finite set of nonzero elements of a UFD have a g.c.d. is an argument that we leave to the reader.

The sequence of theorems just completed, all of which are familiar in the case of the ring Z, shows that the essential divisibility properties of the integers are also characteristic of any integral domain which is also a principal ideal ring.

Regarding the divisibility properties of the integers which we have been using thus far without actually proving them, we note that Theorems 3.27 through 3.32 will serve to establish these properties as soon as we establish the division algorithm, the essential result used in the proof of Theorem 3.27.

Theorem 3.33. *For given integers a and b, with $b > 0$, there exist integers q and r such that*

$$a = bq + r, \qquad \text{and} \qquad 0 \leq r < b.$$

Moreover, the integers q and r having this property are uniquely determined by a and b.

PROOF. There exists some integral multiple, bc, of b not exceeding a, for example,

$$b(-|a|) \leq -|a| \leq a,$$

since $b \geq 1$. Hence the set of integers $a - bc$ contains a nonnegative integer, and, therefore, a least nonnegative integer, say $r = a - bq$.

Now if $r \geq b$, then

$$a - b(q+1) = (a - bq) - b = r - b \geq 0$$

would be a nonnegative integer of the form $a - bc$ and less than r. Thus we conclude that $0 \leq r < b$, and $a = bq + r$.

If, also, $a = bq' + r'$, with $0 \leq r' < b$, then

$$r - r' = b(q - q')$$

has absolute value less than b, yet is divisible by b. This is possible only if $r - r' = 0$. Thus $r = r'$ and, hence, $bq = bq'$. Since $b \neq 0$, we must then have $q = q'$, establishing the asserted uniqueness of both q and r.

In case b is a negative integer, a similar result obtains with the inequality modified to read $0 \leq r < |b|$.

The reader will doubtless recall the method, known as the Euclidean Algorithm and based upon the division algorithm, for finding the g.c.d. of two integers a and b. Clearly, we may assume both a and b are positive, and say $a \geq b$. Then $a = bq + r$ with $0 \leq r < b$. If $r = 0$, then b is the desired g.c.d., and if not, we then apply the division algorithm to b and r, obtaining $b = rq' + r'$, with $0 \leq r' < r$. If $r' = 0$, then r can be easily shown to be the g.c.d. of a and b, and if $r' \neq 0$, we continue the process with r and r', etc. In some finite number of steps, we must obtain a zero remainder, and it is easy to show that the last nonzero remainder is the desired g.c.d.

We have already seen the central role played in the theory of polynomial rings by the analogue of the division algorithm, and one can obtain the g.c.d. of two polynomials by an algorithm similar to the Euclidean Algorithm.

If we look for the properties of the ring of integers, and of rings of polynomials with coefficients in a ring with unity, which are essential to the proofs of the respective division algorithms, we soon notice the similarity of the roles played by the notion of absolute value in Z and the notion of the degree of a polynomial. It would appear, then, that it might be useful to formulate this notion in a way which will apply to a wide class of rings.

Definition. A *Euclidean ring* is a commutative ring R, together with a mapping ϕ from the set of nonzero elements of R to the set of nonnegative integers such that:

(i) If $ab \neq 0$ in R, then $(ab)\phi \geq a\phi$.

(ii) For given a and b, with $b \neq 0$, there exist elements q and r in R such that $a = bq + r$ and either $r = 0$ or $r\phi < b\phi$.

The mapping ϕ is often called a *valuation* on the ring R. We see at once that the integers are a Euclidean ring with absolute value as a valuation, and a ring of polynomials with coefficients in a field is a Euclidean ring with degree as a valuation. A Euclidean ring which is also an integral domain, as are the examples just cited, will be called a *Euclidean domain.*

We obtain a unique factorization theorem for Euclidean domains, as well as the analogues of Theorem 3.29, 3.30, and 3.31 with the following theorem:

Theorem 3.34. *Every Euclidean ring is a PIR.*

PROOF. Let B be an ideal of the Euclidean ring E. If $B = 0$, the zero ideal, then B is principal, so suppose $B \neq 0$. Then we may choose b in B such that $b \neq 0$ and $b\phi$ is minimal in the set $\{c\phi : c \neq 0, c \in B\}$, since this is a nonempty set of nonnegative integers.

Now for given a in B, there exist elements q and r in E such that $a = bq + r$ and either $r = 0$ or $r\phi < b\phi$ by the definition of a Euclidean ring. The element $r = a - bq$ is also in B, hence the minimality of $b\phi$ assures us that $r = 0$ and $a = bq$. Thus every element of B is of the form bq for some q in E and $B = (b)$.

To show that E is a PIR, it remains only to show that E has a unity element. Now E is itself an ideal of E, and, hence, $E = (b)$ for some b in E. Since we have just seen that every element of (b) is of the form bq for some q in E, it follows that there is some element e in E such that $b = be = eb$ (E being commutative). For any element a in E, there is, then, some element q in E such that

$$a = bq = (eb)q = e(bq) = ea = ae,$$

and e is the desired unity element.

It follows at once that a Euclidean ring is a Euclidean domain if and only if it contains no zero-divisors. We may also observe that any field is a Euclidean ring if we use the trivial valuation, i.e., $a\phi = 0$ for every nonzero element of the field, and leave the verification to the reader.

Exercises

1. Show that any nonzero element of a field F is a g.c.d. of any a and b in F.
2. Prove the corollaries to Theorem 3.29.
3. Show that "is an associate of" is an equivalence relation on a ring R with unity.
4. Show that in $Z[x, y]$, any polynomial of degree one is prime.
5. Determine the units and primes of the ring of second-order matrices with integer elements.
6. Show that any field is a Euclidean domain.
7. Show that the ring of polynomials $F[x]$, F a field, is a Euclidean domain.
8. Use the Euclidean Algorithm to compute the g.c.d. of 564 and 756, of 546 and 378.
9. State and prove a "Euclidean Algorithm" for polynomials over a field F.
10. Show that if R is a PID and $a\theta$ is the number of primes in any (hence in every) factorization of $a \neq 0$ in R, then:
    (i) If $a = bc$, then $a\theta \geq b\theta$.
    (ii) If a and b are nonzero in R and neither divides the other, then there exist elements $p, q, r \in R$ such that $r = pa + qb$ and $r\theta \leq$ minimum $(a\theta, b\theta)$.
11. Show that if r and s are nonzero elements of a UFD, then r and s have a g.c.d.

9. Factorization in Polynomial Domains

The study of factorization of polynomials begins early in the treatment of elementary algebra, and plays an important role in many mathematical developments. We turn now to a consideration of element factorization in the particular case that our ring is a *polynomial domain,* that is, a ring of polynomials which is also an integral domain. As we have seen, this is true of any ring of polynomials whose ring of coefficients is itself an integral domain.

If we consider the polynomial domain $F[x]$, where F is a field, x an indeterminate, then the leading coefficient of every nonzero polynomial in $F[x]$ is a unit and, by Theorem 3.21, the division algorithm holds in $F[x]$. Thus if we let the valuation of a nonzero polynomial in $F[x]$ be its degree, it follows that $F[x]$ is a Euclidean domain. Then $F[x]$ is also a PID and the results of Theorems 3.29 through 3.32 are valid in $F[x]$.

In $F[x]$ it is customary to use the term *irreducible* in preference to *prime* for an element having no nontrivial factorizations. Since every nonzero constant (i.e., element of F) is a unit in $F[x]$ as well as in F, we see that every polynomial in $F[x]$ can be expressed as a unit times a monic polynomial, and also that if $d(x)$ is any greatest common divisor of $f(x)$ and $g(x)$, then so is $cd(x)$, where c is any nonzero element of F. Thus if we are to have any hope of being able to refer to *the* g.c.d. of two polynomials, we must somehow specialize our notion of g.c.d. in this case. We therefore adopt the convention that in $F[x]$ *the g.c.d. of two polynomials shall always be monic.* That this restriction is sufficient to make the g.c.d. unique is an argument that we leave to the reader.

For convenience, we summarize the results of the previous section for the case of $F[x]$ in the following theorem:

Theorem 3.35. *Let $f(x)$ and $g(x)$ be nonzero polynomials in $F[x]$, F a field and x an indeterminate, of respective degrees n and m. Then there exist unique polynomials $q(x)$ and $r(x)$ in $F[x]$, where $q(x)$ is zero or of degree $n - m$, and $r(x)$ is zero or of degree less than m, and $f(x) = q(x)g(x) + r(x)$. There also exist polynomials $a(x)$ and $b(x)$ in $F[x]$ such that $a(x)f(x) + b(x)g(x) = d(x)$, where $d(x)$ is the unique greatest common divisor of $f(x)$ and $g(x)$. Further, $d(x)$ may be characterized as the monic polynomial of minimal degree expressible in the form $a(x)f(x) + b(x)g(x)$. If $f(x)$ is irreducible and divides a product of polynomials, then $f(x)$ divides at least one of the factors. Any polynomial $f(x)$ can be factored as a product $f(x) = a_n f_1(x) f_2(x) \cdots f_k(x)$, where a_n is the leading coefficient of $f(x)$ and the factors $f_i(x)$ are monic irreducible elements of $F[x]$ and are unique, apart from order.*

All of the above assertions are translations of previous results, except for the characterization of the g.c.d. of $f(x)$ and $g(x)$, which may be easily established.

In contrast to the case of $F[x]$, F a field, in the case where one is dealing with $D[x]$ where D is only assumed to be an integral domain, these results cannot be so simply asserted. For now Theorem 3.21 cannot be applied to every pair of nonzero polynomials. Thus, for example, in $Z[x]$, if $f(x) = x + 1$ and $g(x) = 2x$, then there do not exist polynomials $q(x)$ and $r(x)$ in $Z[x]$ such that $r(x)$ is zero or of degree zero and $f(x) = q(x)g(x) + r(x)$, the difficulty being, of course, that 2 is not a unit of Z.

Yet in the case of $Z[x]$, at least, we are familiar with the fact that any polynomial can be expressed as the product of its leading coefficient and monic irreducible polynomials. The general result that if D is an integral domain with unique factorization, i.e., a unique factorization domain, then $D[x]$ is also, is another of the many theorems whose proof goes back to Gauss.

Definition. If $D[x]$ is a ring of polynomials in the indeterminate x over an integral domain D, then a polynomial $f(x)$ in $D[x]$ whose coefficients have no common factors other than units is called *primitive*. If D is a unique factorization domain, then it is immediate that any $f(x)$ in $D[x]$ may be written as the product of an element of D, called the *content* of $f(x)$, and a primitive polynomial.

Theorem 3.36 (Gauss's Lemma). *Let D be a UFD, $f(x)$ and $g(x)$ in $D[x]$. Then if $f(x)$ and $g(x)$ are primitive, so is $h(x) = f(x)g(x)$.*

PROOF. Let

$$f(x) = a_0 + a_1x + a_2x^2 + \cdots,$$
$$g(x) = b_0 + b_1x + b_2x^2 + \cdots,$$
$$h(x) = c_0 + c_1x + c_2x^2 + \cdots.$$

If $h(x)$ is not primitive, let the g.c.d. of the c_i be d, where d is then not a unit, and, hence, divisible by some prime, say p, in D. Now let a_r be the first a_j not divisible by p, i.e., a_r is not divisible by p, but for $i < r$ each a_i is divisible by p. Similarly, let b_s be the first b_j not divisible by p. Such an a_r and b_s must exist, since $f(x)$ and $g(x)$ are both primitive.

Consider the coefficient c_{r+s} of x^{r+s},

$$\begin{aligned} c_{r+s} = a_0b_{r+s} &+ a_1b_{r+s-1} + \cdots \\ &+ a_{r-1}b_{s+1} + a_rb_s + a_{r+1}b_{s-1} + \cdots \\ &+ a_{r+s}b_0. \end{aligned}$$

Since c_{r+s}, and every term on the right except the term a_rb_s, is divisible by p, it follows that a_rb_s must also be divisible by p. But this implies that either a_r or b_s is divisible by p, contrary to assumption. Hence the only alternative is that $h(x)$ is primitive, as asserted.

It is easily seen that we could have stated the theorem in the if and only if form, since if $h(x)$ is primitive, clearly $f(x)$ and $g(x)$ must be also.

If D is a unique factorization domain, we may consider the polynomial ring $D[x]$ as imbedded in the polynomial ring $\Delta[x]$, where Δ is the quotient field of D. Our next theorem deals with the relation between the irreducibility of an element $g(x)$ in $D[x]$, when considered as an element of $D[x]$, as compared to its irreducibility when considered as an element of $\Delta[x]$.

Theorem 3.37. *Let Δ be the quotient field of the UFD D, and x an indeterminate. Then:*

(i) *Any $G(x)$ in $\Delta[x]$ may be written in the form $G(x) = ab^{-1}g(x)$, where a and b are in D, $g(x)$ is primitive in $D[x]$ and is uniquely determined by $G(x)$ (to within units of D). Conversely, each primitive $g(x)$ of $D[x]$ is thus determined by a unique (to within units of Δ) $G(x)$ in $\Delta[x]$.*

(ii) *If each $G(x)$ in $\Delta[x]$ thus determines (to within units) a primitive $g(x)$ in $D[x]$, then the product $G(x)H(x)$ determines (to within units) the product $g(x)h(x)$, and conversely.*

(iii) *If $g(x)$ in $D[x]$ and $G(x)$ in $\Delta[x]$ thus correspond, then $g(x)$ is irreducible in $D[x]$ iff $G(x)$ is irreducible in $\Delta[x]$.*

PROOF.

(i) Every coefficient of $G(x)$ is of the form $a_ib_i^{-1}$, where a_i and b_i are in D. Let b be the product of the b_i and we have b in D and $a_i(b_i^{-1}b)$ in D for each i. Now let a be the g.c.d. of the elements $a_i(b_i^{-1}b)$ and we have $a_ib_i^{-1} = (ab^{-1})c_i$, where c_i is in D and the c_i's have no common factors, other than units. Thus $G(x) = ab^{-1}g(x)$ with a and b in D, $g(x)$ primitive in $D[x]$.

Suppose, now, that $G(x) = ab^{-1}g(x) = cd^{-1}h(x)$ are two such representations of $G(x)$. Then $(ad)g(x) = (bc)h(x)$ and, since both $g(x)$ and $h(x)$ are primitive, we must have that $ad = \epsilon bc$, where ϵ is a unit of D. Then $g(x)\epsilon = h(x)$, and $g(x)$ is unique to within units of D.

Since any $g(x)$ in $D[x]$ is also in $\Delta[x]$, the converse is trivial.

(ii) Suppose that

$$G(x) = ab^{-1}g(x) \quad \text{and}$$
$$H(x) = cd^{-1}h(x)$$

with $g(x)$ and $h(x)$ primitive in $D[x]$. Then

$$G(x)H(x) = ac(bd)^{-1}g(x)h(x)$$

and, by Theorem 3.36, $g(x)h(x)$ is again primitive. By the part of this theorem just proved, it follows that $g(x)h(x)$ is unique to within units of D. A similar argument may be applied to obtain the converse part of (ii).

(iii) Suppose, now, that $G(x)$ has the factorization (in $\Delta[x]$) $G(x) = F(x)H(x)$. Then if $G(x) = ab^{-1}g(x)$, $g(x)$ primitive in $D[x]$, it follows from (ii), just proved, that $g(x)$ has a factorization (in $D[x]$) into the product of the two primitive polynomials corresponding to $F(x)$ and $H(x)$. Thus if $g(x)$ is irreducible in $D[x]$, $G(x)$ is also irreducible in $\Delta[x]$. Again, the converse argument is similar.

We are now ready to prove the main theorem on factorization in polynomial rings over unique factorization domains, although it should be noted that the two previous theorems are of considerable interest in themselves.

Theorem 3.38. *If D is a UFD, then so is $D[x]$, where x is an indeterminate over D.*

PROOF. Any $f(x)$ in $D[x]$ can be written in the form $dg(x)$, where d is the g.c.d. of the coefficients of $f(x)$ and $g(x)$ is primitive. Since D is a UFD, d has a factorization into prime factors, which is unique to within units.

Now let $G(x)$ be the essentially unique element of $\Delta[x]$ corresponding to $g(x)$, as in Theorem 3.37. Since $\Delta[x]$ is a ring of polynomials over a field, we have, from Theorem 3.35, that $G(x)$ has a factorization into a finite number of irreducible polynomials $G_i(x)$, which are unique to within units. By Theorem 3.37, each of these $G_i(x)$ corresponds to an essentially unique primitive irreducible $g_i(x)$ in $D[x]$, and, moreover, $g(x)$ must be a unit times the product of the $g_i(x)$.

Since both d and $g(x)$ have prime factorizations, unique to within units of D, so does $f(x) = dg(x)$, and the proof is complete.

Corollary 3.38.1. *If D is a UFD, then so is $D[x_1, x_2, \ldots, x_n]$.*

PROOF. Induction on n.

Exercises

1. Prove that if F is a field and $f(x)$ and $g(x)$ are nonzero in $F[x]$, then $f(x)$ and $g(x)$ have a unique monic g.c.d.
2. Show that the (monic) g.c.d. of nonzero $f(x)$ and $g(x)$ in $F[x]$, F a field, is the monic polynomial of minimal degree which can be expressed in the form

$$a(x)f(x) + b(x)g(x), \quad a(x) \text{ and } b(x) \text{ in } F[x].$$

3. Supply the converse arguments for parts (ii) and (iii) of Theorem 3.37.
4. Prove that if $f(x)$ is an irreducible polynomial in $Z[x]$, Z the ring of integers, then $f(x)$ is also irreducible as an element of $R[x]$, R the field of rational numbers.

10. Maximal, Prime, and Primary Ideals

We have observed before that properties of the positive integers can be translated into properties of the corresponding principal ideals in the ring Z. Of particular interest in the set of positive integers are the primes, which may be characterized in either of two ways. According to the usual definition, a prime is an integer greater than one having no proper divisors. Alternatively, one could define a prime as an integer greater than one such that if it divides a product of integers, then it must divide at least one of the factors.

In terms of ideals, the first characterization becomes: If $P = (p)$, p a prime, then P is a proper ideal of Z with the property that if $P \subseteq Q \subset Z$, it follows that $Q = P$, or P has no proper (ideal) divisors. The second characterization would become: $P = (p)$, p a prime, is such that if $P \supseteq AB = (a)(b) = (ab)$, then either $P \supseteq A$ or $P \supseteq B$, or, equivalently, if $ab \in P$, then either $a \in P$ or $b \in P$. (We leave to the reader the demonstration that, in Z, we have $(a)(b) = (ab)$.)

We now proceed to formulate these properties for more general rings.

Definition. The ideal M of an arbitrary ring R is *maximal* if $M \subset R$ and for any ideal Q of R, $M \subset Q \subseteq R$ implies $Q = R$, that is, if M has R as its unique proper divisor.

Definition. The ideal P in a commutative ring R is *prime* if $ab \in P$ implies $a \in P$ or $b \in P$.

Thus in the ring Z, an ideal is generated by a prime if and only if it is maximal, or, alternatively, if and only if it is a proper prime, i.e., a prime ideal other than 0 or Z. We also see at once that the commutative ring R is an integral domain if and only if R has a unity and the zero ideal 0 is prime in R.

While maximal and proper prime ideals are the same in the ring Z, this is not the case in a general commutative ring. For example, in the ring $Z[x, y]$, the ideals (x), (x, y), and $(x, y, 2)$ are all prime, while only the last, $(x, y, 2)$, is maximal. That (x) is prime is seen from the fact that if a product of two polynomials has x as a factor, then at least one of the polynomials must have x as a factor, since $Z[x, y]$ is an integral domain. The ideal (x, y) consists of all polynomials having zero constant terms so that the lack of zero-divisors in Z shows that (x, y) is prime. That $(x, y, 2)$ is maximal follows from the fact that $(x, y, 2)$ contains all polynomials whose constant terms are divisible by 2, and if an ideal Q were to properly contain $(x, y, 2)$, it would have to contain a polynomial whose constant term was not divisible by 2, say $a_0 + f(x, y)$, where $f(x, y)$ is in (x, y). Then Q would contain both a_0 and 2, and, hence, their g.c.d., which is 1, or $Q = Z[x, y]$. The fact that $(x, y, 2)$ is prime could be argued similarly or obtained as a consequence of the next theorem.

Theorem 3.39. *If R is a commutative ring with unity element e, then any maximal ideal M of R is prime.*

PROOF. Suppose that $ab \in M$ with $a \notin M$. Then, since M is maximal (M, a), the ideal generated by M and a, must be the whole ring R. Hence $e \in (M, a)$, or for some $m \in M$ and $r \in R$, we have

$$e = m + ra.$$

But then

$$b = mb + rab$$

is an element of M, and M is prime.

The above examples of prime ideals in $Z[x, y]$ show that the converse of this theorem is not valid, as does the case of the zero ideal of Z, which is prime, but clearly not maximal.

We may obtain some interesting and useful characterizations of prime and maximal ideals in commutative rings by considering the residue class rings which they define. We see at once that an ideal M is maximal in the ring R if and only if the residue class ring R/M is simple, i.e., has no proper ideals. Similarly, an ideal P of a commutative ring R is prime if and only if the residue class ring R/P has no zero-divisors. We may also obtain the following, somewhat more specialized results:

Theorem 3.40. *Let M be an ideal of the commutative ring R. R/M is a field if and only if the following two conditions are satisfied:*

(i) *M is a maximal ideal of R.*

(ii) *If $x^2 \in M$, then $x \in M$.*

PROOF. Suppose that R/M is a field. Then, since a field has no proper ideals, it follows, from Theorem 3.10, that M is maximal. Since a field has no zero-divisors, $\overline{x^2} = \overline{0}$ implies $\overline{x} = \overline{0}$, or $x^2 \in M$ implies $x \in M$.

Conversely, suppose both (i) and (ii) hold in R. Let a be any fixed element of R not in M and let b be an arbitrary element of R. Then $\overline{a} \neq \overline{0}$ and we must show that there exists an element $x \in R$ such that $\overline{a}\,\overline{x} = \overline{b}$. Now (ii) assures us that $a^2 \notin M$ and, hence, the set $X = \{ax : x \in R\}$ is not contained in M. Then, since M is maximal, we have $(M, X) = R$ and $b \in (M, X)$. This requires that $b = m + ax$ for some $m \in M$ and $x \in R$, whence $\overline{b} = \overline{ax} = \overline{a}\,\overline{x}$, as required. Thus R/M is commutative and its nonzero elements form a group, or R/M is a field.

Corollary 3.40.1. *If R is commutative with unity e, then M is a maximal ideal of R iff R/M is a field.*

PROOF. We need only show that if M is maximal, then $x^2 \in M$ implies $x \in M$. So suppose, on the contrary, that $x \notin M$. Then $(M, x) = R$ and $e = m + rx$ for some $m \in M$ and $r \in R$. But then $x = ex = mx + rx^2$, and if $x^2 \in M$, then $x \in M$, contrary to assumption. Thus $x \notin M$ implies $x^2 \notin M$ or, equivalently, $x^2 \in M$ implies $x \in M$.

Corollary 3.40.2. *A nonzero ideal of Z is maximal iff it is prime.*

PROOF. By Theorem 3.7 and our earlier discussion of prime ideals of Z, it follows that Z/P is a field iff P is a nonzero prime, while, from the preceding corollary, Z/P is a field iff P is maximal.

That this situation generalizes to any principal ideal domain is shown by the next theorem.

Theorem 3.41. *Let R be a PID. Then a nonzero ideal P is prime iff it is maximal.*

PROOF. It is sufficient to show that if P is a nonzero prime ideal, then P is maximal. Now $P = (p)$ for some prime element p of R. If a is any element of R not in P, then the g.c.d. of a and p is the unity element e, and, by Theorem 3.29, $e = ra + sp$ for some $r, s \in R$. Then $(e) = R \subseteq (a, P) \subseteq R$, $(a, P) = R$ and P is maximal.

Since, probably, the most important result concerning primes in the ring Z is that any integer is an essentially unique product of primes, it is natural to ask if the translation of this result, any ideal of Z is a product of prime (or maximal) ideals, holds in general, commutative rings.

That this is not the case is shown by the ideal $(x^2, 2)$ of the ring $Z[x]$, which is neither prime itself nor expressible as a product of primes. The first assertion is obvious. To see the latter, suppose that P is any prime ideal containing $(x^2, 2)$. Then both the elements x and 2 must be in P, or $P \supseteq (x, 2)$. Now $(x, 2)$ is the set of all elements of $Z[x]$ having constant terms divisible by 2. But $(x, 2)$ is maximal, since if $f(x)$ is any element of $Z[x]$ having constant term not divisible by 2, then $(x, 2, f(x))$ must contain 1 and be the entire ring. Hence $P = (x, 2)$ is the only proper prime ideal containing $(x^2, 2)$. But the constant term of every element of P^2 is divisible by 4, so that $(x^2, 2) \nsubseteq P^2$ and $(x^2, 2)$ is not expressible as a product of primes.

To salvage the situation, we need to take another look at what the prime factorization theorem of the integers says. In its usual formulation, the theorem asserts that every integer is an essentially unique product of powers of primes. Now a power of a prime integer has the characterizing property that, if it divides the product of two integers a and b and does not divide a, then it must divide b^n, for some positive integer n. Thus 8 divides the product $4 \cdot 6$, does not divide 4, but does divide 6^3. Formulating this property in terms of ideals, we have the following definition.

Definition. The ideal Q of the commutative ring R is *primary* if $ab \in Q$ and $a \notin Q$ together imply $b^n \in Q$ for some positive integer n.

The above ideal $(x^2, 2)$ of $Z[x]$ is primary, as is every ideal of the ring Z of the form (p^n) where p is a prime integer. Indeed, all primary ideals of Z are of this form. Thus in the ring Z, the primary ideals are powers of prime ideals. This is not true in general, however. For example, consider the ideal (x, y) in the ring $F[x, y]$, where F is a field. Then (x, y) is maximal, since if $f(x, y)$ is any polynomial with nonzero constant term a_0, then $(x, y, f(x, y))$ would contain a_0, hence also $a_0^{-1}a_0 = e$, the unity of F, and would be the entire ring. Then by Theorem 3.39, the ideal (x, y) is prime. Now we have

$$(x, y)^2 = (x^2, xy, y^2) \subset (x^2, y) \subset (x, y),$$

and one can easily show that (x^2, y) is primary, and that (x, y) is the only proper prime ideal containing (x^2, y). Thus the primary ideal (x^2, y) is not a power of any prime ideal in the ring $F[x, y]$.

The concept of primary ideals will enable us to obtain a generalization of the Fundamental Theorem of Arithmetic, valid in a wide class of rings, as we shall see in the next section. At present, we wish to develop relationships between prime and primary ideals.

In Section 4, we defined the radical $\sqrt{A}$ of an ideal A of the commutative ring R to be the set of all elements b of R such that $b^n \in A$ for some positive integer n (which may, of course, depend on b) and saw that $\sqrt{A}$ is an ideal of R.

Theorem 3.42. *If Q is a primary ideal of the commutative ring R, then $\sqrt{Q} = P$ is a prime ideal of R.*

PROOF. If $ab \in P$ and $a \notin P$, then for some n, we have $(ab)^n = a^n b^n \in Q$ and $a^n \notin Q$. Hence $(b^n)^m \in Q$ for some m, since Q is primary, and $b \in P = \sqrt{Q}$. Thus P is a prime ideal of R.

Definition. If Q is a primary ideal of the commutative ring R, then the radical P of Q is called the *associated prime ideal* of Q, and Q is called *a primary ideal belonging to* the prime P, or simply *primary for* P.

While there is, thus, a unique prime ideal associated with a given primary ideal P, it may happen that many different primary ideals all belong to the same prime ideal P. For instance, in the ring $Z[x, y]$, the ideals (x^2, y), (x^2, y^2), (x^2, y^3), etc., are all primary ideals belonging to the prime ideal (x, y).

If Q is primary for P, it follows at once that if $ab \in Q$ and $a \notin Q$, then $b \in P$, and, also, that if A and B are ideals such that $AB \subseteq Q$ and $A \nsubseteq Q$, then $B \subseteq P$. We also recall that, since any ideal is contained in its radical, we have for primary Q belonging to P that $Q \subseteq P \subseteq \sqrt{Q}$. That these properties just mentioned actually are characterizing for primary ideals is shown by the next theorem.

Theorem 3.43. *Let Q and P be ideals of the commutative ring R. Then Q is primary for P if and only if:*

(i) $Q \subseteq P \subseteq \sqrt{Q}$.

(ii) *If $ab \in Q$ and $a \notin Q$, then $b \in P$.*

PROOF. We need only show the sufficiency of the conditions (i) and (ii), having already noted their necessity. Since if $b \in P \subseteq \sqrt{Q}$, we have $b^n \in Q$ for some n, it is clear that Q is primary. To show that $P = \sqrt{Q}$, we need only show that $\sqrt{Q} \subseteq P$. So suppose that $b^n \in Q$ for some positive integer n, and suppose that n is the minimal positive integer such that $b^n \in Q$. Then if $n = 1$, we have $b \in Q \subseteq P$, while if $n > 1$, then $b^n = b^{n-1}b$ and $b^{n-1} \notin Q$, so that $b \in P$ by (ii). Thus if $b \in \sqrt{Q}$, we have $b \in P$, and the proof is complete.

In the ring Z, it is obvious that if $Q_i = (p^{e_i})$, $i = 1, 2, \ldots, n$, are all primary for $P = (p)$, then the product of the Q_i is also primary for P. It is also obvious that the intersection $Q = (p^e)$, where $e =$ maximum $(e_1, e_2, \ldots, e_n)$, of the Q_i is also primary for P. Since the intersection of any set of ideals of a ring is again an ideal of the ring, one might ask if this property holds for arbitrary intersections of ideals all of which are primary for the same prime.

Theorem 3.44. *Let R be a commutative ring:*

(i) *If Q_i, $i = 1, 2, \ldots, n$, are any finite set of ideals of R, all primary for P, then $Q = \cap Q_i$ is primary for P.*

(ii) *If Q is primary for P and A is an ideal of R such that $A \nsubseteq P$, then $Q : A$ is primary for P.*

PROOF.

(i) Since the radical of an intersection of ideals is the intersection of the radicals of the ideals, we have that

$$\sqrt{Q} = \sqrt{\cap Q_i} = \cap\sqrt{Q_i} = \cap P = P$$

and, hence,

$$Q \subseteq Q_i \subseteq P \subseteq \sqrt{Q}.$$

Also, if $ab \in Q$ and $a \notin Q$, then $ab \in Q_i$ and $a \notin Q_i$ for some i, whence $b \in P$. Thus the conditions of the previous theorem are satisfied and Q is primary for P.

(ii) Since $(Q : A)A \subseteq Q \subseteq P$ and $A \not\subseteq P$, we must have $Q : A \subseteq P$. Since $Q \subseteq Q : A$, we have $P = \sqrt{Q} \subseteq \sqrt{Q : A}$ and condition (i) above is satisfied. Now suppose

$$ab \in Q : A \text{ and } a \notin Q : A.$$

Then

$$(ab)A = b(aA) \subseteq Q,$$

but

$$aA \not\subseteq Q \text{ and } b \in P,$$

so that condition (ii) is also satisfied.

Exercises

1. Prove that an ideal P of Z is generated by a prime p iff P is a proper prime ideal of Z, or, equivalently, iff P is a maximal ideal.
2. Define a *multiplicative system* to be a subset S of a ring R such that S is closed under the multiplication of R. Show that for a commutative ring R, the ideal P is prime iff the (set theoretic) complement S of P in R is a multiplicative system.
3. Let R be a UFD. Show that the ideal (p) is prime iff either $(p) = R$ or p is a prime element of R.
4. Let R be a commutative ring, A, B, and P ideals such that $AB \subseteq P$ with P prime. Show that $A \subseteq P$ or $B \subseteq P$.
5. Let R be commutative with unity. Show that an ideal P of R is prime iff R/P is an integral domain.
6. Prove Corollary 3.40.1 directly, i.e., without use of Theorem 3.40.
7. Find a necessary and sufficient condition that a homomorphism map a commutative ring with unity into a field.
8. Show that if R is a commutative ring with ACC and Q is primary for P, then $P^m \subseteq Q$ for some positive integer m.
9. Show that in a commutative ring R, the ideal Q is primary iff all zero-divisors in R/Q are nilpotent; i.e., $\bar{r}\,\bar{s} = \bar{0}$, $\bar{r} \neq \bar{0} \neq \bar{s}$, implies that $\bar{r}^n = \bar{0}$ for some positive integer n.
10. Let α be a homomorphism of the commutative ring R onto R' with radical N, and Q an ideal containing N. Show that Q is primary for P iff $Q\alpha$ is primary for $P\alpha$.
11. Let R be commutative with unity and $M_1, M_2, \ldots, M_r$ distinct maximal ideals of R. Show that $M_1 \cap M_2 \cap \cdots \cap M_r = M_1M_2 \cdots M_r$.
12. Show that if R is commutative with unity and satisfies the DCC, then every proper prime ideal of R is maximal. (*Hint:* Use the result of Exercise 6, Section 7 of this chapter.)
13. Show that part (i) of Theorem 3.44 is false if infinite intersections are allowed. (*Hint:* Consider $\bigcap_{n=1}^{\infty} (p^n)$ for p a prime in Z.)

11. Ideals in Noetherian Rings

As the reader will have observed, many results in ring theory derive from the attempt to obtain extensions to more general rings of the unique prime factorization theorem of the integers. We have seen that any ring of polynomials in a finite number of indeterminates over a unique factorization domain is also a unique factorization domain. In addition to such rings of polynomials, one of the types of rings to receive early and continuing study has been those subrings of the complex numbers composed of all complex numbers of the form $a + bi\sqrt{p}$, where $i^2 = -1$, p is a fixed prime, and a and b are any integers, that is, rings of the form $Z[i\sqrt{p}]$. For such rings, we cannot apply Theorem 3.38, since the element $i\sqrt{p}$ is not an indeterminate over Z. Indeed, while it can be shown that $Z[i]$, the ring of Gaussian integers, is a UFD, this is not, in general, true for $Z[i\sqrt{p}]$.

To see an example of the failure of unique factorization, let us consider the ring $R = Z[i\sqrt{5}]$. Let us define $N(x + yi) = x^2 + y^2$ for any complex number, so that $N(x + yi)$ is the square of the ordinary absolute value, or modulus of the complex number $x + yi$. Then if $r = a + bi\sqrt{5}$ is in R, we have $N(r) = a^2 + 5b^2$, and if, also, $s \in R$, then $N(rs) = N(r)N(s)$. Thus r can be factored in R as a product st only if $N(r)$ can be factored in Z as a product $N(s)N(t)$. Moreover, it is clear that 1 and -1, the units of R, are the only elements s of R such that $N(s) = 1$. Thus in looking for possible factorizations of r in R, we may neglect any trivial factorizations of $N(r)$ in Z. Now consider the element 6 of R. We have

$$6 = 2 \cdot 3 = (1 + i\sqrt{5})(1 - i\sqrt{5}),$$
$$N(2) = 4 = 2 \cdot 2,$$
$$N(3) = 9 = 3 \cdot 3,$$
$$N(1 + i\sqrt{5}) = N(1 - i\sqrt{5}) = 6 = 2 \cdot 3.$$

It is trivial to verify that $a^2 + 5b^2$ can never be either 2 or 3 for integers a and b. Thus all of the elements 2, 3, $1 + i\sqrt{5}$ and $1 - i\sqrt{5}$ are primes of R and, clearly, none is an associate of any other. Thus we have two genuinely different prime factorizations of the element 6 in $Z[i\sqrt{5}]$, so that unique prime factorization of elements does not hold in this ring.

Problems such as this lead to the first realizations by Dedekind and others that *ideal numbers*, or as we now simply say, *ideals*, were needed to save the situation. But we have also seen that prime ideals, the natural ideal formulations of the notion of prime elements, are themselves inadequate, even in rings of polynomials over a field, and we have introduced the notion of a primary ideal as an attempt to improve the situation.

If we now consider the ideal $A = (x^2, xy, 2)$ in the ring $Z[x, y]$, we see that A is not primary, since, while xy is in A, neither x nor any positive power of y is in A. Now, clearly, any ideal which contains A must contain the element 2, and if it is to be a proper ideal, must not contain any polynomial of degree zero other than powers of 2. But a product of such ideals would have all its elements of degree zero divisible by (at least) 4, and, hence, would not contain 2. Thus A is not expressible even as product of primary ideals. However, as the reader may verify, A is expressible as an intersection of primary ideals.

As we shall see, in a wide class of rings every ideal is expressible as a finite intersection of primary ideals. This class of rings is called Noetherian, in honor of Emmy Noether, who first observed the crucial role which the ACC plays in the theory.

Definition. A commutative ring with unity and satisfying the ACC for ideals is called a *Noetherian ring*.

We have immediately from Theorem 3.28 that the maximal condition and the finite basis condition also hold in any Noetherian ring. Thus when we are dealing with a Noetherian ring, we may use whichever of the three conditions ACC, MC, or FBC is most appropriate for the argument at hand. For example, the FBC may be used to show that any ideal of a Noetherian ring and any homomorphic image of a Noetherian ring is also Noetherian.

While we shall not make use of the theorem in this section, one of the basic theorems concerning Noetherian rings is the famous Hilbert Basis Theorem:

Theorem 3.45. *If R is a Noetherian ring, then so is $R[x_1, x_2, \ldots, x_n]$, where $x_1, x_2, \ldots, x_n$ are any finite set of indeterminates over R.*

PROOF. It is clearly sufficient to show that $R[x]$ is Noetherian if R is, as then an inductive argument may be applied to complete the proof. We consider, first, some ideals formed by leading coefficients of elements of an arbitrary ideal A of $R[x]$.

Let M be the set of elements of R consisting of zero and the leading coefficients of all nonzero elements of A. If $f(x)$ of degree n and leading coefficient a, $g(x)$ of degree m and leading coefficient b, are in A and r is in R then, assuming $n \geq m$, we have $f(x) - x^{n-m}g(x)$ and $rf(x)$ are in A, whence $a - b$ and ra are in M. Thus M is an ideal of R and must have a finite basis consisting of the leading coefficients a_i of certain polynomials $f_i(x)$ in A, $i = 1, 2, \ldots, r$. Let $B = (f_1(x), \ldots, f_r(x))$ and B is an ideal of $R[x]$ contained in A. Suppose s is the maximum of the degrees $n_1, \ldots, n_r$ of $f_1(x), \ldots, f_r(x)$.

Let M_k, $k = 0, 1, \ldots, s - 1$, be the set of elements of R consisting of zero and the leading coefficients of all elements of A of degree k. By arguments similar to those used in the case of M, we see that each M_k is an ideal of R and, hence, has a finite basis, say $M_k = (a_{k1}, \ldots, a_{kr_k})$, where a_{kj} is the leading coefficient of $f_{kj}(x)$, an element of degree k in A. As before,

$$B_k = (f_{k1}(x), \ldots, f_{kr_k}(x))$$

is an ideal of $R[x]$ contained in A, $k = 0, 1, \ldots, s - 1$.

Now the ideal $A' = (B, B_{s-1}, \ldots, B_0)$ has a finite basis and is contained in A. If we can show that $A \subseteq A'$, the proof will be complete.

Let $h(x)$ of degree t and leading coefficient a be any element of A. If $t \geq s$, then, since a is in M, we have $a = c_1a_1 + \cdots + c_ra_r$ for some $c_1, \ldots, c_r$ in R, and, hence,

$$h'(x) = h(x) - c_1x^{t-n_1}f_1(x) - \cdots - c_rx^{t-n_r}f_r(x)$$

is an element of A having degree less than t and differing from $h(x)$ by an element of A'. Continuing this procedure, if necessary, we obtain $h(x) = g(x) + f(x)$, where $g(x)$ is an element of A of degree less than s and $f(x)$ is in A'. If we can show that $g(x)$ is in A', we will be finished.

But if $g(x)$ is not zero, then the leading coefficient of $g(x)$ is in some M_k, and, by a process entirely similar to that just used, we have that $g(x) = g_k(x) + g'(x)$, where $g_k(x)$ is in B_k, hence in A', and the degree of $g'(x)$ is less than k. Again continuing, if necessary, we obtain $h(x) = f(x) + g_{s-1}(x) + \cdots + g_0(x)$ is an element of A'. (We note that some of the $g_k(x)$ may be zero, as will be $f(x)$ if $h(x)$ has degree less than s.) Thus $A = A'$ and our proof is complete.

Since any principal ideal ring or any field is a Noetherian ring, this theorem gives us a large set of Noetherian rings. We may remark that, as noted in Section 6, if S is any commutative overring of a commutative ring R and $c_1, \ldots, c_n$ are elements of S, then the mapping of $R[x_1, \ldots, x_n]$ onto $R[c_1, \ldots, c_n]$, defined by $f(x_1, \ldots, x_n) \to f(c_1, \ldots, c_n)$, is a homomorphism. In this situation $R[c_1, \ldots, c_n]$ is Noetherian if R is.

We now return to our objective of showing that in a Noetherian ring, every ideal is a finite intersection of primary ideals.

Definition. Let R be any ring. An ideal A of R is *irreducible* if it can not be expressed as a finite intersection of ideals of R properly containing A. Otherwise A is *reducible.*

We see, at once, that in a commutative ring every prime ideal is irreducible. The converse does not hold, however, as one may see by considering the irreducible ideal (4) of the ring Z. We notice that (4) is primary, however, and proceed to show that this is the general situation in any Noetherian ring.

Theorem 3.46. *Every irreducible ideal in a Noetherian ring R is primary.*

PROOF. We shall show that any nonprimary ideal A of R is reducible. If A is nonprimary, then there exist elements b and c of R such that $cb \in A$, $c \notin A$ and $b^k \notin A$ for all positive integers k. Now $A\colon (b^k) \subseteq A\colon (b^{k+1})$ for all k, since if $rb^k \in A$, then certainly $rb^{k+1} \in A$. By the ACC, there must exist some integer n such that $A\colon (b^n) = A\colon (b^{n+1})$. Clearly $A \subseteq (A + (b^n)) \cap (A + (c))$ and both $A + (b^n)$ and $A + (c)$ are proper divisors of A. Now any element $d \in (A + (b^n)) \cap (A + (c))$ has the form $d = a + rb^n = a' + r'c$ for some $a, a' \in A$ and $r, r' \in R$. Then $rb^{n+1} = (a' - a)b + r'cb$ is in A and r must be in $A\colon (b^{n+1}) = A\colon (b^n)$. But then $rb^n \in A$ and $d = a + rb^n \in A$. Thus the reverse inclusion holds also, and A is reducible.

It is not the case that any primary ideal of a Noetherian ring is necessarily irreducible, as may be seen by considering the ideal (x^2, xy, y^2) in $Z[x, y]$. We leave it to the reader to find a representation of this ideal as an intersection of proper divisors.

Theorem 3.47. *Every ideal of a ring with ACC is a finite intersection of irreducible ideals.*

PROOF. Suppose there is an ideal not so expressible. Then the set of such ideals is not empty, and, by the MC, there must exist a maximal such ideal, that is, an ideal B which is not a finite intersection of irreducible ideals and such that any proper divisor of B is a finite intersection of irreducible ideals. Clearly B is not itself irreducible; hence $B = C \cap D$, where C and D are proper divisors of B. Thus each of C and D is a finite intersection of irreducible ideals, whence B is also. This is a contradiction and our original supposition must be false, so that the theorem is valid.

From these last two theorems, we could immediately conclude that every ideal in a Noetherian ring is a finite intersection of primary ideals. However, if we wish the result to correspond to the Fundamental Theorem of Arithmetic, then some sort of uniqueness of the representation is certainly called for. With this in mind, we proceed to obtain a stronger result.

Definition. A representation of the ideal A of the commutative ring R as a finite intersection

$$A = Q_1 \cap Q_2 \cap \cdots \cap Q_n \text{ of primary ideals } Q_1, Q_2, \ldots, Q_n$$

is called a *primary representation* of A. It is called *irredundant* or *reduced* if no Q_i contains the intersection of the other Q_j's and, moreover, the Q_i's all have distinct (prime) radicals.

Theorem 3.48. *Every ideal A in a Noetherian ring R has a reduced primary representation.*

PROOF. By the preceding two theorems, A has a finite primary representation, $A = Q_1 \cap Q_2 \cap \cdots \cap Q_n$. First, let Q_i' be the intersection of all those Q_j having a given radical P_i. By Theorem 3.44, Q_i' is primary with radical P_i. Now if any of the Q_i' contains the intersection of the remaining Q_k', we may omit it, and, in this way, obtain the desired reduced representation.

Before turning to the question of the uniqueness of reduced primary representations of ideals, let us draw some simple consequences of our existence theorem. It will be useful to note that if R is a commutative ring, A an ideal of R, and P a prime ideal of R such that $P \supseteq A$, then $P \supseteq \sqrt{A}$. For if $r^n \in A \subseteq P$, then $r \in P$, whence $r \in \sqrt{A}$ implies $r \in P$.

Definition. Let A be an ideal of the commutative ring R. A prime ideal divisor P of A such that no prime divisor of A is properly contained in P is called a *minimal* or *isolated* prime of A.

Theorem 3.49. *Let A be an ideal of the commutative ring R such that A has a reduced primary representation. Then A has a finite set $P_1, P_2, \ldots, P_n$ of isolated primes, and $\sqrt{A} = P_1 \cap P_2 \cap \cdots \cap P_n$.*

PROOF. Let $A = Q_1 \cap Q_2 \cap \cdots \cap Q_m$ be a reduced primary representation of A, $\sqrt{Q_i} = P_i$. Any prime $P \supseteq A$ then contains the product of the Q_i, hence contains some Q_j and also its radical P_j. Thus any prime dividing A also divides some P_j and, hence, some P_j minimal in the set $P_1, P_2, \ldots, P_m$. Reindexing if necessary, let these be $P_1, \ldots, P_n$ and the first assertion is established.

Now if $r^k \in A \subseteq Q_i \subseteq P_i$ for all i, then $r \in P_i$ for all i. Thus $r \in P_1 \cap P_2 \cap \cdots \cap P_n$. Conversely, if $r \in P_j$, $j = 1, 2, \ldots, n$, then $r \in P_j$ for all $j = 1, 2, \ldots, m$, and $r^{k_j} \in Q_j$ for some k_j. If k is the maximum of $k_1, k_2, \ldots, k_m$, then $r^k \in Q_1 \cap Q_2 \cap \cdots \cap Q_m = A$.

Corollary 3.49.1. *Any ideal A of a Noetherian ring has a finite set of isolated primes and $\sqrt{A}$ is the intersection of the isolated primes of A.*

PROOF. Immediate from Theorems 3.48 and 3.49.

Reduced representations of ideals in Noetherian rings need not be unique. For example, if F is any field, we have in $F[x, y]$ that

$$(x^2, xy) = (x) \cap (x^2, xy, y^k)$$

for any integer $k > 1$, where (x) is prime and (x^2, xy, y^k) is primary with radical (x, y). However, the prime radicals are unique.

Theorem 3.50. *Let R be a commutative ring and A an ideal of R having a reduced primary representation $A = Q_1 \cap \cdots \cap Q_n$, $n > 1$, with $\sqrt{Q_i} = P_i$. The primes $P_1, \ldots, P_n$ are uniquely determined by the criterion that a prime ideal P of R is one of the P_i if and only if there exists some $c \in R$ such that $c \notin A$ and $A : (c)$ is primary for P.*

PROOF. We show first that each P_i satisfies the given criterion. For given i, there exists $c_i \in \bigcap_{j \neq i} Q_j$ such that $c_i \notin A$, since the representation is reduced. Then $c_i Q_i \subseteq A$ so that $Q_i \subseteq A : (c_i)$. Since $c_i \notin Q_i$, but $c_i(A : (c_i)) \subseteq A \subseteq Q_i$, we have $A : (c_i) \subseteq P_i$. Also, $P_i = \sqrt{Q_i} \subseteq \sqrt{A : (c_i)}$ and condition (i) of Theorem 3.43 is satisfied. If $ab \in A : (c_i)$ and $a \notin A : (c_i)$, then $ac_i \notin A$, hence $ac_i \notin Q_i$. Then $abc_i \in A \subseteq Q_i$ implies $b \in P_i$. Thus condition (ii) of Theorem 3.43 is also satisfied, and $A : (c_i)$ is primary for P_i.

Conversely, let P be a prime of R and c an element of R such that $c \notin A$ and $A : (c)$ is primary for P. Now $A : (c) = (\cap Q_i) : (c) = \cap(Q_i : (c))$. Thus $P = \sqrt{A : (c)} = \cap\sqrt{Q_i : (c)}$. Applying the argument of the first part of the proof, with A replaced, successively, by those Q_i for which $c \notin Q_i$, we obtain for these Q_i that $\sqrt{Q_i : (c)} = P_i$, while, if $c \in Q_j$, then, clearly, $\sqrt{Q_j : (c)} = Q_j : (c) = R$. Thus P is the intersection of some of the P_i, contains their product and, hence, contains one of the P_i and is contained by P_i. Then $P = P_i$ for some i and the proof is complete.

Corollary 3.50.1. *Let the ideal A satisfy the conditions of the theorem. Then, in any reduced primary representations of A, the number of primary ideals is the same.*

PROOF. Immediate from the theorem.

Definition. Let A be an ideal of a commutative ring having a reduced primary representation. The primary ideals occurring in any such representation of A are called *primary components* of A and their uniquely determined set of radicals are called the *associated primes* of A. A prime ideal minimal in the set of associated primes of A is, of course, an isolated prime of A, and all other associated primes of A are called *imbedded primes* of A.

Thus the associated primes of the ideal (x^2, xy) in $F[x, y]$ are (x) and (x, y) and are the radicals of Q_1 and Q_2, where $(x^2, xy) = Q_1 \cap Q_2$ is any reduced primary representation of (x^2, xy). In this case, (x^2, xy) has a unique isolated prime, (x), and a unique imbedded prime (x, y). Since the radical of A is the intersection of the isolated primes of A, it follows that $(x) = \sqrt{(x^2, xy)}$. We notice that in the reduced primary representations of (x^2, xy) which we have previously given, (x), the primary component with radical an isolated prime of (x^2, xy), always occurs. This is true in general, and, indeed, we can prove somewhat more. But first we wish to obtain the following result.

Theorem 3.51. *Let B and C be ideals of the Noetherian ring R having reduced primary representations $B = Q_1 \cap \cdots \cap Q_n$, $C = Q'_1 \cap \cdots \cap Q'_m$ with $\sqrt{Q_i} = P_i$, $\sqrt{Q'_j} = P'_j$. Then the following are all equivalent:*

(i) $B : C = B$.

(ii) *C is not contained in any associated prime of B.*

(iii) *No associated prime of C is contained in any associated prime of B.*

PROOF. Suppose $C \not\subseteq P_i$ for $i = 1, 2, \ldots, n$. Then $Q_i : C = Q_i$ for all i since, clearly, $Q_i : C \supseteq Q_i$ and, if $c \in C$, $c \notin P_i$ then $ac \in Q_i$ implies $a \in Q_i$, whence $Q_i : C \subseteq Q_i$. Thus $B : C = \cap(Q_i : C) = \cap Q_i = B$. On the other hand, if $C \subseteq P_i$, say $C \subseteq P_1$, then, by Corollary 3.28.2, we have $C^r \subseteq Q_1$ for some positive integer r, and, hence, $(Q_2 \cap \cdots \cap Q_n)C^r \subseteq B$. Let s be minimal such that $(Q_2 \cap \cdots \cap Q_n)C^s \subseteq B$, where $(Q_2 \cap \cdots \cap Q_n)C^0 = Q_2 \cap \cdots \cap Q_n$. Then $s \geq 1$, since the representation of B is reduced, whence

$$(Q_2 \cap \cdots \cap Q_n)C^{s-1} \subseteq B : C$$

but is not contained in B. Thus $B : C \neq B$ if $C \subseteq P_i$ for any i, and the equivalence of (i) and (ii) is established.

Clearly if $P'_j \subseteq P_i$ for any i and j, then $C \subseteq P_i$, while conversely, if $C \subseteq P_i$ for some i, then $\prod Q'_j \subseteq P_i$, some $Q'_j \subseteq P_i$, and $P'_j = \sqrt{Q'_j} \subseteq P_i$. Thus (ii) and (iii) are also equivalent, and the proof is complete.

We may observe that in the proof of the equivalence of (i) and (ii), no use was made of the fact that C had a reduced primary representation, so that a slightly stronger result could have been stated.

Definition. Let A be an ideal of a commutative ring having a reduced primary representation. The primary components of A whose radicals are isolated primes of A are called *isolated primary components* of A. More generally, if $P_1, P_2, \ldots, P_k$ are associated primes of A such that no other associated prime of A is contained in any of them, then the intersection of the corresponding primary components, $Q_1 \cap Q_2 \cap \cdots \cap Q_k$, is an *isolated component* of A.

Theorem 3.52. *Let A be an ideal of the commutative ring R having a reduced primary representation*

$$A = Q_1 \cap Q_2 \cap \cdots \cap Q_n, \qquad P_i = \sqrt{Q_i},$$

and let

$$Q_i' = \{c \in R\colon\ A : (c) \nsubseteq P_i\}, \qquad i = 1, 2, \ldots, n.$$

Then Q_i' is an ideal of R,

$$Q_i' \subseteq Q_i.$$

Moreover, any isolated component of A, say $Q_{i_1} \cap \cdots \cap Q_{i_k}$, is the intersection of those Q_j' for which P_j is a maximal element of the finite set $P_{i_1}, \ldots, P_{i_k}$.

PROOF. Suppose $c \in Q_i'$. Then for some $r \in R$, $r \notin P_i$, we have $rc \in A$ and, hence, $r(cs) \in A$, $A : (cs) \nsubseteq P_i$, and $cs \in Q_i'$ for all $s \in R$. If $c, d \in Q_i'$, then there exist s and t not in P_i such that $cs, dt \in A$. Then $(c - d)st \in A$ and $st \notin P_i$, since P_i is prime. Thus $c - d \in Q_i'$ and Q_i' is an ideal of R. Now for $c \in Q_i'$, we have $cs \in A \subseteq Q_i$ for some $s \notin P_i$, whence $c \in Q_i$, $Q_i' \subseteq Q_i$, and the first assertion is established.

Now let B_j be the intersection of those Q_i, $i = 1, 2, \ldots, n$, whose radicals P_i are contained in P_j, where P_j is maximal in the set $P_{i_1}, \ldots, P_{i_k}$. Clearly $Q_{i_1} \cap \cdots \cap Q_{i_k}$ is the intersection of these B_j (recall that, for $i \notin \{i_1, \ldots, i_k\}$, $P_i \nsubseteq P_j$), and it will suffice to prove that each $B_j = Q_j'$. For any P_i, $i = 1, 2, \ldots, n$, such that $P_i \nsubseteq P_j$, there exists $b_i \in P_i$ with $b_i \notin P_j$. For some s_i, we have $b_i^{s_i} \in Q_i$ and, if $b = \Pi b_i^{s_i}$, i such that $P_i \nsubseteq P_j$, then $b \in \cap Q_i$, i such that $P_i \nsubseteq P_j$. But, $b \notin P_j$, since P_j is prime. Thus we have $bB_j \subseteq A$, $b \in A : B_j$ and $b \notin P_j$, so that $A : B_j \nsubseteq P_j$, $B_j \subseteq Q_j'$.

On the other hand, if $P_i \subseteq P_j$, then $Q_j' \subseteq Q_i'$ (if $A : (c) \nsubseteq P_j$ then, certainly, $A : (c) \nsubseteq P_i$ for $P_i \subseteq P_j$), and, hence, by the part of the theorem already established, $Q_j' \subseteq Q_i$. Thus $Q_j' \subseteq B_j$, the intersection of those Q_i for which $P_i \subseteq P_j$.

Hence $B_j = Q_j'$, as required.

Corollary 3.52.1. *Let A satisfy the conditions of the theorem. Then the isolated components of A, and, in particular, the isolated primary components of A, are uniquely determined and must be the same in every reduced primary representation of A.*

PROOF. Immediate from the theorem and the uniqueness of the associated primes of A.

For example, in $Z[x, y]$, the ideal $A = (x^2, 2xy)$ has the reduced primary representation $A = (x^2, xy, y^2) \cap (x) \cap (x^2, 2x, 4)$ and, hence, the associated primes (x, y), (x), and $(x, 2)$. Of these, only (x) is an isolated prime, both (x, y), and $(x, 2)$ being imbedded primes of A. Thus in any reduced primary representation of A, the primary ideal

$$(x) = \{f \in Z[x, y]\colon\ A\colon (f) \not\subseteq (x)\}$$

must appear, as it is an isolated primary component of A. The other isolated components of A are, besides A itself,

$$(x^2, xy) = (x^2, xy, y^2) \cap (x) \text{ and}$$
$$(x^2, 2x) = (x) \cap (x^2, 2x, 4).$$

Thus in any reduced representation $A = Q_1 \cap Q_2 \cap Q_3$ of A by primary ideals Q_1, Q_2, and Q_3, the Q_i must satisfy the following criteria, where we, of course, neglect the order in which the Q_i are written:

$$\sqrt{Q_1} = (x, y), \qquad \sqrt{Q_2} = (x), \qquad \sqrt{Q_3} = (x, 2);$$
$$Q_1 \cap Q_2 = (x^2, xy), \qquad Q_2 = (x), \qquad Q_2 \cap Q_3 = (x^2, 2x)$$

and, of course,

$$Q_1 \cap Q_2 \cap Q_3 = A = (x^2, 2xy),$$

which is automatic if the other conditions are satisfied. The reader may find it interesting to see what possibilities there are for the Q_i which satisfy all of these restrictions.

Exercises

1. Show that $Z[i\sqrt{3}]$ is not a UFD.
2. Show that if R is a Noetherian ring and A is an ideal of R, then both A and R/A are Noetherian rings.
3. Prove that if P is a prime ideal of a commutative ring, then P is irreducible.
4. Show that (x^2, xy, y^2) in $Z[x, y]$ is reducible and primary.
5. Find a reduced primary representation of $A = (x^2, xy, 2)$ in $Z[x, y]$ and determine the associated primes of A, as well as all the isolated components of A.
6. Use Theorem 3.51 to prove the following weakened version of Theorem 3.52: The isolated components of any two reduced primary representations of the ideal A of a Noetherian ring R are necessarily the same.
7. Let A be an ideal of a commutative ring having a reduced primary representation. Show that if all the associated primes of A are maximal (in the set of associated primes of A), then the reduced primary representation of A is unique. Use this result to deduce the prime factorization theorem of the ring Z of integers.
8. Show that in a Noetherian ring R, the ideal A has a prime radical iff A has a unique isolated prime.
9. Show that if R is a Noetherian ring, then the set of nilpotent elements of R is the intersection of the isolated primes of (0).

12. The Characteristic of a Ring

In the ring Z of integers, if b is any nonzero element, then the additive order of b is infinite; that is, if $nb = 0$, then $n = 0$. On the other hand, in the ring Z_p, p a prime, the additive order of every nonzero element is p; that is, $pb = 0$ for every b in the ring. Moreover, if $nb = 0$ and $b \neq 0$, then n is divisible by p.

It is of interest to formalize and generalize such properties of rings, which will be of much importance in our subsequent study of fields.

Definition. In an arbitrary ring R, if there exists a positive integer n such that $nx = 0$ for every x in R, then the least such positive integer n is called the *characteristic* of R and R is said to have (*positive*) *characteristic* n. If no such positive integer exists, that is, if $nx = 0$ for all x in R only if $n = 0$, then R is said to have *characteristic zero.*

We emphasize, again, that nx means $x + x + \cdots + x$, n terms, not n times x, unless it happens that the ring R contains the ring of integers. Thus we are here speaking of the nth natural multiple of x. As noted in Section 2 of Chapter 2, where we first used the notion of natural multiple, one may calculate with natural multiples as though they were real multiplications in which the element n commutes with all other elements, i.e., we have that

$$(nx)y = n(xy) = x(ny), \qquad n(x + y) = nx + ny,$$
$$m(nx) = (mn)x = (nm)x = n(mx), \qquad (n + m)x = nx + mx, \text{ etc.}$$

If R has a unity element, then, for any x in R, we have $nx = n(ex) = (ne)x$ and it follows that the characteristic of R is the least positive integer n such that $ne = 0$ if such an n exists, and is zero, otherwise. If the characteristic is positive, it is not generally true that there may not be a smaller positive integer m such that $mx = 0$ for some nonzero elements of R. But if R is a ring with no divisors of zero, then this may not happen, and the characteristic of R is the common additive order of all the nonzero elements of R.

Theorem 3.53. *If R is a ring with no divisors of zero, then all nonzero elements of R have the same additive order.*

PROOF. We must show that if a and b are nonzero in R, then $na = 0$ if and only if $nb = 0$. If $na = 0$, then $(nb)a = b(na) = 0$ and, since a is not a zero-divisor, we conclude that $nb = 0$. Similarly, $nb = 0$ implies that $na = 0$.

We note that if R is a ring without unity and also without divisors of zero, then we may imbed R in a ring R' with unity and without divisors of zero by the construction given in Section 5 of this chapter. Recall that $R' = (R \times Z)/A$, where A is the ideal of $R \times Z$ consisting of all those elements (r, m) of $R \times Z$ such that $(r, m)(s, 0) = (rs + ms, 0)$ is the identity element $(0, 0)$ of $R \times Z$ for all $s \in R$. Then $n(r, m) \in A$ for all (r, m) in $R \times Z$, that is, $n(r, m)(s, 0) = (nrs + nms, 0) = (0, 0)$, for all $r, s \in R$ and all $m \in Z$, implies that this holds, in particular, if $m = 0$, or $nrs = (nr)s = 0$ for all $r, s \in R$. But this implies, since R has no divisors of zero, that $nr = 0$ for all $r \in R$. Conversely, if $nr = 0$ for all $r \in R$, then for all $(r, m) \in R \times Z$, we have $n(r, m)(s, 0) = 0$, $n(r, m) \in A$. Thus $nR = 0$ iff $nR' = 0$ and we see that R and R' must have the same characteristic. Therefore, we shall freely assume the existence of a unity element when dealing with results concerning the characteristic of a ring R without divisors of zero.

Theorem 3.54. *A ring R of positive characteristic and no zero-divisors must have prime characteristic.*

PROOF. Suppose, on the contrary, that the characteristic n of R is not prime, say $n = rs$ with both r and s positive integers less than n. Then $ne = (rs)e = (re)(se) = 0$ and, since R has no zero-divisors, it follows that either re or se must be zero. (Here e is, of course, the unity of R.) But then the characteristic of R would be less than n, contrary to assumption. Hence the characteristic must be prime.

Corollary 3.54.1. *In a ring with no zero-divisors, the characteristic is the common additive order of all the nonzero elements of the ring, and is either zero or a prime p.*

PROOF. Immediate from Theorems 3.53 and 3.54.

The ring Z of integers and the ring Z_p of integers modulo p are the most natural examples of rings with the respective characteristics zero and p. Just how natural they really are, is apparent from the next result.

Theorem 3.55. *Let R be any ring with unity e. If the characteristic of R is a prime p, then the additive subgroup of R generated by e is isomorphic to Z_p, while if the characteristic of R is zero, then the additive subgroup generated by e is isomorphic to Z.*

PROOF. Let Z' be the additive subgroup of R generated by e, and let the mapping $\alpha: Z \to R$ be defined by $n\alpha = ne$. Then, clearly, $Z\alpha = Z'$. Moreover, α is a homomorphism. For

$$\begin{aligned}(n + m)\alpha &= (n + m)e = (e + e + \cdots + e)_{n+m \text{ terms}} \\ &= (e + e + \cdots + e)_{n \text{ terms}} + (e + e + \cdots + e)_{m \text{ terms}} \\ &= ne + me = n\alpha + m\alpha,\end{aligned}$$

by the associative property of addition in R and the meaning of a natural multiple. Similarly, we have

$$\begin{aligned}(nm)\alpha &= (nm)e = (e + e + \cdots + e)_{nm \text{ terms}} \\ &= (e + \cdots + e)_{n \text{ terms}}(e + \cdots + e)_{m \text{ terms}} \\ &= (ne)(me) = (n\alpha)(m\alpha).\end{aligned}$$

Now if R has characteristic p, the kernel of α is (p) and

$$Z_p = Z/(p) \cong Z' = Z\alpha,$$

while if R has characteristic zero, then the kernel of α is (0) and

$$Z \cong Z/(0) \cong Z' = Z\alpha.$$

If we perform the identification of isomorphic domains, we can then say that every integral domain or division ring must contain either Z or Z_p. With regard to characteristic p however, a word of caution is again in order. We must remember that when we write nx, we are still really dealing with the nth natural multiple of x, and, hence, cannot infer from $nx = 0$ that either n or x is necessarily zero, as we are accustomed to do in an integral domain. It would, of course, follow that if x is not zero, then n must be divisible by the characteristic p, even though n might not be zero.

By arguments entirely similar to those of elementary algebra, one can show that in any integral domain D, the analogue of the celebrated binomial theorem is valid; that is, for $a, b \in D$ and any nonnegative integer n,

$$(a + b)^n = \sum_{r=0}^{n} \binom{n}{r} a^{n-r}b^r,$$

where, as usual, $\binom{n}{r}$ is the binomial coefficient,

$$\binom{n}{r} = \frac{n!}{(n-r)!r!},$$

and, again, we are dealing with the $\binom{n}{r}$th natural multiple of $a^{n-r}b^r$.

In the case of an integral domain of characteristic p, this leads to the result that for all a and b, we have $(a + b)^p = a^p + b^p$, the proof being left to the reader. Also $(a - b)^p = a^p - b^p$ in an integral domain of characteristic p since if p is odd, then $a - b = a + (-e)b$ and $(-e)^p = -e$, while if $p = 2$, then $x = -x$ for all x in the domain, since $x + x = 0$. These observations lead to an interesting extension of the Fermat Theorem:

Theorem 3.56. *The correspondence $a \to a^p$ maps any integral domain D of characteristic p isomorphically onto the subdomain D^p consisting of all pth powers of elements of D.*

PROOF. Exercise.

Exercises

1. Show that natural multiples nx obey the rules:
   (i) $(nx)y = n(xy) = x(ny)$.
   (ii) $n(x + y) = nx + ny$.
   (iii) $(n + m)x = nx + mx$.
   (iv) $m(nx) = (mn)x = n(mx)$.
2. Verify that if R has unity e, then the characteristic of R is the least positive integer n such that $ne = 0$ if such an integer exists, and is zero otherwise.
3. Prove the binomial theorem for arbitrary integral domains.
4. Prove that if D is an integral domain of prime characteristic p, then for all a and b in D, $(a + b)^p = a^p + b^p$.
5. Prove Theorem 3.56.

13. Modules and Vector Spaces

Occupying a position intermediate between that of a group with operator set and that of a ring is the structure known as a module.

Definition. A *left module over* R, or a *left* R*-module*, is an additive Abelian group M with operator set R, where R is a ring, and such that, for all $r, s \in R$ and $x, y \in M$, we have

$$(r + s)x = rx + sx, \qquad (rs)x = r(sx),$$

as well as the usual condition that M be an R-group,

$$r(x + y) = rx + ry.$$

Similarly, M is a *right* R*-module* if M is an additive Abelian R-group, where R is a ring and

$$x(r + s) = xr + xs, \qquad x(rs) = (xr)s,$$

in addition to the usual condition,

$$(x + y)r = xr + yr.$$

If the ring R has a unity element and $ex = x$ $(xe = e)$ for all x in M, then M is called a *unitary* left (right) module. By a *submodule* of a left (or right) R-module M, we shall mean an R-subgroup, the submodule being proper if the subgroup is proper.

Evidently any ring R can be considered either as a left module over itself, or as a right module over itself. If we choose to view R as a left R-module, then the submodules are precisely the left ideals of R, while, if we view R as a right R-module, then the right ideals of R are the submodules. Thus a subset A of the ring R is an ideal (two-sided) if and only if A is both a left and a right submodule of R.

Not only is every ring a module, but every (additive) Abelian group may also be considered as a module, in particular, as a left module over the ring Z of integers. For in defining ng for the integer n and group element g to be the n-fold sum of g with itself, or nth natural multiple of g, we effectively introduced a multiplication of n by g, and, moreover, one which satisfies all the conditions of a unitary module, as may be readily checked. It should be noted that if the group G were not Abelian, then not only would this fact in itself immediately eliminate the possibility of G being a module with respect to any ring R, but, in addition, we would no longer assert the property $n(g + h) = ng + nh$, which is needed if G is to be a left Z-module.

As another, even simpler, illustration, let G be any (additive) Abelian group and R any ring. Then for all $g \in G$ and $r \in R$, let $rg = 0$ and G becomes a left R-module, the module properties being trivial in this case. Such a module is called a *trivial module.*

Since the R-module M is a group M with operator set R, it is at once apparent that the theory of groups with operators can be carried over to the case of modules. Thus we have such notions as the sum of two submodules, or their intersection, just as before.

Definition. If N is a submodule of the (left) R-module M, then we may define the *difference* (or *factor*) R-module, which we will denote by $M - N$ in the present case of modules, just as we defined an $\mathfrak{O}$-factor group for an $\mathfrak{O}$-group G and $\mathfrak{O}$-subgroup H.

Thus the *difference* module $M - N$ is the set of cosets $m + N$ for $m \in M$, with $(m + N) + (m' + N) = (m + m') + N$ and $r(m + N) = rm + N$. The notions of R-homomorphism of an R-module M into an R-module M' and of R-isomorphism, likewise, are translations of previous definitions for the (more general) case of operator groups, and we may obtain homomorphism and isomorphism theorems for modules.

Definition. Let X be a nonempty subset of the R-module M. The intersection of all submodules of M containing X is called the *submodule generated by* X, is denoted by (X), or $(x_1, x_2, \ldots, x_n)$ if $X = \{x_1, x_2, \ldots, x_n\}$, and X is said to be a *generating set* for (X) or, simply, to generate (X). X is a *basis* of (X) if (X) is not generated by any proper subset of X. If $M = (X)$ for some finite subset X, then M is said to be *finitely generated over* R, or to be a *finite* R-*module*. If $M = (x)$, then M is a *cyclic* R-*module*.

The submodule (X) of the R-module M clearly consists of all elements of M having the form

$$a_1x_1 + a_2x_2 + \cdots + a_nx_n + m_1x_1 + m_2x_2 + \cdots + m_nx_n,$$

where $\{x_1, x_2, \ldots, x_n\}$ is any finite subset of X, $a_1, a_2, \ldots, a_n$ are in R, and $m_1, m_2, \ldots, m_n$ are integers. We note that if M is a finite R-module, then M has a finite basis, leaving the proof to the reader.

If M is a unitary R-module, then in the above expression the natural multiples m_ix_i can be omitted since, in this case, $mx = (me)x$, where e is the unity of R. We refer to the resulting expression, $a_1x_1 + a_2x_2 + \cdots + a_nx_n$, as a *linear combination*, with coefficients in R, of $x_1, x_2, \ldots, x_n$. Thus if M is unitary, $(x_1, x_2, \ldots, x_n)$ is the set of all linear combinations of $x_1, x_2, \ldots, x_n$. If $a_1x_1 + a_2x_2 + \cdots + a_nx_n = 0$ implies that $a_1 = a_2 = \cdots = a_n = 0$, then $\{x_1, x_2, \ldots, x_n\}$ is said to be *linearly independent*, the set X is linearly independent if every finite subset of X is linearly independent, and X is *linearly dependent* if X is not linearly independent. If R is a division ring, the reader may readily verify that $\{x_1, x_2, \ldots, x_n\}$ is linearly independent if and only if no x_i is a linear combination of the others.

As in the case of rings, the notions of ascending chain condition, descending chain condition, maximal condition, minimal condition, and finite basis condition, can be applied to modules, the only change necessary being that the term ideal must be replaced throughout by the term submodule. The arguments of Theorem 3.28 can then be applied to show the equivalence of the ACC, MC, and FBC for modules over arbitrary rings. It is natural to ask if there is any connection between the ACC in the ring R and the ACC in the R-module M.

Theorem 3.57. *Let M be a finite unitary (left) R-module. Then, if R satisfies the ACC (DCC) for left ideals, M satisfies the ACC (DCC) for submodules.*

PROOF. Let $\{x_1, x_2, \ldots, x_n\}$ be a generating set of M, and N some submodule of M. For $j = 1, 2, \ldots, n$, let A_j be the set of all elements a_j such that there is some element in N of the form

$$a_jx_j + a_{j+1}x_{j+1} + \cdots + a_nx_n,$$

that is, A_j consists of all the coefficients of x_j of elements of N which are linear combinations of $x_j, x_{j+1}, \ldots, x_n$. It follows that A_j is a left ideal of R.

Now let P be some submodule of M and, similarly, define the left ideals $B_1, B_2, \ldots, B_n$ of R. If $N \subseteq P$, then, clearly, $A_j \subseteq B_j$ for all j, and we assert that if $A_j = B_j$ for all j, then $N = P$. For if

$$x = b_1x_1 + b_2x_2 + \cdots + b_nx_n$$

is any element of P, then b_1 is in $B_1 = A_1$, and there is an element

$$x' = b_1x_1 + a_2x_2 + \cdots + a_nx_n$$

in N. Then $y = x - x' = c_2x_2 + c_3x_3 + \cdots + c_nx_n$, $c_j = b_j - a_j$, is in P, so that c_2 is in $B_2 = A_2$. Repeating the process, we obtain that x is a sum of elements of N, hence is in N and $N = P$.

If $N_1 \subseteq N_2 \subseteq \cdots$ is any ascending chain of submodules of M, we define for each N_i the set A_{ij} of left ideals of R as above and obtain the n ascending chains of left ideals,

$$A_{1j} \subseteq A_{2j} \subseteq \cdots, \qquad j = 1, 2, \ldots, n.$$

If R satisfies the ACC for left ideals, then for each j there exists an index r_j such that $A_{sj} = A_{r_j j}$ for all $s \geq r_j$. We let r be the maximum of $r_1, r_2, \ldots, r_n$ and have that $A_{sj} = A_{rj}$ for all $s \geq r$ and all $j = 1, 2, \ldots, n$. Hence $N_s = N_r$ for all $s \geq r$, and the ACC holds for submodules of M. The proof for the DCC is similar.

One of our chief interests in this section will be to develop those properties of that special type of module called a vector space which we shall need in our study of fields.

Definition. A unitary (left) module M over a division ring D is a (left) *vector space.* The elements of M are called *vectors* and the elements of D are called *scalars* and the composite of a vector v and a scalar d, dv, is called *scalar multiplication* of v by d. A submodule of a vector space is called a *subspace.*

The most familiar examples of vector spaces are probably those of elementary analytic geometry, where the division ring is the field R' of real numbers and the vectors are ordered n-tuples (with $n = 2$ or 3 in the simpler cases) of real numbers $(a_1, a_2, \ldots, a_n)$ with the group addition being;

$$(a_1, a_2, \ldots, a_n) + (b_1, b_2, \ldots, b_n) = (a_1 + b_1, a_2 + b_2, \ldots, a_n + b_n)$$

and scalar multiplication

$$r(a_1, a_2, \ldots, a_n) = (ra_1, ra_2, \ldots, ra_n).$$

Thus we have the so-called *parallelogram law of addition*, where, if we are given the origin $0 = (0, 0, \ldots, 0)$ and the two points $a = (a_1, a_2, \ldots, a_n)$ and $b = (b_1, b_2, \ldots, b_n)$ in Euclidean n-space with a Cartesian coordinate system, then the above sum, $a + b$, represents the fourth vertex in that parallelogram for which a and b are one pair of opposite vertices and 0 and $a + b$ are the other pair.

Such vector spaces, which we usually denote by $V_n(R')$, or by $V_n(D)$ if R' is replaced by some division ring D, also form the most natural examples of finitely generated modules, and one may easily verify that, for example, $V_n(D)$ has the basis $(1, 0, \ldots, 0), (0, 1, 0, \ldots, 0), \ldots, (0, \ldots, 0, 1)$.

For the case of vector spaces, Theorem 3.57 is changed as follows.

Corollary 3.57.1. *If a vector space V is finitely generated, then every subspace of V has a finite basis.*

PROOF. The ACC holds trivially for left ideals in a division ring; hence the ACC holds in V, and it follows that every subspace of V is finitely generated and, hence, has a finite basis.

While the ACC and DCC are not equivalent for modules in general (the ring of integers is a module over itself with ACC, but not DCC), these two conditions are equivalent for vector spaces.

Theorem 3.58. *A vector space V over a division ring D satisfies the ACC if and only if it satisfies the DCC.*

PROOF. If V does not satisfy the ACC, then there exists an infinite properly ascending chain of subspaces $(0) \subset V_1 \subset V_2 \subset \cdots$. For each $i = 1, 2, \ldots$, there is, thus, some x_i in V_i which is not in V_{i-1}, and, hence, x_i is not a linear combination of $x_1, x_2, \ldots, x_{i-1}$. Let $W_i = (x_i, x_{i+1}, \ldots)$ and we have $W_1 \supseteq W_2 \supseteq \cdots$. Now if $W_i = W_{i+1}$ for any i, then we would have x_i in W_{i+1} and, hence, $x_i = a_1x_{j_1} + a_2x_{j_2} + \cdots + a_mx_{j_m}$ for $i < j_1 < j_2 < \cdots < j_m$. If $a_m \neq 0$, then a_m^{-1} is in D and $x_{j_m} = a_m^{-1}(x_i - a_1x_{j_1} - \cdots - a_{m-1}x_{j_{m-1}})$, contrary to the original choice of x_{j_m}. Hence $a_m = 0$, and, repeating the argument, we have, successively, $a_{m-1} = 0, \ldots, a_1 = 0$, whence $x_i = 0$, again a contradiction. Thus $W_1 \supset W_2 \supset \cdots$ is an infinite properly descending chain, and the DCC must then imply the ACC.

On the other hand, if the DCC does not hold in V, then there is some infinite properly descending chain $W_1 \supset W_2 \supset \cdots$ and, hence, for each i some x_i such that $x_i \in W_i$, $x_i \notin W_j$ for $j > i$, and, moreover, x_{i+1} is not a linear combination of $x_1, x_2, \ldots, x_i$. For certainly $x_{i+1} \neq 0$; hence if

$$x_{i+1} = a_1x_1 + a_2x_2 + \cdots + a_ix_i,$$

some $a_j \neq 0$. An argument entirely similar to that in the first part of the proof would then show that $a_1 = 0$, and, successively, $a_2 = 0, \ldots, a_i = 0$, a contradiction. Hence if $V_i = (x_1, x_2, \ldots, x_i)$, we have that $V_1 \subset V_2 \subset \cdots$ is an infinite properly ascending chain. Thus the ACC must also imply the DCC in V.

While for any module a basis is a minimal generating set, in the case of a vector space other equivalent definitions can be given.

Theorem 3.59. *For a subset X of the vector space V, the following are equivalent:*

(i) *X is a basis of V.*
(ii) *X is a linearly independent generating set for V.*
(iii) *X is a maximal linearly independent subset of V (i.e., for any $y \notin X$, the set $X \cup \{y\}$ is linearly dependent).*

PROOF.

(i) implies (ii).

We must show that X is linearly independent. If not, we would have $a_1x_1 + a_2x_2 + \cdots + a_nx_n = 0$ for some $x_1, \ldots, x_n \in X$ and a_i not all zero in D, say $a_1 \neq 0$. Then $x_1 = -a_1^{-1}(a_2x_2 + \cdots + a_nx_n)$, $x_1 \in (X - \{x_1\})$, the space generated by the set complement of x_1 in X, from which it follows that $V = (X - \{x_1\})$, and X is not a minimal generating set for V. Hence X must be linearly independent.

(ii) implies (iii).

Here we must show that X, assumed to be a linearly independent generating set for V, is also a maximal linearly independent set. If y is any element of V, $y \notin X$, then $y = a_1x_1 + a_2x_2 + \cdots + a_nx_n$ for some $a_i \in D$ and $x_i \in X$. Then $0 = -ey + a_1x_1 + \cdots + a_nx_n$, e the unity of D, which implies that $X \cup \{y\}$ is linearly dependent.

(iii) implies (i).

For any $y \in V$, either $y \in X \subseteq (X)$ or $y \notin X$, in which case $X \cup \{y\}$ is linearly dependent and so is some finite subset Y of $X \cup \{y\}$. Clearly $y \in Y$ and, hence, $ay + a_1x_1 + \cdots + a_nx_n = 0$, where $Y = \{y, x_1, \ldots, x_n\}$ and $a, a_1, \ldots, a_n$ are not all zero. Then $a \neq 0$, since, otherwise, $\{x_1, \ldots, x_n\}$ would be linearly dependent. Thus $y = -a^{-1}(a_1x_1 + \cdots + a_nx_n) \in (X)$ and $V = (X)$. The linear independence of X then implies that $x \notin (X - \{x\})$ for any $x \in X$; that is, X is a minimal generating set for V, or a basis.

We turn now to the case of vector spaces which are finitely generated, that is, those vector spaces having finite bases.

Theorem 3.60. *Let the vector space V have a finite basis $X = \{x_1, x_2, \ldots, x_n\}$, and let Y be any basis of V. Then Y consists of exactly n elements.*

PROOF. Let $X \cap Y = \{x_1, x_2, \ldots, x_m\}$, reindexing the x_i if necessary. If $m = n$, then $X \subseteq Y$ and, since X is a maximal linearly independent set and Y is linearly independent, it follows that $X = Y$.

Suppose, then, that $m < n$. Let $X' = \{x_1, \ldots, x_m, x_{m+2}, \ldots, x_n\}$. If $Y \subseteq (X')$, then for any $v \in V$, we would have

$$v = a_1y_1 + \cdots + a_ry_r$$

for some $y_1, \ldots, y_r \in Y$, and, also,

$$y_j = b_{j1}x_1 + \cdots + b_{jm}x_m + b_{j,m+2}\, x_{m+2} + \cdots + b_{jn}x_n.$$

But then

$$\begin{aligned} v = (a_1b_{11} + \cdots + a_rb_{r1})x_1 + \cdots &+ (a_1b_{1m} + \cdots + a_rb_{rm})x_m \\ &+ (a_1b_{1,m+2} + \cdots + a_rb_{r,m+2})x_{m+2} + \cdots \\ &+ (a_1b_{1n} + \cdots + a_rb_{rn})x_n, \end{aligned}$$

which contradicts the minimality of the generating set X. Hence there is some $y \in Y$ such that $y \notin (X')$. Then,

$$a_1x_1 + \cdots + a_mx_m + ay + a_{m+2}x_{m+2} + \cdots + a_nx_m = 0$$

implies $a = 0$, which, in turn, implies

$$a_1 = \cdots = a_m = a_{m+2} = \cdots = a_n = 0.$$

Thus $X' \cup \{y\}$ is linearly independent. The maximality of X as a linearly independent set implies that $X \cup \{y\}$ is linearly dependent and

$$0 = a_1x_1 + \cdots + a_{m+1}x_{m+1} + \cdots + a_nx_n + ay$$

for $a, a_1, \ldots, a_n$ not all zero. Since $X' \cup \{y\}$ is linearly independent, we must have $a_{m+1} \neq 0$, hence, $x_{m+1} \in (X' \cup \{y\})$. Thus $X' \cup \{y\}$ generates V and is a basis of B.

By induction on m, it follows that there exists an n element basis Y' of V having n elements in common with Y. As in the first part of the proof, this implies that $Y = Y'$ and Y has n elements.

The procedure used in the proof of "exchanging" x_{m+1} for an element of Y to obtain a new basis is usually called the Steinitz Exchange Principle.

Definition. If the vector space V over the division ring D has a finite basis of n elements, then V is called a *finite dimensional vector space over D*, and the unique number, n, of elements in any basis of V is called the *dimension of V over D* and is denoted by $[V : D]$. If V has no finite basis, then V is said to be *infinite dimensional* (over D) and we write $[V : D] = \infty$.

Corollary 3.60.1. *Let $V = (X) = (x_1, x_2, \ldots, x_n)$, and $Y = \{y_1, y_2, \ldots, y_r\}$ be a subset of V. Then, if $r > n$, Y is linearly dependent.*

PROOF. Since X generates V, by deleting some of the x_i, if necessary, we may obtain a linearly independent subset of X, say of m elements, $m \leq n$, which also generates V and, hence, is a basis. For Y to be linearly independent would then require that $r \leq m$, the unique number of elements in a maximal linearly independent set.

Corollary 3.60.2. *Let $c_1a_{i1} + c_2a_{i2} + \cdots + c_ra_{ir} = 0$, $i = 1, 2, \ldots, n < r$, be a system of n linear homogeneous equations in r unknowns with coefficients a_{ij} in a division ring D. Then there exist elements $c_1, c_2, \ldots, c_r$, in D and not all zero, which comprise a solution of this system of equations.*

PROOF. Consider the left vector space $V_n(D)$. $V_n(D)$ clearly has a basis $e_1 = (1, 0, \ldots, 0)$, $e_2 = (0, 1, 0, \ldots, 0), \ldots, e_n = (0, \ldots, 0, 1)$. Now let $y_i = a_{1i}e_1 + a_{2i}e_2 + \cdots + a_{ni}e_n = (a_{1i}, a_{2i}, \ldots, a_{ni})$. We have

$$c_1y_1 + c_2y_2 + \cdots + c_ry_r = 0$$

if and only if

$$c_1a_{i1} + \cdots + c_ra_{ir} = 0, \qquad i = 1, 2, \ldots, n.$$

But if $r > n$, then $\{y_1, y_2, \ldots, y_r\}$ is linearly dependent, and the required $c_1, c_2, \ldots, c_r$, in D and not all zero, must exist.

Similarly, the system of homogeneous linear equations

$$a_{i1}c_1 + a_{i2}c_2 + \cdots + a_{ir}c_r = 0, \qquad i = 1, 2, \ldots, n < r,$$

a_{ij} in D may be shown to have a nontrivial solution by considering the right vector space $V_n(D)$.

We conclude this section with the following easy and useful theorem.

Theorem 3.61. *Let V be a vector space of dimension n over the division ring D. Then $X = \{x_1, x_2, \ldots, x_n\}$ is a basis of V if and only if every vector in V is a unique linear combination of $x_1, x_2, \ldots, x_n$.*

PROOF. If X is a basis, then for $x \in V$, we have $x = a_1x_1 + \cdots + a_nx_n$. If, also, $x = b_1x_1 + \cdots + b_nx_n$, then

$$0 = x - x = (a_1 - b_1)x_1 + \cdots + (a_n - b_n)x_n$$

and the linear independence of X requires that

$$a_i = b_i, \; i = 1, 2, \ldots, n.$$

Conversely, if every $v \in V$ is a unique linear combination of $x_1, x_2, \ldots, x_n$, then, in particular, the vector 0 must be such a unique linear combination, namely $0 = 0x_1 + 0x_2 + \cdots + 0x_n$. The uniqueness implies that X is linearly independent and, hence, a basis of V.

Exercises

1. Show that if M is a left R-module, then the subset L of M is a submodule if and only if L is an R-subgroup of M.
2. Show that A is a left ideal of the ring R iff A is a submodule of R, viewed as a left R-module.
3. Let the ring R with no divisors of zero be considered as a left R-module. Show that the only module homomorphisms of R which are also ring homomorphisms of R are the trivial ones $\alpha: r\alpha = 0$ for all r in R, and $\beta: r\beta = r$ for all r in R.
4. If R is a commutative ring with unity, show that the cyclic submodules of R regarded as an R-module are the principal ideals of R. Is this true if R has no unity element?
5. Show that the system of linear homogeneous equations
$$x_1a_{1j} + x_2a_{2j} + \cdots + x_na_{nj} = 0; \qquad j = 1, 2, \ldots, m,$$
with a_{ij} in a division ring D, has a nontrivial solution in D (i.e., a solution $c_1, c_2, \ldots, c_n$ in D with the c_i not all zero) if $n > m$, without the use of Theorem 3.60.
6. Show that if V is a vector space of dimension n and W is a subspace of V having as basis $\{x_1, x_2, \ldots, x_r\}$, $r < n$, then there exist $x_{r+1}, x_{r+2}, \ldots, x_n$ in V such that $\{x_1, \ldots, x_r, x_{r+1}, \ldots, x_n\}$ is a basis of V.
7. Let the vector space V of dimension n be generated by $\{y_1, y_2, \ldots, y_m\}$, $m \geq n$. Show that some subset $\{y_{i_1}, y_{i_2}, \ldots, y_{i_n}\}$ is a basis of V.

CHAPTER 4

Fields

1. Prime Fields

We now turn to the study of that special type of ring called a field. We have already seen several examples of fields, including those of such great importance to analysis and other branches of mathematics, the real and complex number fields. The study of fields would be justified by these applications if by nothing more. But since so many of the most important results which we obtained for rings apply to the case of fields (for example, the unique factorization of polynomials with coefficients in a field), it would seem apparent that the properties of fields should be of considerable interest in themselves. It is to be expected, of course, that we shall be able to obtain much more in the way of results for fields than for arbitrary rings, since in fields we have both the additive Abelian group and the multiplicative Abelian group (of nonzero elements) to work with.

Since a field is, in particular, an integral domain, it follows from Corollary 3.54.1 and Theorem 3.55 that every field F has a characteristic which is either zero or a positive prime, and that F contains an isomorphic copy of either the integers or the integers modulo p, respectively. Now Z_p is itself a field, and, since the additive group of Z_p contains no proper subgroups, it follows that Z_p contains no proper subfields. In the case of a field of characteristic zero, the subdomain isomorphic to Z must be contained in a subfield isomorphic to the rational numbers, since we know that the rational numbers, being the quotient field of the integers, are the smallest field containing the integers. We are thus led to the following definition:

Definition. Let D be a division ring. A subset F of D which is itself a field will be called a *subfield* of D.† Now the intersection of any number of subfields of D is again a subfield of D. Thus if D contains any subfields, then D contains a unique subfield P, called the *prime subfield of* D, which is contained in every subfield of D. Since P is characterized as that subfield of D which itself has no proper subfields, we shall further define a *prime field* to be a field containing no proper subfields.

Now we can state and prove the following theorem.

† Recall that a field must contain at least two elements, so that 0 does not constitute a field by itself (see page 78).

Theorem 4.1. *Let D be a division ring. Then D contains a prime subfield isomorphic to either Z_p or R, the field of rational numbers, according to whether the characteristic of D is a prime p or is zero.*

PROOF. Suppose, first, that the characteristic of D is p. Then, by Theorem 3.55, the additive subgroup of D generated by the unity element e of D is isomorphic to Z_p. But Z_p is a field, and, clearly, every subfield of D must contain the additive subgroup generated by e. Thus the result is established in the case of characteristic p.

Now suppose the characteristic of D is zero. Then, again by Theorem 3.55, the additive subgroup of D generated by e is isomorphic to Z, and any subfield of D must contain this additive subgroup. But the smallest field containing Z is its quotient field R, by Theorem 3.19, and, since D is a division ring, D must contain multiplicative inverses of all nonzero elements in the isomorphic copy of Z; hence D contains a subfield isomorphic to R, which must, therefore, be the prime subfield of D.

Corollary 4.1.1. *If P is a prime field, then P is isomorphic to either R or Z_p for some prime p.*

PROOF. Exercise.

As a consequence of the fact that a field of characteristic p always has as its prime subfield an isomorphic copy of Z_p, the field of integers modulo p, we often refer to a field of prime characteristic as a *modular field*.

As all the fields of classical analysis, the rational, real, and complex number fields are fields of characteristic zero, all must have (a field isomorphic to) R as prime subfield. It might then seem that modular fields are of abstract interest only. However, such is not the case, as there are, in fact, a great many applications of the theory of finite fields, which must, of course, have prime characteristic.

While a finite field must have prime characteristic, it is not the case that a field of prime characteristic need be finite. For example, consider the quotient field $Z_2(x)$ of the domain of polynomials $Z_2[x]$ with coefficients in Z_2. Here the prime subfield is certainly Z_2, hence the characteristic is 2, and yet it is easy to verify that the field $Z_2(x)$ contains an infinite number of elements.

The notation used here for the quotient field of a ring of polynomials in an indeterminate x over an integral domain will be used throughout the rest of the book.

Definition. Let D be an integral domain, F a field containing D, c an element of F, and x an indeterminate. Then

$D(x)$ will denote the quotient field of the polynomial ring $D[x]$,
$D(c)$ will denote the quotient field of the ring $D[c]$.

Thus $D(x)$ and $D(c)$ denote the *fields of all rational functions in x and c*, respectively, with coefficients in D.

Rather than give examples of finite fields other than those isomorphic to the finite prime fields at this time, we shall delay such examples until we have considered the next topic, extensions of fields, at which time it will be easy to give many such examples.

Exercises

1. Prove that if $\{F_i : i \in I\}$ is any set of subfields of the field F, then $\cap F_i$, $i \in I$, is a subfield of F.
2. Prove Corollary 4.1.1.
3. Let R be the field of rational numbers. Show that

$$R[x]/(x^2 + 1)$$

is a field and determine its characteristic.

4. Let D be an integral domain and x an indeterminate. Prove that D, $D[x]$, and $D(x)$ all have the same characteristic. Is this still the case if x is replaced by c, where c is some element of a field containing D?

2. Extensions of Fields

Definition. If F is a subfield of the field K, then K is an *extension field* or *superfield* of F. If M is any set of elements of K, then by $F(M)$ we mean the intersection of all subfields of K containing both F and M, and $F(M)$ is called the *extension field of F obtained by adjunction of the elements in M*.† If the set M consists of a single element $c \notin F$ then $F(c)$ is said to be a *simple extension* of F.

In order to classify the types of extensions which a field may have, we shall need several definitions, including the following one.

Definition. Let $c \neq 0$ be an element of K, K an extension field of the field F. If c satisfies a polynomial equation with coefficients not all zero in F, that is, if

$$a_n c^n + \cdots + a_1 c + a_0 = 0$$

in K with the a_i all in F and not all zero, then c is said to be *algebraic over F*. If c is not algebraic over F, then c is *transcendental over F*. A simple extension of F is *algebraic* or *transcendental* according as the *adjoined element* generating the extension is *algebraic* or *transcendental.*

For example, if R is the field of rational numbers, then $R(\sqrt{2})$ is an algebraic extension of R, since $\sqrt{2}$ satisfies $x^2 - 2 = 0$, while $R(\pi)$ is a transcendental extension of R.

We may now classify all possible simple extensions of the field F, in the sense of isomorphism.

† We leave it to the reader to verify that $F(M)$ actually is a field.

Theorem 4.2. *Let K be a superfield of the field F, and c any element of K such that c is transcendental over F. Then the simple extension $F(c)$ is isomorphic to $F(x)$, the field of all rational functions of the indeterminate x with coefficients in F, and the isomorphism α can be chosen so that F remains elementwise fixed, that is, $a\alpha = a$ for all a in F.*

PROOF. Since $F(c)$ is a field and contains both F and c, it must consist of all rational expressions in c, that is, all expressions of the form $f(c)(g(c))^{-1}$, where $f(c)$ and $g(c)$ are polynomials in c with coefficients in F, and $g(c)$ is not the zero polynomial. Now consider the mapping α' from the domain $F[x]$ onto $F[c]$ defined by $f(x)\alpha' = f(c)$. Two distinct elements $f(x)$ and $g(x)$ of $F[x]$ cannot have equal images under α', since $f(c) = g(c)$ would imply that $f(c) - g(c) = 0$, which is impossible, since c is transcendental over F. Thus α' is 1–1 and is, evidently, an isomorphism, since the rules for addition and multiplication are identical in $F[x]$ and $F[c]$. Clearly if a is in F, then $a\alpha' = a$, so that F is elementwise fixed under α'. We now apply Theorem 3.19 to obtain, from the isomorphism α' of the integral domains $F[x]$ and $F[c]$, the unique extension of α' to an isomorphism α of the respective quotient fields $F(x)$ and $F(c)$.

Theorem 4.3. *Let c be an element of the field K algebraic over the field F. Then $F(c) = F[c]$ and is isomorphic to $F[x]/(p(x))$, where $p(x)$ is the unique monic polynomial irreducible in $F[x]$ having c as a root (in K). c is a root of the polynomial $g(x)$ in $F[x]$ if and only if $g(x)$ is divisible in $F[x]$ by $p(x)$.*

PROOF. As in the preceding proof, consider the mapping defined by $f(x)\alpha = f(c)$. If N is the kernel of α, then we have that $F[x]/N$ and $F[c]$ are isomorphic. Now, since c is algebraic over F, N cannot consist of 0 alone, and cannot be the entire ring $F[x]$, since $F[c]$ consists of more than one element. Thus N is a proper ideal. Since $F[x]$ is a PID, N must be a principal ideal, say $N = (p(x))$, and $p(x)$ must be prime since $F[x]/N \cong F[c]$, which, as a subset of the field $F(c)$, can have no divisors of zero. F being a field, we may choose $p(x)$ to be monic. Since $N = (p(x))$, an element $g(x)$ of $F[x]$ has c as a root if and only if $g(x)$ is divisible in $F[x]$ by $p(x)$. Thus if $q(x)$ is any monic irreducible polynomial in $F[x]$ having c as a root, we have each of $p(x)$ and $q(x)$ dividing the other and, since both are monic, this is possible only if $p(x) = q(x)$. Hence $p(x)$ is unique, as asserted.

Now, since $F[x]$ is a PID, it follows from Theorem 3.41 that the prime ideal $(p(x))$ is also maximal. Then, by Corollary 3.40.1, we have that $F[x]/(p(x))$ is a field. Hence $F[c]$ is a field, and, since $F(c)$ is the minimal field containing $F[c]$, we must have $F[c] = F(c)$.

This completes the proof.

Definition. For c an element algebraic over the field F, the unique monic irreducible polynomial $p(x)$ in $F[x]$ having c as a root is called the *minimum polynomial of c over F*, and the degree of $p(x)$ is called the *degree of c over F*.

Note that both the *minimum polynomial* and *degree* of an algebraic element depend on the field F over which it is being considered, so that one must be careful not to speak simply of the *minimum polynomial* or the *degree* of the element c without specifying the field F, unless the latter is amply clear from the context. For example, the complex number $\sqrt{2} + i$ has degree 2 over the field R' of real numbers, and degree 4 over the field R of rational numbers.

It is the fact that $F[c] = F(c)$ for c algebraic over F which underlies the familiar operation of *rationalizing the denominator*, which one encounters in elementary algebra. As an example, suppose that we consider the field R of rational numbers and the element $\sqrt{3}$ in the superfield R' of real numbers, whose minimum polynomial over R is $x^2 - 3$. Now the element $1/(a + b\sqrt{3})$, for a and b not both zero in R, is clearly in $R(\sqrt{3})$ and, hence, also in $R[\sqrt{3}]$. Thus there must exist a polynomial in $\sqrt{3}$ with rational coefficients having the same value as $1/(a + b\sqrt{3})$.

The only question remaining is how to find this polynomial. Of course, in the simple example above, we know how to find the required polynomial by means of elementary algebra, but we wish here to develop a method which will generalize to more complicated examples, such as finding the inverse of the element $a + b\sqrt[3]{2} + c\sqrt[3]{4}$ in the field $R(\sqrt[3]{2})$.

Returning to our original problem, suppose we wish the inverse of

$$f(\sqrt{3}) = -2 + \sqrt{3}.$$

Now, since $p(x) = x^2 - 3$ is prime and $f(x)$ is not divisible by $p(x)$, there must exist polynomials $r(x)$ and $s(x)$ such that

$$1 = r(x)p(x) + s(x)f(x).$$

But in the field $R(\sqrt{3}) = R[x]/p(x)$, this becomes

$$1 = f(\sqrt{3})s(\sqrt{3}),$$

since $p(\sqrt{3}) = 0$. (We should write $(p(x))$, rather than $p(x)$, to be correct in identifying the ideal generated by $p(x)$, but it is customary to omit the second pair of parentheses, a custom which we shall follow.) Thus $s(\sqrt{3})$ is the required inverse, and it only remains to find $s(x)$. This may be done by the use of the Euclidean Algorithm, in which we have, successively,

$$\begin{aligned} x^2 - 3 &= (x + 2)(x - 2) + 1, \\ 1 &= 1(x^2 - 3) + (-x - 2)(x - 2), \\ 1 &= 0 + (-\sqrt{3} - 2)(\sqrt{3} - 2). \end{aligned}$$

Thus in this simple case, $r(x) = 1$, $s(x) = -x - 2$, and the inverse of $f(\sqrt{3}) = \sqrt{3} - 2$ is

$$s(\sqrt{3}) = -\sqrt{3} - 2.$$

In more complicated cases, the major problem is, of course, the use of the algorithm in finding $s(x)$ and $r(x)$. The reader should practice this procedure sufficiently to become familiar with it.

The isomorphism established in Theorem 4.3 between the fields $F(c)$ and $F[x]/p(x)$, where $p(x)$ is the minimum polynomial of c over F, is of greater importance than may be at first apparent. For it actually allows us to state (and prove) the following theorem:

Theorem 4.4. *Let $p(x)$ be irreducible over the field F. Then there exists a simple algebraic extension field of F generated by a root c of $p(x)$.*

PROOF. By Theorem 4.3, this extension field $F(c)$, if it exists, must be isomorphic to $F[x]/p(x)$. Now, as argued in the proof of Theorem 4.3, $F[x]/p(x)$ is a field, since $F[x]$ is a PID and the prime ideal generated by $p(x)$ is, therefore, also maximal. No nonzero element of F can be in $(p(x))$, since $p(x)$ is prime and thus has degree at least one, the elements of F being either zero or of degree zero in $F[x]$.

Thus in the homomorphism of $F[x]$ onto $F[x]/p(x)$, F is mapped isomorphically onto a copy of itself, F', which may be identified with F. The elements of $F[x]/p(x)$, that is, cosets of elements $f(x)$ in $F[x]$, then become polynomials $f(c)$ in the element c with (the same) coefficients in F, where c is the coset of x, $c = x + (p(x))$. We may, thus, identify $F[x]/p(x)$ with $F[c] = F(c)$. Since the coset of $p(x)$ is the zero coset, it follows that $p(c) = 0$ and the theorem is proved.

Corollary 4.4.1. *If $f(x)$ is any polynomial of positive degree over the field F, then $f(x)$ has a root in some extension field of F.*

PROOF. We need merely express $f(x)$ as a product of irreducible factors and then apply the theorem to any of these factors.

Theorem 4.4 and its corollary, due to Kronecker, constitute one of the most fundamental results in all of algebra. Indeed, it could well be argued that this is the "fundamental theorem of algebra" rather than the result concerning roots of polynomials over the complex number field which is traditionally given this title. For this result assures us that given any polynomial over any field, there must exist an extension field in which the polynomial has a root, a result of great generality. Moreover, the proof of the theorem does more than merely prove existence, as it also provides a method for constructing the required field.

This process of formally adjoining to a field a constructed root of any polynomial over that field can be applied to any field whatever. The most familiar example is that of the real field R' and the irreducible polynomial $x^2 + 1$ in $R'[x]$. (How does one know that $x^2 + 1$ is irreducible over R'?) Here it is customary to designate the coset of x in $R'[x]/(x^2 + 1)$ by the letter i, the "imaginary" square root of -1. We could, of course, equally well adjoin the coset $-i$ of $-x$, and would obtain the same extension field of R' in either case. We shall soon see that the fact that adjoining either root of $x^2 + 1$ to R' leads to the same extension field is not peculiar to this case, but is true for any irreducible polynomial over any field, provided we interpret "the same field" to mean an isomorphic field.

For another example of formal field adjunction, consider the prime field Z_3 and the polynomial $x^2 + x + 2$. That $x^2 + x + 2$ is irreducible over Z_3 is not obvious and will require proof. (To see the need for proof, suppose that we had taken, instead, the polynomial $x^2 + x + 1 = (x + 2)^2$, or $x^2 + 2 = (x + 1)(x + 2)$, where we are here writing the elements of Z_3 simply as 0, 1, and 2. These examples should suffice to show that polynomials which we are accustomed to thinking of as irreducible, over the real field R', are not necessarily irreducible when considered over other fields. There is, of course, no logical reason why we should expect them to be irreducible over other fields, but the natural tendency to do so can sometimes be rather strong.)

To show that $x^2 + x + 2$ is irreducible over Z_3, we may reason as follows:

Possible values of x:	0	1	2
Corresponding values of x^2:	0	1	1
Corresponding values of $x^2 + x + 2$:	2	1	2

Thus for any c in Z_3, we have $c^2 + c + 2 \neq 0$, while if $x^2 + x + 2$ were reducible over Z_3, it would be a product of first degree factors and, hence, would have a root in Z_3.

Alternatively, we could argue that if $x^2 + x + 2 = (ax + b)(cx + d)$ for some a, b, c, d in Z_3, then we must have $ac = 1$, $ad + bc = 1$, and $bd = 2$. Now in Z_3 the only possible factorizations of 1 are $1 \cdot 1$ and $2 \cdot 2$, and the only factorization of 2 is $1 \cdot 2$. Thus we may assume, without loss of generality, that $b = 1$ and $d = 2$. Also we must have either $a = c = 1$ or $a = c = 2$. Then $ad + bc = 2a + c = 3a = 0 \neq 1$ and the factorization is not possible.

Now let r be a "root" of $p(x)$, that is, the residue class of x in $Z_3[x]/p(x)$. (The other root of $p(x)$ is then $2r + 2$.) Since $r^2 = -2 - r = 1 + 2r$, it follows that for any $f(x)$ in $Z_3[x]$, $f(r) = a + br$ for some a and b in Z_3. Moreover, if $a + br = c + dr$, then $(a - c) + (b - d)r = 0$, and we must have $a = c$ and $b = d$, since $p(x)$ is irreducible and r cannot, therefore, satisfy any equation of degree lower than that of $p(x)$. Thus $Z_3[r] = Z_3(r)$ consists of the nine elements

$$0, 1, 2, r, 1 + r, 2 + r, 2r, 1 + 2r, 2 + 2r.$$

The inverses of the nonzero elements are, in order,

$$1, 2, 1 + r, r, 1 + 2r, 2 + 2r, 2 + r, 2r.$$

We observe that, since $(2 + r)^2 = r^2 + 4r + 4 = r^2 + r + 2 + 2$ and $r^2 + r + 2 = 0$, it follows that $(2 + r)^2 = 2$. Thus we may also consider $r + 2$ as a "square root" of 2 (over the prime field Z_3) and write $r + 2 = \sqrt{2}$, or $r = 1 + \sqrt{2}$, the same result we would obtain if we were to "solve" the equation $x^2 + x + 2 = 0$ in the usual manner, remembering, of course, that in the computation of the solution, we are working over the field Z_3.

The fact that this field, $Z_3(r)$, is of order $9 = 3^2$ is typical of the general case. In fact, we shall later see if F is any finite field, then F is of order p^n for p the order of the prime field of F and n some positive integer.

We may observe that in the example just considered, as in the case of the adjunction of either i or $-i$ to the field of real numbers, whether we adjoin r or $2r + 2$, the roots of our polynomial $p(x) = x^2 + x + 2$ over Z_3, we obtain the "same" field. The general theorem covering this situation is as follows:

Theorem 4.5. *Let u and v be two roots of the polynomial $p(x)$, irreducible over the field F. Then, $F(u)$ and $F(v)$ are isomorphic under an isomorphism such that u corresponds to v and every element of F to itself.*

PROOF. Let $f(u)$ in $F(u)$ correspond to $f(v)$ in $F(v)$, i.e., two polynomials correspond iff they have exactly the same coefficients. Now $f(u) = g(u)$ iff $f(u) - g(u) = 0$ iff $p(x)$ divides $f(x) - g(x)$ iff $f(v) - g(v) = 0$ iff $f(v) = g(v)$, so that the correspondence is 1–1. The other properties of an isomorphism follow trivially from the definitions of $F(u)$ and $F(v)$.

Thus, while the field $Z_3(r)$, with r the residue class of x in the mapping of $Z_3[x]$ onto $Z_3[x]/(x^2 + x + 2)$, is certainly formally different from the field $Z_3(\sqrt{2})$ obtained by adjoining the element we get by "solving" the equation $x^2 + x + 2 = 0$ over the field Z_3, we are assured, by this last theorem, that the difference between these two extension fields is only formal and, hence, their properties are identical.

Exercises

1. Show that if M is a subset of the superfield K of the field F, then $F(M)$, the intersection of all subfields of K containing both F and M, is a field.
2. Show that an element c of the superfield K of F is, respectively, transcendental or algebraic over F according as the natural mapping $f(x) \to f(c)$ of $F[x]$ onto $F[c]$, x an indeterminate, is or is not an isomorphism.
3. Let c be an element of the superfield K of F and x an indeterminate. Show that there exists an ideal A of $F[x]$ such that $F[c] \cong F[x]/A$.
4. Show that $c = \sqrt{2} + i$ has degree four over the rational number field R but degree two over the real number field R', and give the minimum polynomial of c in each case.
5. Find the inverse in $R[\sqrt[3]{2}] = R(\sqrt[3]{2})$ of $2 - \sqrt[3]{2} + \sqrt[3]{4}$ by the method of this section.
6. Given the field R' of real numbers, construct "the" field of complex numbers in the two essentially distinct ways:
   (a) Construct C as the set of all ordered pairs of real numbers, with suitably defined addition and multiplication.
   (b) Construct C' from R' and the polynomial $x^2 + 1$ by Theorem 4.4.
7. Exhibit the isomorphism of the fields C and C' constructed in Exercise 5.
8. Prove that $x^2 + 1$ is irreducible over the real number field R'.
9. Show that $f(x) = x^2 + x + 1$ is irreducible over Z_5 and let $r = x + (f(x))$ in $Z_5[x]/(f(x))$. Let s be the "other root" of $f(x)$ over Z_5 and exhibit the isomorphism of $Z_5(r)$ and $Z_5(s)$.

3. Finite Extensions

If K is any extension field of the field F, then, since the elements of K are an additive Abelian group and admit multiplication by the elements of the field F, we may consider K as a vector space over F.

Definition. If the extension field K of F has, as a vector space, finite dimension over F, then K is called a *finite extension of* F, and the dimension, n, of K over F is called the *degree* of the extension, $n = [K : F]$.

For example, in the last example of the previous section, the degree of $Z_3(r)$ over Z_3 is 2, since 1 and r form a basis of $Z_3(r)$ over Z_3. Similarly, the complex number field C has degree 2 over the real number field R', with 1 and i serving as a basis. (Thus the use of the Argand diagram to "graph" sets of complex numbers.)

Theorem 4.6. *Let $K = F(r)$ be a simple algebraic extension of F, where the minimum polynomial of r over F is of degree n. Then $[K : F] = n$ and every element of K can be represented uniquely in the form;*

$$a_0 + a_1 r + \cdots + a_{n-1} r^{n-1}; \qquad a_0, a_1, \ldots, a_{n-1} \in F.$$

PROOF. We need only show that $\{1, r, \ldots, r^{n-1}\}$ is a basis of K over F and both assertions will follow at once. That these elements are linearly independent over F, is a consequence of the fact that any linear combination of them with coefficients in F is a polynomial in r of virtual degree $n - 1$ and, thus, cannot be zero unless it is the zero polynomial. On the other hand, since r is of degree n over F, we have that r^k, for any $k \geq n$, must be a linear combination of $1, r, \ldots, r^{n-1}$. Thus every element of K is such a linear combination and $\{1, r, \ldots, r^{n-1}\}$ is a linearly independent generating set for K over F, that is, a basis.

This completes the proof of the theorem.

This result gives us another method of calculating the inverse of an element in the algebraic extension $F(r)$. For if we are given any nonzero element,

$$f(r) = a_0 + a_1 r + \cdots + a_{n-1} r^{n-1},$$

we may assume that $f(r)^{-1}$ has the form

$$f(r)^{-1} = b_0 + b_1 r + \cdots + b_{n-1} r^{n-1}$$

and seek to determine the coefficients $b_0, b_1, \ldots, b_{n-1}$. This we may do by calculating the formal product of $f(r)$ and $f(r)^{-1}$, which must be the element $1 = 1 + 0r + \cdots + 0r^{n-1}$. Since $\{1, r, \ldots, r^{n-1}\}$ is a basis for $F(r)$ over F, the coefficients in this expression for 1 are unique, and we may, therefore, equate coefficients of the corresponding powers of r and solve the resulting system of equations for the desired

$$b_0, b_1, \ldots, b_{n-1}.$$

As an example, suppose we wish to find the inverse of

$$1 + \sqrt[3]{2} + \sqrt[3]{4}.$$

We then obtain, in the field $R(\sqrt[3]{2})$,

$$(1 + \sqrt[3]{2} + \sqrt[3]{4})(a + b\sqrt[3]{2} + c\sqrt[3]{4}) = 1 + 0\sqrt[3]{2} + 0\sqrt[3]{4}$$

and need to determine a, b, and c. Carrying out the multiplication and collecting coefficients of 1, $\sqrt[3]{2}$, and $\sqrt[3]{4}$, we have

$$(a + 2b + 2c) + (a + b + 2c)\sqrt[3]{2} + (a + b + c)\sqrt[3]{4} = 1 + 0\sqrt[3]{2} + 0\sqrt[3]{4}.$$

From this, we obtain the system of linear equations

$$a + 2b + 2c = 1,$$
$$a + b + 2c = 0,$$
$$a + b + c = 0.$$

This system has the unique solution

$$a = -1, b = 1, c = 0.$$

We thus conclude that

$$(1 + \sqrt[3]{2} + \sqrt[3]{4})^{-1} = -1 + \sqrt[3]{2}.$$

Definition. If K is any superfield of F, then K is termed *algebraic over* F if every element of K is algebraic over F. Otherwise, K is *transcendental over* F.

To see that this definition is consistent with our earlier definition that $F(r)$ is *algebraic* over F if r is *algebraic* over F, we prove the following result:

Theorem 4.7. *If K is a finite extension of F, $[K : F] = n$, then every element of K is algebraic of degree at most n over F.*

PROOF. Let t be any element of K. Then $1, t, \ldots, t^n$ are $n + 1$ elements in a space of dimension n, and hence must be linearly dependent, i.e.,

$$a_0 + a_1t + \cdots + a_nt^n = 0,$$

for some $a_0, a_1, \ldots, a_n$ in F and not all zero. But then t satisfies a polynomial equation of virtual degree n over F, and, hence, is algebraic of degree at most n over F.

Definition. If $c_1, c_2, \ldots, c_k$ are algebraic over the field F, then $F(c_1, c_2, \ldots, c_k)$ is a *finite algebraic extension of* F.

In connection with this definition, the question of consistency with previous definitions again arises, and is answered by the following theorem.

Theorem 4.8. *K is a finite extension field of F if and only if K is a finite algebraic extension field of F.*

PROOF. Suppose, first, that K is finite over F, $[K : F] = n$. Then there are elements $c_1, c_2, \ldots, c_n$ of K which constitute a basis of K over F, and the previous theorem assures us that each c_i is algebraic over F. Thus $K = F(c_1, c_2, \ldots, c_n)$ is a finite algebraic extension of F.

Conversely, let $K = F(c_1, c_2, \ldots, c_r)$ with each c_i algebraic over F. Let $F_0 = F$ and $F_i = F_{i-1}(c_i)$ for $i = 1, 2, \ldots, r$. Since c_i is algebraic over F, it is certainly algebraic over $F_{i-1} \supseteq F$, and we may take $\{v_{i_1}, v_{i_2}, \ldots, v_{im_i}\}$ to be a basis of F_i over F_{i-1}. Then any element of $K = F_r$ is a linear combination of $v_{r_1}, \ldots, v_{rm_r}$ with coefficients in F_{r-1}. Now each of these coefficients is itself a linear combination of $v_{r-1_1}, \ldots, v_{r-1m_{r-1}}$, with coefficients in F_{r-2}, from which it follows that the $m_r m_{r-1}$ elements $v_{r_i} v_{r-1_j}$ generate K over F_{r-2}. Continuing the process, we have that the $m_1 m_2 \cdots m_r$ elements $v_{1_i} v_{2_j} \cdots v_{r_k}$ generate K over F. But then, by Corollary 3.57.1, it follows that K has a finite basis over F.

We note that the dimension m_i of $F_i = F_{i-1}(c_i)$ over F_{i-1} may well be less than the degree n_i of c_i over F. For example, if $K = R(\sqrt{2}, \sqrt[4]{2})$, R as usual being the field of rational numbers, then, while $\sqrt[4]{2}$ has degree 4 over R, the degree (dimension) of $R(\sqrt{2}, \sqrt[4]{2})$ over $R(\sqrt{2})$ is only 2.

The result obtained in the above proof, that the $m_1 m_2 \cdots m_r$ elements $v_{1_i} v_{2_j} \cdots v_{r_k}$ generate $F(c_1, c_2, \ldots, c_r)$ over F, where $[F_i : F_{i-1}] = m_i$, can be improved.

Theorem 4.9. *Let $\{v_1, v_2, \ldots, v_n\}$ be a basis of K over F and $\{u_1, u_2, \ldots, u_m\}$ a basis of L over K. Then the mn elements $u_j v_k$ are a basis of L over F.*

PROOF. It remains only to show that the elements $u_j v_k$ are linearly independent over F. Suppose that

$$\sum_{j,k} f_{jk} u_j v_k = 0; f_{jk} \in F; j = 1, 2, \ldots, m; k = 1, 2, \ldots, n.$$

Then

$$\sum_j \Big(\sum_k f_{jk} v_k\Big) u_j = 0,$$

and the linear independence of the u_j over K then implies that

$$\sum_k f_{jk} v_k = 0 \text{ for each } j = 1, 2, \ldots, m.$$

The linear independence of the v_k now implies that all the f_{jk} must be zero, thus establishing the linear independence over F of the mn elements $u_j v_k$.

From this result, many conclusions may be drawn, some of which we list for simplicity in the form of a single corollary, leaving the straightforward proofs to the reader.

Corollary 4.9.1. *Let K be a finite extension of the field F and L a finite extension of K. Then*

(i) $[L:F] = [L:K][K:F]$.
(ii) *The degree over F of an element of K must divide $[K:F]$.*
(iii) *An element of K generates K over F iff its degree over F is $[K:F]$.*
(iv) *L is algebraic over F.*
(v) *If $[K:F] = 2^m$ and $p(x)$ is irreducible over F and of degree 3, then $p(x)$ is irreducible over K also.*

As an illustration, let R be the field of rationals,

$$K = R(\sqrt{3}) \quad \text{and}$$
$$L = K(\sqrt[3]{2}).$$

Then $[K:R] = 2$, with basis $\{1, \sqrt{3}\}$. Since $x^3 - 2$ remains irreducible over K (why?), we have $[L:K] = 3$, with basis $\{1, \sqrt[3]{2}, \sqrt[3]{4}\}$. Thus the six elements

$$1, \sqrt[3]{2}, \sqrt[3]{4}, \sqrt{3}, \sqrt{3}\sqrt[3]{2}, \text{ and } \sqrt{3}\sqrt[3]{4}$$

together constitute a basis of L over R.

Since the degree of an element of K over R must, in this case, divide 2, the degree is either 1 or 2. For instance, the element $k = 1 + \sqrt{3}$ is not in R and, hence, must be of degree 2 over R. Noting that $k^2 = 4 + 2\sqrt{3}$, we readily see that the minimum polynomial of k over R is

$$x^2 - 2x - 2.$$

The reader may find it worthwhile, as an exercise, to exhibit the relationship between $R(\sqrt{3})$ and $R(k)$, k a root of $x^2 - 2x - 2$.

The final statement of the corollary leads to a proof of the impossibility of trisecting a general angle by Euclidean methods, that is, by the use of straight-edge (as contrasted to ruler) and compass only. By appealing to analytic geometry, we see that specifying an angle is equivalent to specifying its cosine, some real number r. Now the rational numbers can all be constructed from a given unit by Euclidean methods, as can sums, differences, products and quotients of given numbers. Thus the problem of angle trisection effectively begins with the field $R(r)$. Trisecting the angle would be equivalent to obtaining the cosine of one third of the angle; this cosine must satisfy the equation $4x^3 - 3x - r = 0$. Since equations of circles are of degree 2 and those of lines are of degree 1, their intersections can result in obtaining solutions of equations of degree a power of 2 only. Thus Euclidean methods result in fields of degree 2^m over $R(r)$. But the above cubic polynomial can be shown to be, in general, irreducible and the impossibility of trisecting the general angle then follows. (A particularly simple case results from considering a 60° angle, so that $r = \frac{1}{2}$ and the corresponding polynomial $8x^3 - 6x - 1$ can be easily shown to be irreducible over R.)

The problem of duplicating the cube is similar. We may assume the given cube to be a unit cube, so that its duplication requires solving the equation $x^3 - 2 = 0$. But this polynomial $x^3 - 2$ is irreducible over R, and the impossibility of the Euclidean construction follows at once by arguments similar to those above. (It should be pointed out that it is not necessary to use such powerful methods to obtain these results; doing so is somewhat like going trout fishing with dynamite — effective, but not very sporting.)

Theorem 4.9 and its corollary deal strictly with finite algebraic extensions of a field. But it is possible to have algebraic extensions of a field which are not finite. For example, the so-called *field of algebraic numbers*, which consists of all numbers or elements algebraic over the field R of rationals, is certainly algebraic over R but is not a finite extension. (Why?) As a matter of interest, and for later use in building the real number system, we have the following result for such nonfinite algebraic extensions:

Theorem 4.10. *If L is a field algebraic over K and K is algebraic over F, then L is algebraic over F.*

PROOF. Let u be any element of L. Then u is a root of some polynomial

$$g(x) = r_0 + r_1x + \cdots + r_mx^m$$

in $K[x]$. The coefficients $r_0, r_1, \ldots, r_m$ are all algebraic over F. Thus the field

$$G = F(r_0, r_1, \ldots, r_m)$$

is a finite extension of F. Then, by Corollary 4.9.1 (iv), we have $G(u)$ algebraic over F. Thus u is algebraic over F and, since u was abritrary in L, the result follows.

Exercises

1. In the method given in this section for obtaining
$$f(r)^{-1} = b_0 + b_1r + \cdots + b_{n-1}r^{n-1}$$
in $F[r]$, r algebraic of degree n over F, prove that the coefficients $b_0, b_1, \ldots, b_{n-1}$ will always be obtained as the unique solution of a system of n linear equations in n unknowns.
2. Prove that every element of a simple algebraic extension field $F(r)$ is algebraic over F.
3. If K is a superfield of F such that $[K : F] = 1$, prove that $K = F$.
4. Let r be a root of $x^2 + x + 1$ and s a root of $x^3 + 2$ over R. Find $[R(r) : R]$ and $[R(r, s) : R(r)]$. Also find bases for $R(r)$ over R and for $R(r, s)$ over $R(r)$ and, thus, a basis for $R(r, s)$ over R.
5. Prove all five parts of Corollary 4.9.1.
6. Prove that $x^3 - 2$ is irreducible over $R(\sqrt{3})$.
7. Show that the field of algebraic numbers is not a finite extension of the field of rational numbers.

4. Splitting Fields

Definition. Let $f(x)$ be any polynomial over the field F and K a superfield of F. $f(x)$ is said to *split* in K if $f(x)$ can be written as a product of linear factors in $K[x]$, that is, if there exist elements $k_1, k_2, \ldots, k_n$ in K such that

$$f(x) = a_n(x - k_1)(x - k_2) \cdots (x - k_n),$$

where a_n is, of course, the leading coefficient of $f(x)$. K is a *splitting field* of $f(x)$ if $f(x)$ thus splits in K and, moreover, $K = F(k_1, k_2, \ldots, k_n)$.

As an extension of Corollary 4.4.1, we have the following theorem.

Theorem 4.11. *Any polynomial $f(x)$ over any field F has a splitting field K.*

PROOF. The theorem is merely a restatement of Corollary 4.4.1 if the degree of $f(x)$ is 1; hence we proceed by mathematical induction on the degree n of $f(x)$. Suppose that the result is valid for all polynomials of degree less than n and all fields F. Now the polynomial $f(x)$ must have some irreducible factor $p(x)$, since we are assuming that n is greater than one. By Corollary 4.4.1 again, there exists an extension field $F(r)$ of F where r is a root of $p(x)$. Thus $f(x)$ has the root r in $F(r)$ and, by Theorem 3.23, we have $f(x) = (x - r)g(x)$ in $F(r)[x]$. Now the degree of $g(x)$ is $n - 1$ and the inductive assumption assures us that there is a splitting field

$$\begin{aligned} K &= F(r)(r_2, r_3, \ldots, r_n) \\ &= F(r, r_2, \ldots, r_n) \end{aligned}$$

of $g(x)$ over $F(r)$, where $r_2, r_3, \ldots, r_n$ are the roots of $g(x)$. Thus in $K[x]$ we have

$$\begin{aligned} f(x) = (x - r)g(x) &= (x - r)a_n(x - r_2) \cdots (x - r_n) \\ &= a_n(x - r)(x - r_2) \cdots (x - r_n), \end{aligned}$$

and K is a splitting field of $f(x)$.

That we could call the field K just obtained *the* splitting field of $f(x)$ follows from the next result:

Theorem 4.12. *Let $f(x)$ be any polynomial over the field F, and let $\bar{f}(x)$ be the corresponding polynomial over an isomorphic field $\overline{F}$, with K and $\overline{K}$ splitting fields of $f(x)$ and $\bar{f}(x)$, respectively. Then the isomorphism between F and $\overline{F}$ can be extended to one between K and $\overline{K}$.*

PROOF. Let the given isomorphism of F and $\overline{F}$ be given by $a \leftrightarrow \bar{a}$ for a in F and $\bar{a}$ in $\overline{F}$, so that if

$$f(x) = a_0 + a_1x + \cdots + a_nx^n,$$

then

$$\bar{f}(x) = \bar{a}_0 + \bar{a}_1x + \cdots + \bar{a}_nx^n.$$

We proceed by induction on the degree $m = [K : F]$. If $m = 1$, the result is trivial, since then $K = F$. So suppose that $m > 1$ and the theorem is valid for splitting fields of any pair of corresponding polynomials of degree less than m over any isomorphic base fields. Not all the roots of $f(x)$ are in F, since m is greater than one, hence there must be some irreducible factor $p(x)$ of $f(x)$ also having degree greater than one, say d. Let $\overline{p}(x)$ be the corresponding polynomial over $\overline{F}$, also of degree d over $\overline{F}$. Then K and $\overline{K}$ contain roots r and $\overline{r}$ of $p(x)$ and $\overline{p}(x)$, respectively. As in the proof of Theorem 4.5, the correspondence

$$a_0 + a_1 r + \cdots + a_{d-1} r^{d-1} \leftrightarrow \overline{a}_0 + \overline{a}_1 \overline{r} + \cdots + \overline{a}_{d-1} \overline{r}^{d-1}$$

is easily shown to be an extension of the isomorphism between F and $\overline{F}$ to an isomorphism between $F(r)$ and $\overline{F}(\overline{r})$. Now K is a splitting field of $f(x)$ over $F(r)$ and $[K : F(r)] = m/d < m$. Similarly, $\overline{K}$ is a splitting field of $\bar{f}(x)$ over $\overline{F}(\overline{r})$ and $[\overline{K} : \overline{F}(\overline{r})] = m/d < m$. By the inductive assumption, the isomorphism of $F(r)$ and $\overline{F}(\overline{r})$, itself an extension of that of F and $\overline{F}$, can be extended to an isomorphism of K and $\overline{K}$. The proof is thus complete.

Definition. Two extension fields K and K' of the field F are called *equivalent over* F if there exists an isomorphism $\alpha: K \to K'$ such that $f\alpha = f$ for all f in F.

For example, if R is the field of rational numbers, then $R(\sqrt{\pi}) \cong R(\sqrt[3]{\pi})$, but the two fields are not equivalent over $R(\pi)$.

We see that any given polynomial over any given field thus has, in the sense of isomorphism, a unique splitting field. We recall that, by Theorem 4.5, the fields $F(r)$ and $F(s)$ are isomorphic if r and s are any two roots of the same irreducible polynomial $p(x)$ over F. It should *not* be inferred from these results, however, that if r and s are two roots of any polynomial $f(x)$ over F, then $F(r)$ and $F(s)$ are necessarily isomorphic. That this is not the case may be seen by considering the polynomial

$$\begin{aligned} f(x) &= x^5 - 2x^3 - 2x^2 + 4 \\ &= (x^2 - 2)(x^3 - 2) \end{aligned}$$

over the field R of rational numbers. Clearly $\sqrt{2}$ and $\sqrt[3]{2}$ are roots of $f(x)$, but $R(\sqrt{2})$ and $R(\sqrt[3]{2})$ are of respective degrees 2 and 3 over R and, thus, certainly not isomorphic. This lack of isomorphism is, of course, the result of the reducibility of $f(x)$ over R. The splitting field

$$R(\sqrt{2}, \sqrt[3]{2}, \theta) \text{ of } f(x), \qquad \text{where } \theta = -\tfrac{1}{2} + \sqrt{3}\, i/2,$$

is, of course, essentially unique.

It is interesting to observe that the field $R(\sqrt{2}, \sqrt[3]{2})$ is actually a simple extension, $R(\sqrt[6]{2})$ of R. For consider the generating elements of $R(\sqrt{2}, \sqrt[3]{2})$ and the product $\sqrt{2}(\sqrt[3]{2})^2 = 2\sqrt[6]{2}$. Thus $\sqrt[6]{2}$ is in the field $R(\sqrt{2}, \sqrt[3]{2})$ and also, clearly, generates this field. The minimum polynomial of $\sqrt[6]{2}$ over R must then be the irreducible monic polynomial $x^6 - 2$.

As another example of this latter phenomenon, consider the field $R(\sqrt{2}, \sqrt{3})$, which is of degree 4 over R. The element $\sqrt{2} + \sqrt{3}$ is in $R(\sqrt{2}, \sqrt{3})$ and, in fact,

$$R(\sqrt{2}, \sqrt{3}) = R(\sqrt{2} + \sqrt{3}),$$

that is, is a simple extension of R. For we have that

$$(\sqrt{2} + \sqrt{3})^3 - 9(\sqrt{2} + \sqrt{3}) = 2\sqrt{2}$$

is an element of $R(\sqrt{2} + \sqrt{3})$, and, hence, so is $\sqrt{2}$. But then

$$\sqrt{3} = (\sqrt{2} + \sqrt{3}) - \sqrt{2}$$

is also in $R(\sqrt{2} + \sqrt{3})$, and our assertion follows. It may also be verified that the minimum polynomial of $\sqrt{2} + \sqrt{3}$ over R is $x^4 - 10x^2 - 1$.

Exercises

1. Prove that $R(\sqrt{\pi}) \cong R(\sqrt[3]{\pi})$. Are these fields equivalent over R?

2. Determine the splitting fields (over R) of

(a) $x^3 + 2$.

(b) $x^3 + x + 2$.

3. Let $f(x)$ be a polynomial of degree n over R and K its splitting field. What can you say about $[K : R]$? Does the same result hold if R is replaced by an arbitrary field F?

4. Prove that simple algebraic extensions K and L of the field F cannot be equivalent over F if $[K : F] \neq [L : F]$. What if $[K : F] = [L : F]$?

5. Separability

The examples given at the end of the previous section lead one to suspect that in many cases the algebraic extension $F(r_1, r_2, \ldots, r_n)$ of F can be expressed as a simple extension $F(r)$ for some suitably chosen r. That this is indeed the case is shown by the next theorem and its corollary. But, first, we need the following definition:

Definition. The irreducible polynomial $p(x)$ in $F[x]$ is *separable* if it has no repeated roots in its splitting field, that is, if in the factorization of $p(x)$ over the splitting field into a product of first degree factors no factor is repeated. An arbitrary polynomial $f(x)$ in $F[x]$ is separable if each of its irreducible factors is separable.

An element r, algebraic over F, is *separable* if its minimum polynomial over F is separable. If every element of the algebraic extension field K of F is separable, then K is said to be *separable*. That this is always the case if F has characteristic zero will be seen shortly.

Theorem 4.13. *Let F be a field with an infinite number of elements and r and s algebraic over F with s separable. Then there exists an element t in $F(r, s)$ such that $F(r, s) = F(t)$.*

PROOF. Let $f(x)$ and $g(x)$, of respective degrees n and m, be the minimum polynomials of r and s, with roots $r = r_1, r_2, \ldots, r_n$ and $s = s_1, s_2, \ldots, s_m$, respectively, in some extension field of F. We may choose c in F such that

$$t = r + cs \neq r_i + cs_j, \text{ i.e., } c \neq \frac{r_i - r}{s - s_j},$$

for all i, and all j greater than 1, since the irreducibility of $g(x)$ and the separability of s combine to guarantee that $s - s_j \neq 0$, and we have assumed that there are an infinite number of elements in F.

Then $g(x)$ and $f(t - cx)$ have the common root s of multiplicity 1 in the field $F(r, s)$; hence, as elements of $F(t)[x]$, they must have a greatest common divisor $h(x)$, also having s as a root. Now $g(x)$ and $f(t - cx)$ have no roots other than s in common in any field, since the other roots of $g(x)$ are $s_2, \ldots, s_m$, none of which is a root of $f(t - cx)$, by the choice of c. Hence the only root of $h(x)$ in any field is the simple root s, and $h(x)$ must, therefore, be of degree 1, $h(x) = x - s$. But this means that s is in $F(t)$, and, hence, $r = t - cs$ is also in $F(t)$. Thus we have $F(r, s) \subseteq F(t) \subseteq F(r, s)$, and the result follows.

Corollary 4.13.1. *If F is a field with an infinite number of elements and $r_1, r_2, \ldots, r_n$ are algebraic over F with $r_2, \ldots, r_n$ separable, then there exists an element t in $E = F(r_1, r_2, \ldots, r_n)$ such that $E = F(t)$.*

PROOF. Induction on n.

It thus appears that separability will play an important role in the theory of fields, as simple extensions are certainly by far the easiest to work with. It is, therefore, desirable to determine some criteria by which the separability of elements may be judged.

For F any field, the integral domain $F[x]$ constitutes an infinite dimensional vector space over F. Consider the mapping of $F[x]$ onto $F[x]$ defined by:

$$D\colon f(x) = a_n x^n + a_{n-1}x^{n-1} + \cdots + a_1 x + a_0$$
$$\rightarrow n a_n x^{n-1} + (n-1)a_{n-1}x^{n-2} + \cdots + a_1 = f'(x).$$

It is not difficult to verify that for any a and b in F, and any $f(x)$ and $g(x)$ in $F[x]$, we have

$$(af(x) + bg(x))' = af'(x) + bg'(x),$$

so that D is an F-endomorphism of the vector space $F[x]$ and the kernel of D is F. Since the mapping D coincides with the notion of derivative operator (for polynomial functions) from analysis, we shall use the same terminology here and call D the *derivative mapping* and $f'(x)$ the derivative of $f(x)$.

Theorem 4.14. *For any field F, an irreducible polynomial $f(x)$ in $F[x]$ is separable if and only if $f(x)$ and $f'(x)$ are relatively prime, that is, the g.c.d. $d(x)$ of $f(x)$ and $f'(x)$ is 1.*

PROOF. Suppose that $d(x) = 1$. If

$$f(x) = (x - r)^k g(x)$$

in a splitting field of $f(x)$, where r is a root of multiplicity k of $f(x)$ and, hence, is not a root of $g(x)$, then we have

$$\begin{aligned} f'(x) &= k(x - r)^{k-1} g(x) + (x - r)^k g'(x) \\ &= (x - r)^{k-1}[kg(x) + (x - r)g'(x)]. \end{aligned}$$

Hence $d(x)$ is divisible over the splitting field of $f(x)$ by the factor $(x - r)^{k-1}$ and $d(x)$ must, therefore, have degree at least $k - 1$. But, since the degree of $d(x)$ is zero, this implies that $k = 1$ and r is a simple root. Similarly, all roots of $f(x)$ must be simple and $f(x)$ is separable.

Conversely, suppose that $f(x)$ is separable and r is a root of $f(x)$. Then

$$f(x) = (x - r)g(x),$$

where r is not a root of $g(x)$. We then have

$$f'(x) = g(x) + (x - r)g'(x)$$

and

$$f'(r) = g(r) \neq 0.$$

Thus r is not a root of $d(x)$. But every root of $d(x)$ must be a root of $f(x)$. Hence $d(x)$ has no roots at all, and, being monic, must be 1.

This result is our basic criterion for determining separability of an irreducible polynomial, and, consequently, for determining the separability of any polynomial. However, in many cases it is possible to avoid computing the g.c.d., which can be a laborious process, by use of the following theorems.

Theorem 4.15. *An irreducible polynomial $f(x)$ over a field F is separable if and only if its derivative is not zero.*

PROOF. Since $f(x)$ is irreducible, its only divisors are itself and elements of F. If $f'(x) \neq 0$, then the g.c.d. of $f(x)$ and $f'(x)$ is clearly 1, while if $f'(x) = 0$, then the g.c.d. is $f(x)$ itself, which, being an irreducible polynomial, is not 1. The result now follows at once from the previous theorem.

Theorem 4.16. *If F is of characteristic zero, then any irreducible polynomial in $F[x]$ is separable.*

PROOF. Since $f(x)$ is irreducible, it must be of positive degree, say n. Then

$$f'(x) = na_n x^{n-1} + \cdots + a_1 \neq 0,$$

since $na_n \neq 0$.

Theorem 4.17. *If F is of characteristic p, then an irreducible polynomial $f(x)$ in $F[x]$ is not separable if and only if $f(x) = g(x^p)$, for some $g(x)$ in $F[x]$.*

PROOF. By Theorem 4.15, $f(x)$ is not separable if and only if $f'(x) = 0$. Now

$$f'(x) = na_nx^{n-1} + (n-1)a_{n-1}x^{n-2} + \cdots + a_1,$$

so that

$$f'(x) = 0 \quad \text{iff} \quad ja_j = 0, \quad j = 1, 2, \ldots, n.$$

But

$$ja_j = 0 \quad \text{iff} \quad \text{either } a_j = 0 \text{ or } j \equiv 0 \pmod{p}.$$

This latter condition is clearly equivalent to

$$f(x) = g(x^p)$$

for some $g(x)$ in $F[x]$, i.e., $f'(x) = 0$ iff all coefficients of $f(x)$ are zero except, possibly, those whose indices are divisible by p.

The property of irreducibility has played a most important role not only in the theorems just given but in many of our considerations thus far. It would then seem appropriate to consider the problem of determining the irreducibility of a polynomial over a field, and we shall turn our attention to this question in the next section.

Exercises

1. Determine an element t such that

$$R(t) = R(r, s),$$

where r is a root of $x^2 + x + 1$ and s is a root of $x^2 + 4$. How many choices for t are there?

2. Determine an element t such that

$$Z_5(t) = Z_5(r, s),$$

where r is a root of $x^2 + x + 1$ and s is a root of $x^2 + 4$. How many choices for t are there?

3. For a field F and indeterminate x, prove that $F[x]$ is an infinite dimensional vector space over F.
4. Prove that the derivative mapping D is an F-endomorphism of the vector space $F[x]$ with kernel F.
5. Show that if the word "irreducible" is deleted in Theorem 4.14 the "if" part remains valid, but the "only if" part is not valid.
6. Prove that if F is of characteristic zero, then any element of $F[x]$ is separable.

6. Irreducibility in $F[x]$

We shall not treat the problem of irreducibility in $F[x]$ in complete generality. The interested reader may, however, find in the first edition of van der Waerden's *Moderne Algebra* (but not in the second edition or its English translation) a method of determining in a finite number of steps the reducibility of any polynomial over an arbitrary field.

In the case of polynomials over the field R of rational numbers, we already know that the question of irreducibility can be reduced to a question of irreducibility over the domain Z of integers. More generally, if F is the quotient field of any unique factorization domain D, then we may reduce the question of irreducibility over F to one of irreducibility over D. Now in the special and important case of the field R and domain Z, we have that not only does every element of Z have an essentially unique prime factorization but, even more, there are only a finite number of possible factorizations, since in Z we have only the two units, 1 and -1. Similarly, in any unique factorization domain D with only a finite number of unit elements, any element of D will have only a finite number of possible factorizations. Let us see if we can put this property to use.

Suppose that we have a polynomial $f(x)$ of degree n greater than zero over a unique factorization domain D possessing only a finite number of units. In seeking a factorization of $f(x)$, it is evidently sufficient to consider only those possible factors of degree at most $n/2$, since any factor of higher degree would give rise to another factor of degree at most $n/2$.

Suppose that our polynomial $f(x)$ has the factorization $g(x)h(x)$. Then for any element c in D, we must have $f(c) = g(c)h(c)$. One may show that for any set of $n + 1$ distinct elements $c_0, c_1, \ldots, c_n$ in D and any set of $n + 1$ elements $d_0, d_1, \ldots, d_n$ in D, there is at most one element $f(x)$ of $D[x]$ of degree n such that $f(c_i) = d_i$, $i = 0, 1, \ldots, n$. Thus if we choose $n + 1$ distinct values $c_0, c_1, \ldots, c_n$ in D, the corresponding values $f(c_0), f(c_1), \ldots, f(c_n)$ provide a complete description of our polynomial $f(x)$. The factor $g(x)$ which we are seeking must, of course, satisfy the requirement that $g(c_i)$ is a factor of $f(c_i)$ for each $i = 0, 1, \ldots, n$. We notice, at this point, that in seeking the factor $g(x)$, if indeed it exists, it would be sufficient to select values $c_0, c_1, \ldots, c_m$ in D, where m is the greatest integer not exceeding $n/2$, since the corresponding values $f(c_0), f(c_1), \ldots, f(c_m)$ with their factors would determine the possible polynomials $g(x)$ of degree not exceeding $n/2$.

To proceed with the determination, we select for $g(c_i)$ some factor of $f(c_i)$, $i = 0, 1, \ldots, m$, and find the polynomial $g(x)$ having the values $g(c_i)$ at $x = c_i$, if there is such a polynomial in $D[x]$. If there is, it is unique, and we then use ordinary division to see whether this possible $g(x)$ is actually a factor of $f(x)$ or not. If it is not, then we take another selection of factors of the $f(c_i)$ as our set of $g(c_i)$'s and repeat the process. If we eventually find in this way a $g(x)$ which is a proper factor of $f(x)$, then we start in all over again seeking factors of each of $g(x)$ and $h(x)$.

This process, while finite, is likely to be lengthy, especially if we are unfortunate or unwise enough to choose values c_i such that the corresponding $f(c_i)$ have many possible factors.

As a simple illustration of the procedure, let us take the polynomial

$$f(x) = x^5 - x - 1 \quad \text{in } Z[x].$$

Here we shall be looking for factors $g(x)$ of degree at most 2, and so we may take 3 values of the c_i's. We select -1, 0, and 1, since

$$f(-1) = -1, \quad f(0) = -1, \quad \text{and} \quad f(1) = -1,$$

each of which has only the two factors -1 and 1.

Even in this simple case, we see that there are eight possibilities for the triple

$$(g(-1),\ g(0),\ g(1)).$$

We note, however, that since if $g(x)$ is a factor of $f(x)$, then so is $-g(x)$, we need consider only four of the triples, say

$$(-1, -1, -1), (-1, -1, 1), (-1, 1, -1), \text{and } (-1, 1, 1),$$

the other four being negatives of these. Letting

$$g(x) = ax^2 + bx + c$$

and determining the coefficients in each case, we obtain the respective possibilities

$$\begin{aligned} g(x) &= -1, \\ g(x) &= x^2 + x - 1, \\ g(x) &= -2x^2 + 1, \\ \text{and} \quad g(x) &= -x^2 + x + 1, \end{aligned}$$

and we may then determine that none of these is a proper factor of

$$f(x) = x^5 - x - 1.$$

Thus

$$x^5 - x - 1$$

is irreducible as an element of either $Z[x]$ or of $R[x]$.

This procedure for determining the reducibility of an element of $D[x]$, D a unique factorization domain with a finite number of units, is due to Kronecker and is quite general. However, it is evident that we shall wish criteria which are easier to apply.

In the case of the domain Z, a criterion due to Eisenstein is often very useful, as when it is applicable, it gives the answer very quickly and easily.

Theorem 4.18 (Eisenstein's Criterion). *The polynomial*

$$f(x) = a_nx^n + a_{n-1}x^{n-1} + \cdots + a_0$$

is irreducible as an element of $Z[x]$ *if there exists a prime* p *such that* p *does not divide* a_n, p *does divide all* a_i *for* $i < n$, *and* p^2 *does not divide* a_0.

PROOF. Suppose that such a prime p exists and that, contrary to the assertion, $f(x)$ is reducible, say $f(x) = g(x)h(x)$, where

$$g(x) = b_mx^m + \cdots + b_0,$$
$$h(x) = c_{n-m}x^{n-m} + \cdots + c_0, \qquad 0 < m < n.$$

Since $a_0 = b_0c_0$ is divisible by p but not by p^2, we see that exactly one of b_0, c_0, is divisible by p. To be definite, suppose that $b_0 \equiv 0 \pmod{p}$ and $c_0 \not\equiv 0 \pmod{p}$.

Not all the b_i can be divisible by p, since this would mean that $f(x)$ and, hence, a_n would also be divisible by p. So, suppose that b_j is the first b_i not divisible by p, i.e.,

$$b_j \not\equiv 0 \pmod{p}, \qquad b_i \equiv 0 \pmod{p}, \qquad 0 \le i < j \le m.$$

Then

$$a_j = b_jc_0 + b_{j-1}c_1 + \cdots + b_0c_j \not\equiv 0 \pmod{p},$$

since neither b_j nor c_0 is divisible by p, while every other term in the expansion of a_j is divisible by p. But this is possible only if $j = n$, contrary to the assumption that $m < n$. Hence no such factorization of $f(x)$ can exist, and $f(x)$ is indeed irreducible.

We may immediately generalize this result to the case of polynomials over any unique factorization domain. Of course, if there exist no prime elements in the domain, as is the case for a field, then the criterion, while still valid, is of no use.

We may extend the usefulness of the Eisenstein criterion by means of two simple observations: First, it is readily shown that $f(x)$ is irreducible if and only if $f(x - c)$ is irreducible, where c is any element of the domain of coefficients. Second, we note that the Eisenstein criterion depends essentially upon the fact that if $f(x)$ is any polynomial over a unique factorization domain and is reducible, then $f(x)$ must also be reducible modulo any element q of the domain. Thus if $f(x) = g(x)h(x)$, then certainly $f(x) \equiv g(x)h(x) \pmod{q}$. Conversely, if $f(x)$ is irreducible modulo q for any q whatever in the coefficient domain, then $f(x)$ is irreducible.

As illustrations of these notions, we see at once that $x^2 + 2x + 6$ is irreducible over Z by taking the Eisenstein criterion with $p = 2$. Similarly, we see that $2x^5 - 6x^3 + 9x^2 - 15$ is irreducible over Z by taking $p = 3$. More generally, we have that $x^n + a$ is irreducible over Z for any positive integer n and any integer a which is not divisible by any square. (Proof?)

The Eisenstein criterion is not directly applicable to the case of the so-called *cyclotomic polynomial*

$$f(x) = x^{p-1} + x^{p-2} + \cdots + x + 1 = \frac{x^p - 1}{x - 1}, \quad p \text{ a prime},$$

again considered over the domain Z. However, if we consider $f(x + 1)$, we see that

$$f(x+1) = \frac{(x+1)^p - 1}{(x+1) - 1} = \frac{x^p + px^{p-1} + \cdots + px}{x}$$
$$= x^{p-1} + px^{p-2} + \frac{p(p-1)}{2}x^{p-3} + \cdots + p,$$

which is clearly irreducible by the Eisenstein criterion.

As an example of the second type of extension mentioned above consider, again over Z, $f(x) = x^5 - x^2 + 1$. Now if we consider $f(x)$ modulo 2, the only possible irreducible factors of degree at most $\frac{5}{2}$ are x and $x + 1$ of degree 1, and $x^2 + x + 1$ of degree 2. (x and $x + 1$ are the only polynomials of degree 1 over Z_2, while the other possible polynomials of degree 2 are x^2, $x^2 + x$, and $x^2 + 1$, all of which are divisible by one of x and $x + 1$.) It is easy to verify that none of these are divisors, modulo 2, of $f(x)$, which must, therefore, be irreducible over Z.

It is perhaps appropriate to remark that the converse of the argument just applied is not valid; that is, a polynomial may well be reducible modulo q and yet be irreducible over the given domain. For example, $x^2 + 2x + 6$ was seen to be irreducible over Z, yet it is reducible modulo 2, since $x^2 + 2x + 6 \equiv x^2 \pmod 2$.

As an example of the use of the Eisenstein criterion for a domain other than Z, consider the polynomial $x^2 + tx + t$ as an element of $F[t][x]$. The element t of $F[t]$ is certainly irreducible, being of degree 1, and, hence, $x^2 + tx + t$ is also irreducible in $F[t][x]$. Notice that if we had chosen to consider this polynomial as an element of $F[x][t]$, then the criterion would not have applied, although it is immediate that, since $x^2 + tx + t$ is of degree one in t, it must be irreducible as a polynomial in t.

When one must resort to the method of Kronecker, it is often useful to modify the method to suit the case at hand. For example, if, instead of considering merely 3 values c_i for the polynomial $f(x) = x^5 - x - 1$, we had chosen to consider the 5 values $-2, -1, 0, 1, 2$, we would have obtained the following data:

$$\begin{aligned}
f(-2) &= -31; \text{ hence } g(-2) = \pm 1, \pm 31;\\
f(-1) &= -1; \text{ hence } g(-1) = \pm 1;\\
f(0) &= -1; \text{ hence } g(0) = \pm 1;\\
f(1) &= -1; \text{ hence } g(1) = \pm 1;\\
f(2) &= 29; \text{ hence } g(2) = \pm 1, \pm 29.
\end{aligned}$$

Noticing, further, that $g(x)$ must be of the form $x \pm 1$, neither of which is a factor of $f(x)$ since $f(-1) = f(1) = -1 \neq 0$, or of the form $g(x) = x^2 + ax + b$, we may now quickly eliminate all possibilities for a and b. First, we must have $b = \pm 1 = g(0)$. Then we have $g(1) = 1 + a \pm 1$, whence $a = -3, -1$, or 1. Then $g(-2) = 4 - 2a + b \neq \pm 31$ and $g(2) = 4 + 2a + b \neq \pm 29$. Hence $g(x)$ would have to take on one of the values 1 or -1 at least three times, which is impossible for a polynomial of degree 2, and, again, we conclude that $f(x)$ is irreducible over Z.

Our next result concerns the special case of a binomial.

Theorem 4.19. *Let p be a prime integer and c an element of the field F. Then $x^p - c$ is irreducible over F if and only if $x^p - c$ has no root in F.*

PROOF. Suppose that F has characteristic p. If r is a root of $x^p - c$, then $r^p = c$, whence

$$(x - r)^p = x^p - r^p = x^p - c$$

and all the roots of $x^p - c$ are equal to r. Now if $x^p - c$ is reducible over F, that is, if $x^p - c = g(x)h(x)$, where $g(x)$ is a proper divisor of $x^p - c$, say the degree of $g(x)$ is m, $0 < m < p$. Then the constant term of $g(x)$ is an element of F, which we may write in the form $(-1)^m b$, for some b in F. Since the m roots of $g(x)$ must all be equal to r, it follows that $r^m = b$. But, since m is less than the prime p, m is prime to p and there exist integers s and t such that $1 = ms + pt$. But then

$$r^{ms} = b^s = r^{1-pt} = r^1 r^{-pt} = rc^{-t},$$

so that $r = b^s c^t$ and r is an element of F. Thus if $f(x) = x^p - c$ is reducible, then $f(x)$ has a root in F.

Conversely, if $x^p - c$ has a root r in F, then $x^p - c$ has the factor $x - r$ and is reducible.

Now suppose that the characteristic of F is not p. Then if r and q are roots of $x^p - c$, we have

$$(qr^{-1})^p = cc^{-1} = 1,$$

from which it follows that $q = rw$, where $w = q^{-p+1}r^{p-1}$ and $w^p = 1$. It follows that the roots of $x^p - c$ are of the form

$$r, rw_1, rw_2, \ldots, rw_{p-1},$$

where $w_i^p = 1$. If, now, $x^p - c$ is reducible, as above, then we may assume the roots of $g(x)$ to be $r, rw_1, \ldots, rw_{m-1}$. The constant term of $g(x)$ being $(-1)^m b$, as before, with b in F, we have that the product of the roots of $g(x)$ is

$$b = r^m w_1 w_2 \cdots w_{m-1} = r^m v,$$

where $v^p = 1$.

With $1 = ms + pt$, as before, we have

$$r^{ms} = v^{-s}b^s = r^{1-pt} = rc^{-t}$$

and $r = v^{-s}b^sc^t$. It then follows that

$$r^p = 1^{-s}(b^sc^t)^p = (b^sc^t)^p = c,$$

since r is a root of $x^p - c$, and the element b^sc^t of F is also a root of $x^p - c$. Again the converse is obvious.

A similar result holds for the case of certain trinomials over a field of finite characteristic.

Theorem 4.20. *Let c be an element of the field F of characteristic p. Then $x^p - x - c$ is irreducible over F if and only if $x^p - x - c$ has no root in F.*

PROOF. Suppose r is a root of $x^p - x - c$. Then for $k = 0, 1, \ldots, p - 1$, we have

$$(r + k)^p = r^p + k^p = r + c + k.$$

Thus $x^p - x - c$ has the roots

$$r, r + 1, r + 2, \ldots, r + p - 1,$$

all of which are distinct. Now if $x^p - x - c$ is reducible, say of the form $g(x)h(x)$, then the sum of the roots of $g(x)$ must be an element of F, say b. This sum must be of the form $mr + s$, where s is some integer. Since m is less than p, it follows that m has an inverse in F, and, hence, $r = (b - s)/m$, an element of F. Again the converse is immediate.

Exercises

1. Show that if D is an integral domain, $c_0, c_1, \ldots, c_n$ are $n + 1$ distinct, but otherwise arbitrary, elements of D and $d_0, d_1, \ldots, d_n$ are any $n + 1$ elements of D, then there exists at most one $f(x)$ in $D[x]$ such that $f(c_i) = d_i$, $i = 0, 1, \ldots, n$. What can be said about the existence of $f(x)$?
2. Show that $x^n + a$ is irreducible in $Z[x]$ if n is any positive integer and a is any integer not divisible by any square.
3. Show that if c is any element of the integral domain D, then $f(x)$ is irreducible in $D[x]$ iff $f(x - c)$ is irreducible in $D[x]$.
4. Let $f(x)$ in $Z[x]$ have degree $n > k > 0$ and suppose that $a_n \not\equiv 0$, $a_k \not\equiv 0 \pmod{p}$, $a_{k-1} \equiv \cdots \equiv a_0 \equiv 0 \pmod{p}$, and $a_0 \not\equiv 0 \pmod{p^2}$. Show that $f(x)$ has a factor $g(x)$ of degree at least k which is irreducible in $Z[x]$.
5. Show that $x^5 + x^4 - 1$ is irreducible in $Z[x]$.
6. Show that if c is an element of the field F of characteristic p, then $x^p - x - c$ is separable, whether reducible or not.
7. Show that Theorem 4.20 is false if F has characteristic zero instead of characteristic p.

7. Finite Fields

If F is a finite field, we already know that F has prime characteristic p and contains (an isomorphic copy of) the prime field Z_p. We wish now to complete our description of the possible finite fields.

Theorem 4.21. *If F is a finite field of characteristic p, then F has p^n elements, where n is some positive integer, and $n = [F : Z_p]$.*

PROOF. Since F has only a finite number of elements and is a vector space over the prime field Z_p, F is certainly finitely generated over Z_p and, hence, has a finite basis over Z_p consisting of n elements for some positive integer n. Now every element of F is a unique linear combination of these n basis elements with coefficients in Z_p. Since there are p choices for each coefficient, it follows that there are exactly p^n elements in F.

Definition. A finite field of p^n elements is often called a *Galois field* and denoted by $GF(p^n)$.

Theorem 4.22. *The multiplicative group of a finite field F of p^n elements is cyclic of order $p^n - 1$. Moreover, every element of F satisfies the equation*

$$x^{p^n} - x = 0.$$

PROOF. The multiplicative group G of nonzero elements of F clearly consists of $p^n - 1$ elements and, thus, is a finitely generated Abelian group. Then, by Theorem 2.32, G is the direct product of cyclic subgroups $G_1, G_2, \ldots, G_m$, where the order of G_i divides the order of G_{i+1}. Thus the order of every element of G divides the order r of the generator t of G_m. Every element of G must then satisfy the equation

$$x^r - 1 = 0.$$

Now the polynomial $x^r - 1$, an element of $F[x]$, can have at most r distinct roots in the field F by Corollary 3.23.1. Thus the order of G is at most r, $p^n - 1 \leq r$. But, since the order of G_m must divide the order of G, we have $r \leq p^n - 1$. Thus $r = p^n - 1$, $G = G_m$, and G is cyclic of order $p^n - 1$. Since every nonzero element of F satisfies the equation $x^{p^n-1} - 1 = 0$, it follows that every element of F satisfies the equation $x^{p^n} - x = 0$.

Theorem 4.23. *Let F be a finite field, r and s algebraic over F. Then $F(r, s) = F(t)$ for some t in $F(r, s)$.*

PROOF. Since $F(r, s)$ is algebraic over F, $F(r, s)$ is finite over F and, hence, is itself a finite field. Then the multiplicative group of $F(r, s)$ is cyclic with generator t, and, hence, $F(r, s) = F(t)$, as asserted.

We thus see that the result of Theorem 4.13 holds in the case of finite fields also, and indeed in this case we do not need the hypothesis that one of r and s is separable, although elements algebraic over a finite field can easily be shown to be separable.

Corollary 4.23.1. *Let F be a finite field of characteristic p, $[F : Z_p] = n$. Then there exists t in F such that t is algebraic of degree n over Z_p and $F = Z_p(t)$.*

PROOF. Exercise.

Having seen that every finite field F consists of roots of a polynomial $x^{p^n} - x$ for some positive integer n, p the characteristic of F, it is natural to ask if such a field exists for every p and n.

Theorem 4.24. *For any prime p, there exists a field F of arbitrary (finite) degree n over Z_p, and moreover, F consists of the roots of the polynomial $f(x) = x^{p^n} - x$ over Z_p.*

PROOF. Let K be the splitting field of $f(x)$ over Z_p, and let r in K be a root of $f(x)$, $f(x) = (x - r)^k g(x)$ in $K[x]$, where r is not a root of $g(x)$. Then $f'(x) = -1$ is divisible in $K[x]$ by $(x - r)^{k-1}$, which implies that $k - 1 = 0$ and r is a simple root of $f(x)$. Thus all the roots of $f(x)$ in K are distinct, and $f(x)$ has p^n roots in K. It is readily verified that the product of roots of $f(x)$ in K is again a root of $f(x)$ in K and that the inverse of a nonzero root of $f(x)$ in K is again a root of $f(x)$ in K. That the sum of roots is a root is a consequence of the fact that $(a \pm b)^p = a^p \pm b^p$, from which it follows, by induction on n, that $(a \pm b)^{p^n} = a^{p^n} \pm b^{p^n}$. Thus the roots of $f(x)$ constitute a field of p^n elements, which must then be the splitting field K of $f(x)$. It follows that the degree of K over Z_p is n and the proof is complete.

Corollary 4.24.1. *There exists an irreducible polynomial of arbitrary degree n over the prime field Z_p.*

PROOF. Exercise.

Definition. Let F be any field. A root of the polynomial $x^n - 1$ in $F[x]$ is called an nth *root of unity*. The *order* of an nth root, α, of unity is the least positive integer m such that $\alpha^m = 1$. An nth root of unity having order n is called a *primitive* nth *root of unity*.

Theorem 4.25. *Let n be an arbitrary positive integer and F any field whose characteristic is not a divisor of n (zero is not a divisor of n). Then there exists a finite extension K of F such that K contains a primitive nth root α of unity. Moreover, if α is a primitive nth root of unity, then $F(\alpha)$ is the splitting field of $f(x) = x^n - 1$ over F and $f(x)$ has exactly n distinct roots in $F(\alpha)$, which roots form a cyclic (multiplicative) group generated by any primitive nth root of unity in $F(\alpha)$.*

PROOF. By an argument similar to that of Theorem 4.24, we see that under the given conditions, $f(x)$ has n distinct roots $\alpha_1, \alpha_2, \ldots, \alpha_n$ in its splitting field K over F.

If F has prime characteristic p, then K contains K', the splitting field of $f(x)$ over Z_p. But K' is finite and, hence, has a cyclic multiplicative group G. Since products and inverses of roots of unity are again roots of unity, it follows that the roots $\alpha_1, \alpha_2, \ldots, \alpha_n$ of $f(x)$ in K' form a subgroup H of G, and H must also be cyclic, since every subgroup of a cyclic group is cyclic. Clearly, α is a generator of H if and only if α has order n in H, that is, α is a primitive nth root of unity.

If F has characteristic zero, then we let

$$\alpha = \cos\frac{2\pi}{n} + i\sin\frac{2\pi}{n},$$

where $i^2 = -1$ and have, by De Moivre's Theorem, that α is a primitive nth root of unity and that

$$\alpha, \alpha^2, \ldots, \alpha^{n-1}, \alpha^n = 1$$

are the n distinct roots of unity in $F(\alpha)$, the splitting field of $f(x)$ over F. Clearly these n powers of α form a cyclic group H, and, again, an element of H generates H if and only if it is a primitive nth root of unity.

Definition. Let

$$\alpha_1, \alpha_2, \ldots, \alpha_m$$

be the primitive nth roots of unity in the splitting field K of $x^n - 1$ over some field F whose characteristic does not divide n. The polynomial

$$\Phi_n(x) = (x - \alpha_1)(x - \alpha_2)\cdots(x - \alpha_m) \qquad \text{in } K[x]$$

is called the nth *cyclotomic polynomial.*

Theorem 4.26. *Let n, F, K, and $\Phi_n(x)$ be as in the above definition. Then $\Phi_n(x)$ has coefficients in Z or Z_p, according as the characteristic of F is zero or a prime, and $\Phi_n(x)$ is a divisor of $f(x) = x^n - 1$ in $Z[x]$ or $Z_p[x]$, respectively.*

PROOF. We proceed by induction on n. In $K[x]$, we have

$$f(x) = (x - \alpha_1)(x - \alpha_2)\cdots(x - \alpha_m)\cdots(x - \alpha_n).$$

Since each α_i is a primitive dth root of unity for exactly one positive divisor d of n, we see that

$$f(x) = \Pi\Phi_d(x),$$

where the product is taken over the finite set of positive divisors d of n.

Since $\Phi_1(x) = x - 1$, the result holds for $n = 1$, and so we assume it for all $d < n$. Then

$$f(x) = \Phi_n(x)g(x), \qquad \text{where } g(x) = \Pi_{d<n}\,\Phi_d(x).$$

By our inductive assumption, $g(x)$ is a divisor of $f(x)$ in $Z[x]$ or $Z_p[x]$, respectively, and, hence, so is $\Phi_n(x)$.

We saw earlier that a finite integral domain is necessarily a field, and the proof was extremely simple. One might naturally wonder whether the requirement of finiteness might not, similarly, enable us to drop some other one of the usual requirements for a field and then obtain it as a consequence. In particular, since we have seen no examples thus far of finite division rings which are not fields, we might conjecture that all finite division rings are fields. This result is indeed true, but proving it is far from being as elementary as in the case of a finite integral domain. However, we are now in position to give a proof of this most interesting result.

Theorem 4.27 (Wedderburn). *A finite division ring D is a field.*

PROOF. Being finite, D has prime characteristic and contains Z_p. Let $K = \{k : k \in D,\ kd = dk \text{ for all } d \in D\}$, and it follows that K is a subfield of D. For, if $k, k' \in K$, then $(k - k')d = kd - k'd = dk - dk' = d(k - k')$, so $k - k'$ is in K, $kk'd = dk'k$, so kk' is in K, and, if $k \neq 0$, then $kd = dk$ implies that $dk^{-1} = k^{-1}d$, so k^{-1} is in K. Thus K is a subdivision ring of D and, being commutative, is a field, say of q elements. Now D is a vector space over K of finite dimension, say n. Then D has q^n elements and the multiplicative group G of D has $q^n - 1$ elements, and, clearly, G contains all nonzero elements of K.

We shall suppose that $n > 1$ and obtain a contradiction. For any $g \in G$, $g \notin K$, we let $D_g = \{d : dg = gd\}$ and we may verify, as above, that D_g is a division ring and, clearly, D_g contains K. Since D is also a vector space over D_g, we have that D_g contains q^d elements for some positive integer d dividing n, and the multiplicative group G_g of D_g thus has order $q^d - 1$. Now G_g is the normalizer of g in G, and, hence, by Theorem 2.38 the number of conjugates of g in G is the index $\dfrac{q^n - 1}{q^d - 1}$ of G_g in G. Decomposing G into conjugate classes, we thus obtain

$$q^n - 1 = (q - 1) + \sum \frac{q^n - 1}{q^{d_i} - 1},$$

where the sum is taken over a finite set of proper divisors d_i of n.

Now $\Phi_n(x)$ divides $\dfrac{x^n - 1}{x^{d_i} - 1}$ for each d_i, since $\Phi_n(x) = \Pi(x - \alpha_j)$, α_j a primitive nth root of unity, and no such $x - \alpha_j$ can occur in the factorization of $x^{d_i} - 1$, since $d_i < n$. Moreover, the quotient is a polynomial with integers as coefficients. Thus $\Phi_n(q)$ is an integer dividing $q^n - 1$ and all $\dfrac{q^n - 1}{q^{d_i} - 1}$, and, hence, also dividing $q - 1$. But $\Phi_n(q) = \Pi(q - \alpha_j)$ and, taking moduli, we have that

$$|\Phi_n(q)| = \prod |q - \alpha_j| > q - 1,$$

since $|q - \alpha_j| > q - 1 \geq 1$ for all j (being the number of elements in a field, q is at least 2). But this contradicts the statement that $\Phi_n(q)$ is a divisor of $q - 1$.

Hence we must have $n = 1$ and $D = K$ is a field.

Exercises

1. Show that any finite field is isomorphic to $Z[x]/A$ for some ideal A.
2. Show that any two finite fields of p^n elements are isomorphic.
3. Show that any finite field is separable over its prime field.
4. Prove Corollary 4.23.1.
5. Carry through the details of the argument in the proof of Theorem 4.24 that the roots of $x^{p^n} - x$ in the splitting field of $x^{p^n} - x$ over Z_p themselves constitute a field.
6. Prove Corollary 4.24.1.
7. Let b be an element of the Galois field $GF(p^n)$. Prove that there exists a unique element c in $GF(p^n)$ such that $c^p = b$.
8. Show that if m and n are positive integers such that m divides n, then $p^m - 1$ divides $p^n - 1$, and, hence, $x^{p^m-1} - 1$ divides $x^{p^n-1} - 1$ or $x^{p^m} - x$ divides $x^{p^n} - x$. Thus show that $GF(p^n)$ contains a unique subfield $GF(p^m)$, and that every subfield of $GF(p^n)$ is of this form.
9. Find a polynomial irreducible over $GF(3)$ having a primitive eighth root of unity as one of its roots in $GF(9)$.
10. Let F be a field with characteristic not dividing n and let K be the splitting field of $x^n - 1$ over F. Show that K contains exactly $\phi(n)$ primitive nth roots of unity, where $\phi(n)$ is the Euler ϕ function, i.e., $\phi(1) = 1$ and $\phi(n)$, $n > 1$, is the number of natural numbers less than n and relatively prime to n.

8. Galois Theory

In this section, we shall give a brief glimpse of one of the most elegant parts of abstract algebra. It is of particular interest as it brings together much of our development thus far. In our presentation, we shall follow the approach of Artin to the Galois theory. Before giving the fundamental results of the theory, we need to obtain some preliminary theorems concerning isomorphisms of a field K into a field K', and also a certain type of field extension called a normal extension.

Theorem 4.28. *Let K and K' be fields and $\alpha_1, \alpha_2, \ldots, \alpha_n$ distinct isomorphisms of K into K'. Then*

$$a_1(k\alpha_1) + a_2(k\alpha_2) + \cdots + a_n(k\alpha_n) = 0$$

for all k in K and some fixed $a_1, a_2, \ldots, a_n$ in K' implies

$$a_1 = a_2 = \cdots = a_n = 0.$$

PROOF. We proceed by induction on n. If $n = 1$ and $a_1(k\alpha_1) = 0$ for all k in K, then $a_1(1\alpha_1) = a_1 = 0$, since $1\alpha_1$ is the unity element of K'. Assume now that the result holds for any m distinct isomorphisms, $1 \leq m < n$. Suppose $a_1(k\alpha_1) + a_2(k\alpha_2) + \cdots + a_n(k\alpha_n) = 0$ for all k in K and a_1, $a_2, \ldots, a_n$ not all zero in K'. Our inductive assumption then implies $a_i \neq 0$

for all i. Since α_1 and α_n are distinct, there must exist some h in K such that $h\alpha_1 \neq h\alpha_n$. Now let $k = hg$ for any g in K. We have

$$a_1(h\alpha_1)(g\alpha_1) + a_2(h\alpha_2)(g\alpha_2) + \cdots + a_n(h\alpha_n)(g\alpha_n) = 0,$$

and multiplying by $(h\alpha_n)^{-1}$, we obtain

$$b_1(g\alpha_1) + b_2(g\alpha_2) + \cdots + b_n(g\alpha_n) = 0, \qquad b_i = a_i(h\alpha_i)(h\alpha_n)^{-1}.$$

Thus $b_n = a_n$, and subtracting this last equation from

$$a_1(g\alpha_1) + a_2(g\alpha_2) + \cdots + a_n(g\alpha_n) = 0,$$

we have

$$(a_1 - b_1)(g\alpha_1) + (a_2 - b_2)(g\alpha_2) + \cdots + (a_{n-1} - b_{n-1})(g\alpha_{n-1}) = 0$$

and

$$a_1 - b_1 = a_1[1 - (h\alpha_1)(h\alpha_n)^{-1}] \neq 0,$$

since $h\alpha_1 \neq h\alpha_n$. But this contradicts our inductive assumption, and we conclude that the result holds for all n.

Definition. Isomorphisms $\alpha_1, \alpha_2, \ldots, \alpha_n$ of the field K into the field K' such that

$$a_1(k\alpha_1) + a_2(k\alpha_2) + \cdots + a_n(k\alpha_n) = 0$$

for all k in K implies $a_1 = a_2 = \cdots = a_n = 0$ are called *linearly independent over* K'.

Definition. Let K and K' be fields and $A = \{\alpha_i : i \in I\}$ be a set of isomorphisms of K into K'. An element k in K is called *fixed for* A if $k\alpha_i = k\alpha_j$ for all i and j in I. The set of all k in K which are fixed for A is denoted by K_A.

The reason for the term *fixed* is that we shall apply this notion in the case of a group A of automorphisms of K, in which case the identity automorphism, which we shall denote by ϵ, being a member of A, the fixed elements of K are indeed left fixed by all elements of A.

Theorem 4.29. *Let K, K' and A be as in the above definition. Then K_A is a subfield of K.*

PROOF. Let $h, k \in K_A$ and $\alpha, \beta \in A$. Then $(h - k)\alpha = h\alpha - k\alpha = h\beta - k\beta = (h - k)\beta$ and K_A is an additive subgroup of K. If $k \neq 0$, then $(hk^{-1})\alpha = (h\alpha)(k^{-1}\alpha) = (h\alpha)(k\alpha)^{-1} = (h\beta)(k\beta)^{-1} = (h\beta)(k^{-1}\beta) = (hk^{-1})\beta$ and the nonzero elements of K_A form a multiplicative subgroup of the multiplicative group of K. Thus K_A is a subfield of K.

Definition. Let K, K' and A be as in the previous definition. K_A is called the *fixed field of K for A.*

Theorem 4.30. *Let* $A = \{\alpha_1, \alpha_2, \ldots, \alpha_n\}$ *be a set of* n *distinct isomorphisms of a field* K *into a field* K'. *Then* $[K : K_A] \geq n$.

PROOF. Suppose the conclusion to be false, so that K has a basis $\{u_1, u_2, \ldots, u_m\}$, $m < n$, over K_A. Then, by Corollary 3.60.2, there exist $c_1, c_2, \ldots, c_n$, not all zero in K', such that

$$c_1(u_i\alpha_1) + c_2(u_i\alpha_2) + \cdots + c_n(u_i\alpha_n) = 0, \qquad i = 1, 2, \ldots, m.$$

Let k be any element of K and $k = f_1u_1 + f_2u_2 + \cdots + f_mu_m$ for some $f_1, f_2, \ldots, f_m$ in K_A. Recalling that $f_i\alpha_j = g_i$ for some $g_i \in K'$ and all $j = 1, 2, \ldots, n$, we have

$$\begin{aligned} c_1(k\alpha_1) &+ c_2(k\alpha_2) + \cdots + c_n(k\alpha_n) \\ &= c_1(f_1u_1 + \cdots + f_mu_m)\alpha_1 + \cdots + c_n(f_1u_1 + \cdots + f_mu_m)\alpha_n \\ &= [c_1g_1(u_1\alpha_1) + \cdots + c_1g_m(u_m\alpha_1)] + \cdots \\ &\quad + [c_ng_1(u_1\alpha_n) + \cdots + c_ng_m(u_m\alpha_n)] \\ &= g_1[c_1(u_1\alpha_1) + \cdots + c_n(u_1\alpha_n)] + \cdots \\ &\quad + g_m[c_1(u_m\alpha_1) + \cdots + c_n(u_m\alpha_n)] \\ &= 0. \end{aligned}$$

But this contradicts the result of Theorem 4.28, and, hence, the desired conclusion, $[K : K_A] \geq n$, must hold.

Corollary 4.30.1. *Let* $A = \{\alpha_1, \alpha_2, \ldots, \alpha_n\}$ *be a set of distinct automorphisms of a field* K. *Then* $[K : K_A] \geq n$.

PROOF. Immediate from the theorem.

To see that $[K : K_A]$ may exceed n, consider the set $A = \{\epsilon, \alpha, \beta\}$ of automorphisms of $R(\sqrt{2}, \sqrt{3})$, where ϵ is the identity map, $(a + b\sqrt{2} + c\sqrt{3} + d\sqrt{6})\alpha = a - b\sqrt{2} + c\sqrt{3} - d\sqrt{6}$, and $(a + b\sqrt{2} + c\sqrt{3} + d\sqrt{6})\beta = a + b\sqrt{2} - c\sqrt{3} - d\sqrt{6}$, for all $a, b, c, d \in R$. The reader may verify that α and β are automorphisms, and that $R(\sqrt{2}, \sqrt{3})_A = R$, while $[R(\sqrt{2}, \sqrt{3}) : R] = 4 > 3$. However, in the event that A is a finite group of automorphisms the inequality may be replaced by an equality.

Theorem 4.31. *Let* K_A *be the fixed field of the field* K *for the group*

$$A = \{\alpha_1 = \epsilon, \alpha_2, \ldots, \alpha_n\}$$

of automorphisms of K. *Then* $[K : K_A] = n$.

PROOF. We have $[K : K_A] \geq n$. Suppose $[K : K_A] > n$ so that there are elements $u_1, u_2, \ldots, u_{n+1}$ of K linearly independent over K_A. Then there exist $c_1, c_2, \ldots, c_{n+1}$ in K and not all zero satisfying the system of n linear homogeneous equations in $n + 1$ unknowns:

$$\text{(i)}\ x_1(u_1\alpha_i) + x_2(u_2\alpha_i) + \cdots + x_{n+1}(u_{n+1}\alpha_i) = 0, \quad i = 1, 2, \ldots, n.$$

From among all such nontrivial solutions of (i), select one having the minimum possible number, m, of nonzero members. We have $m > 1$, since $m = 1$ would imply $c_1(u_1\alpha_1) = 0$, and, hence, $c_1 = 0$, contrary to the assumption that the c_j are not all zero. ($u_1\alpha_1 \neq 0$, since $u_1 \neq 0$ and α_1 is an automorphism.) Now we may assume that $c_1, \ldots, c_m$ are not zero and $c_{m+1} = \cdots = c_{n+1} = 0$ and also that $c_m = 1$. (Otherwise, we would multiply all the c_j by c_m^{-1} to obtain the desired set of c's.) We thus obtain

$$\text{(ii)}\ c_1(u_1\alpha_i) + c_2(u_2\alpha_i) + \cdots + c_{m-1}(u_{m-1}\alpha_i) + u_m\alpha_i = 0, \qquad i = 1, 2, \ldots, n.$$

Setting $i = 1$, we have, since $\epsilon = \alpha_1$ is the identity automorphism,

$$c_1u_1 + \cdots + c_{m-1}u_{m-1} + u_m = 0,$$

from which it follows that $c_1, \ldots, c_{m-1}$ are not all in K_A, since $u_1, \ldots, u_m$ are linearly independent over K_A. Suppose that c_1 is not in K_A. Then

$$c_1 - c_1\alpha_j \neq 0$$

for some α_j, and applying α_j to the left side of (ii), we have

$$(c_1(u_1\alpha_i))\alpha_j + \cdots + (c_{m-1}(u_{m-1}\alpha_i))\alpha_j + (u_m\alpha_i)\alpha_j = 0, \qquad i = 1, 2, \ldots, n,$$

or

$$\text{(iii)}\ (c_1\alpha_j)(u_1\alpha_{ij}) + \cdots + (c_{m-1}\alpha_j)(u_{m-1}\alpha_{ij}) + u_m\alpha_{ij} = 0, \qquad i = 1, 2, \ldots, n,$$

where $\alpha_{ij} = \alpha_i\alpha_j$. Since A is a group, the elements $\alpha_{1j}, \alpha_{2j}, \ldots, \alpha_{nj}$ are merely a permutation of $\alpha_1, \alpha_2, \ldots, \alpha_n$. We may thus renumber the equations (iii) and subtract from (ii) to obtain

$$(c_1 - c_1\alpha_j)(u_1\alpha_i) + \cdots + (c_{m-1} - c_{m-1}\alpha_j)(u_{m-1}\alpha_i) = 0, \qquad i = 1, 2, \ldots, n.$$

But then $c_1 - c_1\alpha_j, \ldots, c_{m-1} - c_{m-1}\alpha_j, 0, \ldots, 0$ is a nontrivial solution of (i) having fewer than m nonzero members. Thus the supposition that $[K : K_A] > n$ is false, and $[K : K_A] = n$.

Now let K be an extension field of F and consider the set of all automorphisms α of K such that $f\alpha = f$ for all f in F, that is, those automorphisms α of K such that $K_\alpha \supseteq F$. If α and β are two such automorphisms, then so are $\alpha\beta$ and α^{-1}. The identity automorphism ϵ leaves F fixed and the composition of automorphisms is associative. Thus, this set of automorphisms is a group.

Definition. Let K be a superfield of F. The group $G_{K/F}$ of all automorphisms α of K for which $K_\alpha \supseteq F$ is called the *automorphism group of K over F*. If $[K : F]$ is finite and $K_{G_{K/F}} = F$, that is, F is the fixed field for $G_{K/F}$, then K is *normal over F*, and $G_{K/F}$ is then called the *Galois group of K over F*.

We note that not all finite extension fields are normal. For example $K = R(\sqrt[3]{2})$ is not normal over the field R of rationals. For suppose that α is an automorphism of K with $K_\alpha \supseteq R$. Then $\sqrt[3]{2}\alpha = a + b\sqrt[3]{2} + c\sqrt[3]{4}$ for some a, b, c in R, from which we have

$$(\sqrt[3]{2}\alpha)^3 = (a + b\sqrt[3]{2} + c\sqrt[3]{4})^3 = a' + b'\sqrt[3]{2} + c'\sqrt[3]{4}.$$

Computation of the coefficients a', b', c', together with the fact that $(\sqrt[3]{2}\alpha)^3 = (\sqrt[3]{2})^3\alpha = 2\alpha = 2$, yields the equations

$$a^3 + 2b^3 + 4c^3 + 12abc = 2,$$
$$a^2b + 2b^2c + 2c^2a = 0,$$
$$ab^2 + 2bc^2 + ca^2 = 0.$$

But the only rational numbers satisfying these equations can be shown, by elementary algebra, to be $a = c = 0$, $b = 1$. Thus $\sqrt[3]{2}\alpha = \sqrt[3]{2}$ and the only automorphism of K leaving R fixed is the identity automorphism ϵ, $G_{K/R} = E = \{\epsilon\}$ and $K_E = K \neq R$, so that $R(\sqrt[3]{2})$ is not normal over R.

In the Galois theory, normal extension fields will play a most important role. Since not all finite extensions are normal, we shall wish to develop criteria for determining the normality of an extension field K of F, without the necessity of first computing the group G of automorphisms of K over F and then determining the fixed field of G. We first prove the following theorem.

Theorem 4.32. *Let K be normal over F. Then K is separable over F and, moreover, every element k of K is a root of a polynomial $f(x)$ in $F[x]$ which splits in K.*

PROOF. Let $G_{K/F} = \{\alpha_1 = \epsilon, \alpha_2, \ldots, \alpha_n\}$, where $n = [K : F]$. For $k \in K$, let $k = k_1, k_2, \ldots, k_m$ be the distinct elements of the set $\{k\alpha_i : i = 1, 2, \ldots, n\}$. Since $G_{K/F}$ is a group, we have $k_i\alpha_j = k\alpha_i\alpha_j = k_r$ for some r, and also $k_i\alpha_r = k_j\alpha_r$ implies $k_i = (k_i\alpha_r)\alpha_r^{-1} = (k_j\alpha_r)\alpha_r^{-1} = k_j$, so that $k_1\alpha_j, k_2\alpha_j, \ldots, k_m\alpha_j$ are distinct. Hence the factors of $f(x) = (x - k_1)(x - k_2)\cdots(x - k_m)$ are merely permuted by any α_i of $G_{K/F}$. Thus the coefficients of $f(x)$ remain unaltered by any α_i of $G_{K/F}$ and must be in F, since K is normal over F. Hence $k = k_1$ is a root of a separable polynomial $f(x)$ in $F[x]$ and $f(x)$ splits in K.

Theorem 4.33. *A field K is normal over F if and only if K is the splitting field of a separable polynomial in $F[x]$.*

PROOF. Assume, first, that K is normal over F. Then $[K: F] = n$ for some n, and we may take $\{u_1, u_2, \ldots, u_n\}$ as a basis of K over F. Now each u_i is a root of a separable irreducible polynomial $f_i(x)$ in $F[x]$ which splits in K. Let $f(x) = f_1(x)f_2(x)\cdots f_n(x)$. Then $f(x)$ is separable and splits in K. Since $f(x)$ has $u_1, u_2, \ldots, u_n$ as roots, the splitting field K_0 of $f(x)$ must contain $K = F(u_1, u_2, \ldots, u_n)$. But since all the roots of $f(x)$ are in K, we have $K_0 \subseteq K$, hence $K_0 = K$ and the necessity of our condition is established.

Conversely, assume that K is the splitting field of the separable polynomial $f(x)$ in $F[x]$. We proceed by induction on the number m of roots of $f(x)$ in K, but not in F. Clearly if $m = 0$, then $K = F$ and K is normal over F, since then $G_{K/F} = \{\epsilon\}$, and $F = K$ is the fixed field for the identity automorphism ϵ. Assume that the result holds for all pairs of fields such that $f(x)$ has fewer than $m \geq 1$ roots outside the base field.

Now $f(x) = p_1(x)p_2(x) \cdots p_r(x)$ for $p_i(x)$ irreducible and separable in $F[x]$, and, since $m \geq 1$, we may assume that $p_1(x)$ has degree d greater than 1. Let k be a root of $p_1(x)$ so that $[F(k) : F] = d$.

Since $p_1(x)$ is irreducible and separable, its roots $k = k_1, k_2, \ldots, k_d$ are all distinct. Then, by Theorem 4.5, there exist isomorphisms $\alpha_1', \alpha_2', \ldots, \alpha_d'$ such that $\alpha_i'\colon F(k) \to F(k_i)$ with $k\alpha_i' = k_i$ and F fixed under α_i'. Since K is a splitting field of $f(x)$ over both $F(k)$ and $F(k_i)$, by Theorem 4.12 the isomorphism α_i' can be extended to an automorphism α_i of K which maps k on k_i and leaves F fixed, $i = 1, 2, \ldots, d$.

Suppose now that t is an element of K which is fixed under all automorphisms in $G_{K/F}$. Since $f(x)$ has fewer than m roots outside $F(k)$, by our inductive assumption K is normal over $F(k)$, and, hence, any element fixed under $G_{K/F(k)} \subseteq G_{K/F}$ must lie in $F(k)$. Thus t has the form

$$t = a_0 + a_1 k + \cdots + a_{d-1}k^{d-1}, \qquad a_0, a_1, \ldots, a_{d-1} \in F.$$

We then have

$$t\alpha_i = t = a_0 + a_1 k_i + \cdots + a_{d-1}k_i^{d-1}, \qquad i = 1, 2, \ldots, d.$$

But this implies that

$$g(x) = (a_0 - t) + a_1 x + \cdots + a_{d-1}x^{d-1}$$

has the d distinct roots $k_1, k_2, \ldots, k_d$ in K, which, by Corollary 3.23.1, implies that $g(x)$ is the zero polynomial and $t = a_0$ is in F. Thus F is the fixed field of $G_{K/F}$ and K is normal over F, as required.

Theorem 4.34. *Let K be a finite extension field of F. Then K is normal over F if and only if every element of K is a root of a separable polynomial $f(x)$ in $F[x]$ which splits in K.*

PROOF. The necessity of the condition follows from Theorem 4.32. Conversely, let $\{u_1, u_2, \ldots, u_n\}$ be a basis of K over F, and suppose the condition on elements of K is satisfied, where u_i is a root of the separable polynomial $f_i(x)$ in $F[x]$ and $f_i(x)$ splits in K. Then $f(x) = f_1(x)f_2(x) \cdots f_n(x)$ is separable, K is the splitting field of $f(x)$ and K is normal over F by Theorem 4.33.

Corollary 4.34.1. *Let $K \supseteq L \supseteq F$ be fields with K normal over F. Then K is normal over L.*

PROOF. Immediate from the theorem and the fact that $L[x] \supseteq F[x]$.

Theorem 4.35. *Let K be a normal extension field of F, $[K : F] = n$. Then $G_{K/F}$ has order n.*

PROOF. Theorem 4.31 and the definition of K normal over F.

Theorem 4.36. *Let H be a (finite) group of automorphisms of the field K and $F = K_H$. Then, $H = G_{K/F}$.*

PROOF. If H has order n, then $[K : F] = n$ by Theorem 4.31. Since H leaves F fixed, we have $H \subseteq G_{K/F}$. Let m be the order of $G_{K/F}$ and we have $m \geq n$. If $H \neq G_{K/F}$, then $m > n$ and, by Theorem 4.30, we have $[K : F] \geq m > n$, a contradiction. Hence $H = G_{K/F}$.

Corollary 4.36.1. *Let $H_1 \neq H_2$ be two groups of automorphisms of the field K. Then $K_{H_1} \neq K_{H_2}$.*

PROOF. If $K_{H_1} = K_{H_2} = F$, then, by the theorem, we would have $H_1 = G_{K/F} = H_2$, contrary to hypothesis.

Theorem 4.37 (The fundamental theorem of the Galois theory). *Let K be a normal extension of the field F, $G = G_{K/F}$, L and L' subfields of K which contain F, and H and H' subgroups of G. Let $o(H)$ be the order of H and $i(H)$ be the index of H in G. Then:*

(i) *There is a 1–1 correspondence between subfields L, $K \supseteq L \supseteq F$, and subgroups H of G given by $L \leftrightarrow H$ iff $H = G_{K/L}$ iff $L = K_H$. Moreover, if L and H correspond, then $[K : L] = o(H)$ and $[L : F] = i(H)$.*

(ii) *Let L and H, L' and H' correspond. Then $L' \subseteq L$ iff $H' \supseteq H$ and, in such a case, $[L : L'] =$ index of H in H'.*

(iii) *Let L and H, L' and H' correspond. Then there exists α in G such that $L' = L\alpha$ iff $H' = \alpha^{-1}H\alpha$.*

(iv) *Let L and H correspond. Then L is normal over F iff H is normal in G, and, in such a case, $G_{L/F} \cong G/H$,* i.e., *$G_{L/F} \cong (G_{K/F})/(G_{K/L})$.*

PROOF.

(i) Suppose $K \supseteq L \supseteq F$. Since K is normal over F, K is normal over L. Set $H = G_{K/L}$ and we have that $L = K_H$ by the normality of K over L. Conversely, let H be a subgroup of G. Then H determines a subfield $L = K_H$ and, K being normal over L, we have $H = G_{K/L}$. Since, by Corollary 4.36.1, distinct subgroups of G have distinct fixed fields, the correspondence is 1–1.
If L and H correspond, then $o(H) = [K : L]$ since K is normal over L, and $o(H)i(H) = o(G) = [K : F] = [K : L][L : F]$ implies that $i(H) = [L : F]$, since all numbers involved are finite.

(ii) If $L' \subseteq L$, then every α in G leaving L fixed must also leave L' fixed, hence, $H' = G_{K/L'} \supseteq G_{K/L} = H$. If, conversely, $H' \supseteq H$, then clearly $L' = K_{H'} \subseteq K_H = L$. In such a situation, K being normal over both L and L', we replace F in (i) by L' and G by H' to obtain $[L : L'] =$ index of H in H'.

(iii) If there exists α in G such that $L' = L\alpha$, then $[L : F] = [L' : F]$. Then, by part (i), H and H' have the same index in G, hence $o(H) = o(H')$. We have that $o(H) = o(\alpha^{-1}H\alpha)$ also, since these subgroups are conjugate. Now, for any k' in L', we have $k' = k\alpha$ for some k in L, and $k\beta = k$ for any β in H. Hence $k'(\alpha^{-1}\beta\alpha) = k(\beta\alpha) = k\alpha = k'$, whence

$L' \subseteq K_{\alpha^{-1}H\alpha}$. Then, by (ii), we have $H' \supseteq \alpha^{-1}H\alpha$. Now $o(H') = o(\alpha^{-1}H\alpha)$ implies $H' = \alpha^{-1}H\alpha$.

Conversely, suppose $H' = \alpha^{-1}H\alpha$. Then, for k in L, we have $k\alpha(\alpha^{-1}\beta\alpha) = k(\beta\alpha) = k\alpha$ for all β in H, and thus $L\alpha \subseteq K_{H'} = L'$. Now $o(H') = o(H)$ implies that $[K : L] = [K : L']$, so that $[L : F] = [L\alpha : F] = [L' : F]$. Hence $L\alpha = L'$, as required.

(iv) We shall prove the following sequence of results in order to establish (iv):

(a) L is normal over F iff $o(G_{L/F}) = [L : F]$.

(b) $o(G_{L/F}) = [L : F]$ iff every isomorphism of L leaving F fixed is an automorphism of L over F.

(c) Every isomorphism of L over F is an automorphism of L over F iff H is normal in G.

(d) If this is the case, then $G_{L/F} \cong G/H$.

The proofs are as follows:

(a) Suppose L is normal over F. Then $o(G_{L/F}) = [L : F]$ by Theorem 4.35. Conversely, if $o(G_{L/F}) = [L : F]$, let F' be the fixed field of $G_{L/F}$. Then $F \subseteq F' \subseteq L$ and, by Theorem 4.31, we have $[L : F'] = o(G_{L/F})$, so that $F = F'$ and L is normal over F.

(b) For any α in G, α determines an isomorphism of L leaving F fixed. On the other hand, if γ is an isomorphism of L leaving F fixed, then, since K is normal over F, K is the splitting field of some $f(x)$ in $F[x]$, and, under γ, we have $f(x)$ in $L[x]$ corresponds to $f(x)$ in $L\gamma[x]$, so that, by Theorem 4.12, γ can be extended to an automorphism of K over F.

Now by (i), H has $m = i(H) = [L : F]$ distinct (right) cosets $H = H\alpha_1, H\alpha_2, \ldots, H\alpha_m$ in G. For k in L and β in H, we have $k\beta\alpha_i = k\alpha_i$ for all i, since $L = K_H$. Thus elements of G in the same cosets of H determine the same isomorphism of L. Conversely, if $k\alpha = k\alpha'$ for all k in L, then $k\alpha'\alpha^{-1} = k$, or $\alpha'\alpha^{-1}$ is in H so that α and α' are in the same coset of H. Thus the number of distinct isomorphisms of L leaving F fixed is $m = i(H)$. If $o(G_{L/F}) = m$, then every isomorphism of L leaving F fixed must be an automorphism of L over F, since every automorphism of L is an isomorphism of L. Conversely, if every isomorphism of L over F is an automorphism, then $o(G_{L/F})$ is the number, m, of these isomorphisms.

(c) Every isomorphism of L over F is an automorphism iff $L\alpha = L$ for all α in G. But, by (iii), $L\alpha = L$ iff $H = \alpha^{-1}H\alpha$, which is the condition that H be normal.

(d) If L is normal over F, then the distinct automorphisms of L over F, by the argument of (b), correspond uniquely to cosets of G modulo H, and this 1–1 correspondence is clearly an isomorphism of $G_{L/F}$ and G/H since, for α and α' in G, we have that $\alpha\alpha'$ corresponds to the coset $(H\alpha)(H\alpha') = H(\alpha\alpha')$.

Let K be the splitting field of $f(x)$ in $F[x]$. Then $G_{K/F}$ is the *Galois group of the equation* $f(x) = 0$. For α in $G_{K/F}$ and r a root of $f(x)$, we have $f(r\alpha) = (f(r))\alpha = 0\alpha = 0$ since F is fixed under α, and, hence, α maps roots of $f(x)$ on roots of $f(x)$. Since α is an automorphism, distinct roots have distinct images under α, and we conclude that each α in $G_{K/F}$ induces a permutation π_α of the set of distinct roots $r_1, r_2, \ldots, r_n$ of $f(x)$. Since $\pi_{\alpha\beta} = \pi_\alpha\pi_\beta$, the mapping $\alpha \to \pi_\alpha$ is a homomorphism of $G_{K/F}$ into the group of all permutations of $r_1, r_2, \ldots, r_n$. Since $K = F(r_1, r_2, \ldots, r_n)$, if $\pi_\alpha = \pi_\beta$ then $r_i\alpha = r_i\beta$ for all i and $\alpha = \beta$. Thus $G_{K/F}$ is isomorphic to the group $G_0 = \{\pi_\alpha : \alpha \in G_{K/F}\}$.

In general, G_0 is not the full group S_n of all permutations of $r_1, r_2, \ldots, r_n$, but merely a subgroup of S_n. If $f(x)$ is irreducible, however, then G_0 is *transitive*, that is, for given r_i and r_j, there exists π in G_0 such that $r_i\pi = r_j$. For in this case $F(r_i) \cong F(r_j)$ with $r_i \to r_j$ and F fixed. This isomorphism may then be extended to an automorphism α in $G_{K/F}$, and we have that $r_i\pi_\alpha = r_j$ as required.

One of the earlier and still most interesting applications of the Galois theory is to the question of the solvability of the equation $f(x) = 0$, $f(x)$ in $F[x]$. We know that there exists a splitting field of $f(x)$, but one is often concerned with the question of whether roots of $f(x)$ can be found by using only the field operations of F, together with the extraction of roots.

An extension field K of F is called an *extension by radicals* if there exists a finite chain of fields

$$F = L_0 \subseteq L_1 \subseteq \cdots \subseteq L_m = K$$

such that

$$L_i = L_{i-1}(r_i),$$

r_i a root of $f_i(x) = x^{n_i} - a_i$, a_i in L_{i-1}, $i = 1, 2, \ldots, m$. The polynomial $f(x)$ in $F[x]$ (or the equation $f(x) = 0$) is called *solvable by radicals* if its splitting field is contained in an extension by radicals of F. If F is of characteristic zero, then it may be shown that $f(x)$ is solvable by radicals if and only if the Galois group G_0 of $f(x)$ is solvable, that is, there exists a finite chain of subgroups $G_0 \supseteq G_1 \supseteq \cdots \supseteq G_m = E$ such that G_i is normal in G_{i-1} and G_{i-1}/G_i is Abelian, $i = 1, 2, \ldots, m$. However, we shall prove here only part of the result, as this is the easiest part to establish and, moreover, leads to the famous result of Abel, that a polynomial of degree greater than four is not, in general, solvable by radicals, one of the classic theorems of algebra.

Theorem 4.38. *If $f(x)$ in $F[x]$, F of characteristic zero, is solvable by radicals, then its Galois group G is solvable.*

PROOF. We shall assume, for the moment, that F has as many roots of unity as we may need in our arguments, and, as a final step in the proof, show that this imposes no essential restriction.

The splitting field L of $f(x)$ lies in an extension K of F by radicals. Now, in the above notation, L_1 is normal over $L_0 = F$, since, along with r_1, we have er_1 in L_1, where e is any n_1-root of unity, and, thus, L_1 is the splitting field of the separable polynomial $f_1(x)$ in $L_0[x]$. If L_2 is not normal over F, then we replace L_2 by the field L_2', obtained by adjoining to L_2 the roots of

$$g(x) = (x^{n_2} - a_2\beta_1)(x^{n_2} - a_2\beta_2) \cdots (x^{n_2} - a_2\beta_k),$$

where $\beta_1, \beta_2, \ldots, \beta_k$ is the set of automorphisms of L_1 over L_0. Now $g(x)$ is in $F[x]$, since its coefficients are $-(a_2\beta_1 + a_2\beta_2 + \cdots + a_2\beta_k)$, $(a_2\beta_1)(a_2\beta_2) + (a_2\beta_1)(a_2\beta_3) + \cdots + (a_2\beta_{k-1})(a_2\beta_k), \ldots, (-1)^k(a_2\beta_1)(a_2\beta_2) \cdots (a_2\beta_k)$, each of which is fixed under all β_i and hence is in F. Thus the field L_2' is an extension by radicals which is normal over F. Continuing in this way, we obtain the desired normal extension by radicals K' containing K, so we may as well assume that K is itself normal over F.

We now assert that the group H_i of L_i over L_{i-1} is Abelian. For if we let $e_1, e_2, \ldots, e_{n_i}$ be the n_i distinct n_i-roots of unity, then, $r_ie_1, r_ie_2, \ldots, r_ie_{n_i}$ are the n_i distinct roots of $f_i(x) = x^{n_i} - a_i$. Thus if α and β are in H_i, then $r_i\alpha = r_ie_j$, $r_i\beta = r_ie_k$ for some j and k, and, since e_j and e_k are in F, we have $r_i\alpha\beta = r_ie_je_k = r_ie_ke_j = r_i\beta\alpha$. Thus α and β commute on r_i and, hence, on all of $L_{i-1}(r_i)$.

Since each L_i is normal over L_{i-1}, we have, by the fundamental theorem, that G_i is normal in G_{i-1}, where G_i is the group of K over L_i. Thus in the chain $G_0 \supseteq G_1 \supseteq \cdots \supseteq G_m = E$, we have each group normal in the preceding. But since G_{i-1}/G_i is isomorphic to the group H_i of L_i over L_{i-1}, we see that G_{i-1}/G_i is Abelian. Thus G_0, the group of K over F, is solvable.

Now $f(x)$ is separable, since F has characteristic zero; hence L, the splitting field of $f(x)$, is normal over F. Thus the group H of K over L is normal in G_0 and the group G of L over F is isomorphic to G_0/H. Then the natural homomorphism of G_0 onto G_0/H maps G_i onto HG_i/H, and the series

$$G_0/H = HG_0/H \supseteq HG_1/H \supseteq \cdots \supseteq HG_m/H = E$$

has each group normal in the preceding and all factor groups Abelian, since $(HG_{i-1}/H)/(HG_i/H)$ is a homomorphic image of G_{i-1}/G_i.

Finally, if F does not contain enough suitable roots of unity, we may adjoin the required roots of unity to F and obtain a field F' which is a normal extension of F by radicals. Then, as in the first part of the proof, we may obtain a normal extension K' of F by radicals which contains the splitting field L of F and whose group G_0' over F' is solvable. If G_0 is now the group of K' over F, then G_0/G_0' is isomorphic to the group of F' over F and is Abelian. Thus G_0 is solvable and we proceed, as before, to deduce the solvability of G, and, thus, complete the proof.

To obtain the theorem of Abel, one needs now to show that, for given n, there exists an $f(x)$ of degree n whose group is the symmetric group S_n, and then show that S_n is not solvable for $n > 4$. These proofs we shall not give here, but leave it to the interested reader to develop them or find them in the literature.

Exercises

1. Show that if $\alpha_1, \alpha_2, \ldots, \alpha_n$ are distinct isomorphisms of the group G into the multiplicative group of a field, then $\alpha_1, \alpha_2, \ldots, \alpha_n$ are linearly independent.

2. For each of the following polynomials over R, determine its splitting field and the group of automorphisms of the splitting field over R.

(a) $f(x) = x^4 - 2x^2 + 2$,

(b) $g(x) = x^5 - 1$.

3. Show that the splitting fields in Exercise 2 are normal over R, and determine, in each case, all intermediate fields and which of the intermediate fields are normal over R.

4. Prove that $R(\sqrt[3]{2})$ is not normal over R. ($\sqrt[3]{2}$ is, of course, the real cube root of 2.)

5. Let $[K : F] = 2$. Prove that K is normal over F if F has characteristic not 2. What can be said if F has characteristic 2?

6. For each of the following, find the degree of K over R, the smallest extension L of K normal over R and the Galois group of L over R. (All indicated roots are real roots.)

(a) $R(\sqrt{2}, \sqrt{3})$,

(b) $R(\sqrt{2}, \sqrt[3]{2})$,

(c) $R(\sqrt{2} + \sqrt[3]{2})$,

(d) $R(\sqrt[3]{2}, \sqrt[3]{-2})$.

7. What are the possible degrees over R of the splitting field of

$$x^4 + ax^3 + bx^2 + cx + d$$

in $R[x]$? For each such degree, find an $f(x)$ of degree four in $R[x]$ whose splitting field has this degree over R.

8. In Exercise 7, can a field normal over R be found in each case?

9. The Fundamental Theorem of Algebra

It would seem inappropriate to leave our discussion of fields without some mention of the so-called *Fundamental Theorem of Algebra:*

Theorem 4.39. *$C = R'(i)$, i a root of $x^2 + 1$ in $R'[x]$, R' the field of real numbers, is the splitting field for any polynomial in $C[x]$.*

This theorem is certainly one of the most famous and useful in algebra. Yet, as a striking example of the basic unity of mathematics, all of the over one hundred known proofs of the theorem make use of arguments essentially nonalgebraic in character.

We shall give the outlines of three proofs of this theorem, leaving it to the reader to supply the topologic or analytic portions of the proofs. Our first proof will follow the lines of the first proof of Gauss, the first known proof of the result. (This proof, given in 1799, was the first of five given by Gauss.)

FIRST PROOF. Let $f(z) = z^n + a_{n-1}z^{n-1} + \cdots + a_0$ be any element of $C[z]$. To show that $f(z)$ actually splits in C, it suffices to show that $f(z)$ has a root in C, so that $f(z) = (z - z_0)g(z)$, and then, by repeating the argument, we obtain our desired result. We may assume that $n > 1$, since, otherwise, the result is trivial. Let us represent z in the form $x + iy$, and obtain $f(z) = u + iv$, where $u = u(x, y)$ and $v = v(x, y)$ are elements of $R'[x, y]$. Then we have that $f(z_0) = 0$ if and only if $f(z_0) = u_0 + iv_0$ with $u_0 = v_0 = 0$. Thus we consider the equations $u = 0$ and $v = 0$, and their graphs in the xy-plane. If these graphs intersect at some point (x_0, y_0), then

$$f(x_0 + iy_0) = f(z_0) = 0$$

and we have the desired root of $f(z)$ in C.

Now from

$$z = x + iy = r(\cos\theta + i\sin\theta),$$

we see that as r becomes very large, $f(z)$ approaches the value

$$z^n = r^n(\cos n\theta + i\sin n\theta) = u' + iv',$$

by the use of De Moivre's theorem. But $u' = 0$ if and only if $\cos n\theta = 0$, and $v' = 0$ if and only if $\sin n\theta = 0$. Both of these latter equations have graphs consisting of n straight lines through the origin, the angle θ for $\cos n\theta = 0$ being $\pi/2n$, $3\pi/2n, \ldots, (2n - 1)\pi/2n$ and that for $\sin n\theta = 0$ being 0, $\pi/n, 2\pi/n, \ldots, (n - 1)\pi/n$. For example, if we take $n = 3$, we obtain as graphs of $u' = 0$ and $v' = 0$:

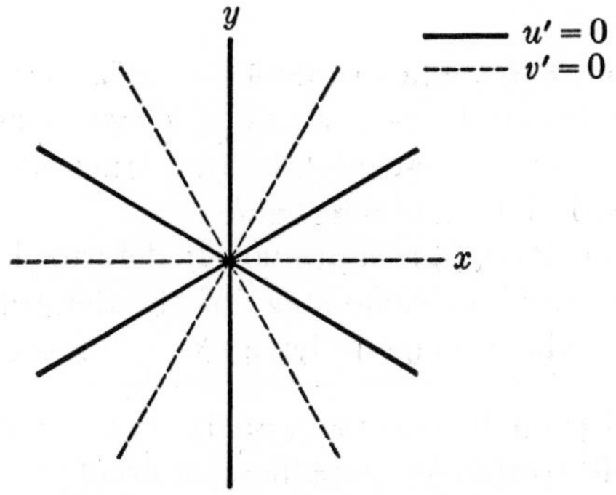

Now consider $u = 0$ and $v = 0$. Outside some large circle with center at the origin, we must have $u = 0$ and $v = 0$ asymptotic, respectively, to $u' = 0$ and $v' = 0$, from which it is apparent that the branches of $u = 0$ and of $v = 0$ must alternate. By means of the continuity properties of $u = 0$ and $v = 0$, one may then show that these curves must indeed intersect in at least one point (x_0, y_0), and we have the desired zero, $z_0 = x_0 + iy_0$, of $f(z)$.

SECOND PROOF. This also depends heavily on geometric (or topologic) argument and proceeds along the following lines: Let

$$w = f(z) \qquad \text{with } f(z) = u + iv,$$

as before. Now consider the two *complex planes* for z and w, respectively. Since $w = f(z)$ is a continuous function of z, the image C'_r of the circle C_r: $|z| = r$ in the z-plane is a closed curve in the w-plane. Now, either C'_r passes through the origin, in which case we are finished, or C'_r must encircle the origin m_r times for some nonnegative integer

$$m_r = \frac{1}{2\pi}\int_{C'_r} d\phi,$$

where $w = \rho(\cos\phi + i\sin\phi)$.

If $r = 0$, then C'_r is a single point. If r is sufficiently large, then we assert that $m_r = n$, the degree of $f(z)$. We let

$$z = r(\cos\theta + i\sin\theta),$$

and we have

$$f(z) = z^n\left(1 + \sum_{j=0}^{n-1} a_j z^{j-n}\right) = \rho(\cos\phi + i\sin\phi).$$

Hence

$$\phi = n\theta + \text{arc}\left(1 + \sum_{j=0}^{n-1} a_j z^{j-n}\right).$$

Now if r is sufficiently large, we have that $1 + \sum_{j=0}^{n-1} a_j z^{j-n}$ has a graph contained entirely within the circle $|w - 1| < \frac{1}{2}$. Hence as z describes C_r counterclockwise, the net change in ϕ is evidently $2\pi n$, from which we conclude that $m_r = n$ for r sufficiently large, as asserted.

Now, as r increases from 0, C'_r is continuously deformed. By a theorem from topology, we conclude that at some stage of the deformation, C'_r must pass through the origin, at which point we have $f(z) = 0$, as desired.

If we use powerful enough tools from analysis, the argument can be made simple indeed, as is illustrated by the following proof:

THIRD PROOF. If, contrary to the theorem, the polynomial $f(z)$ of positive degree is never zero for any z, then the function $1/f(z)$ is regular in the entire complex plane and is certainly bounded, since $1/f(z)$ actually approaches zero as $|z|$ becomes infinite. But then Liouville's theorem tells us that $1/f(z)$ must be a constant. This means that $f(z)$ is itself a constant, contrary to assumption. We thus conclude that there must be a complex zero of $f(z)$.

Having thus briefly indicated some of the types of argument used in proving the Fundamental Theorem of Algebra, it is perhaps appropriate to point out some of its deficiencies. These are essentially due to the fact that it deals only with polynomials over a particular field, C, while there are many fields which are properly contained in, or properly contain, C, or have prime characteristic and, hence, are only distantly related to C. We have seen that if we are given any polynomial over any field, then there exists an essentially unique splitting field for the polynomial. While this result is certainly important, we should like to know even more. Given an arbitrary field, does there exist a superfield in which every polynomial over the given field splits, and is it perhaps unique? In the case of the real number field, the complex field is, of course, the unique field with the required property. Or in a form closer to that for the Fundamental Theorem of Algebra, given any field, does there exist an essentially unique extension field K such that every polynomial over K splits in K?

Definition. A field K is called *algebraically complete* or *algebraically closed* if every polynomial with coefficients in K splits in K.

It may be shown that given any field F, there exists an algebraically complete algebraic extension field K of F and K is unique to within equivalence over F. However, the proof involves heavy use of the Well-Ordering Axiom or the Axiom of Choice of general set theory, and, hence, will be delayed until we have considered these axioms in the Appendix.

Exercises

1. Show that every irreducible polynomial over the real field R' is of degree 1 or 2.

2. Show that every polynomial over the real field R' of odd degree has a root in R':
(a) by use of the Fundamental Theorem of Algebra, and
(b) without the use of this theorem.

3. Complete the proofs of the Fundamental Theorem of Algebra given in this section.

The Well-Ordering Axiom

In many branches of mathematics, one of the most useful general methods of proof is that of mathematical induction. Since the method is based upon the inductive axiom of the positive integers, or natural numbers, it follows that it cannot be applied in transfinite situations, that is, in those situations where the number of possible cases to be considered is essentially larger than the set of positive integers. By "essentially larger" we mean that there are more cases than can be put into 1–1 correspondence with the set of positive integers. If, for example, we ask whether, in a completely general ring, it is true that every ideal is contained in some maximal ideal, it may well be the case that we can construct a properly ascending chain of ideals beginning with the given ideal but not reaching a maximal ideal in any countable number of steps. That is, the properly ascending chain may contain an ideal for each positive integer, yet not reach a maximal ideal. To handle questions of this sort, we need more powerful tools (that is, more powerful axioms) than are supplied by the axiom of (finite) mathematical induction. These tools are supplied by the assumption of axioms known as the Axiom of Choice, the Well-Ordering Axiom, Zorn's Lemma, or others of equivalent power. In order to discuss them, we need some preliminary notions.

Definition. By a *partially ordered set* (POS), we mean a set S, together with a binary relation, $\leq$, on some subset T of $S \times S$ such that:

(i) For all a in S, (a, a) is in T, i.e., $a \leq a$ for all a in S.

(ii) If (a, b) and (b, a) are in T, then $a = b$, i.e., if both $a \leq b$ and $b \leq a$, then $a = b$.

(iii) If (a, b) and (b, c) are in T, then (a, c) is in T, i.e., if both $a \leq b$ and $b \leq c$, then $a \leq c$.

In a partially ordered set, if both $a \leq b$ and $a \neq b$, then we write, simply, $a < b$ or $b > a$.

Definitions. A *simply ordered*, or *linearly ordered*, set is a POS, S, such that at least one of $a \leq b$ or $b \leq a$ holds for all a and b in S. A *chain* is another term for a simply ordered set. A chain S is *well-ordered* if for any nonempty subset T of S, there exists an element c in T such that $c \leq x$ for all x in T, i.e., every nonempty subset T has a "smallest" or "least" element.

Definition. Two well-ordered sets A and B are (*order*) *isomorphic* if there exists a 1–1 correspondence, α, between their elements such that for any x and y in A, $x \leq y$ iff $x\alpha \leq y\alpha$.

It is easily verified that this notion of isomorphism of well-ordered sets is an equivalence relation on the class of all such sets.

An *ordinal number* is an (order) equivalence class of well-ordered sets. This is in contrast to a *cardinal number*, which is an equivalence class of sets without regard to order. That is, two sets are cardinally equivalent merely if there exists a 1–1 correspondence between their elements. We note also that zero is both a cardinal and an ordinal number, namely that of the empty set.

To illustrate some of these notions, we note that the set of positive integers is well-ordered in the usual ordering. The set of positive rational numbers, however, is not well-ordered in the usual ordering, as there is, for example, no smallest rational number greater than 2, or no smallest positive rational whose square is at least 2. We can assign a well-ordering to the positive rationals if, for example, we define

$$\frac{a}{b} \leq \frac{c}{d} \text{ if } b < d,$$

$$\text{or} \qquad \text{if } b = d \text{ and } a \leq c,$$

where the latter orderings are the usual ones for the positive integers, and we agree that all rational numbers are to be expressed in "lowest terms." The reader may find it instructive to assign a well-ordering to the set of polynomials in one indeterminate with coefficients in a well-ordered ring, for instance, the ring of integers with the ordering

$$0 < -1 < 1 < -2 < 2 < -3 < 3 < \cdots.$$

Definition. If A is a well-ordered set and y is in A, then the set of all x in A such that $x \leq y$ is called the *initial segment of* y *in* A, and is denoted by $\mathrm{IS}(y)$.

We now quote a few lemmas, the proofs of which are not too difficult and will be left to the reader:

Lemma 1. *A chain C is well-ordered if, for every c in C, the set of elements of C less than c is well-ordered.*

Lemma 2. *For any ordinal number α, the set of ordinals less than α is well-ordered and has ordinal α.*

Lemma 3. *Any two ordinals α and β are comparable, that is, either*

$$\alpha \leq \beta \qquad \textit{or} \qquad \beta \leq \alpha.$$

Lemma 4. *Any set of ordinals is well-ordered.*

Let S be any set and $P(S)$ the set of all nonempty subsets of S. By a *choice function on* S, we mean a mapping f from $P(S)$ into S, such that for any element T of $P(S)$, i.e., nonempty subset T of S, Tf is an element of T.

With these preliminary definitions and results, we are able to state and prove our principal theorem:

Theorem A–1. *The following statements are equivalent:*

(i) *Any nonempty set A has a choice function.* (Zermelo's Axiom of Choice)

(ii) *Any nonempty set A can be well-ordered.* (Well-Ordering Axiom)

(iii) *Any POS, P, has a maximal subchain, i.e., a subchain not properly contained in any other subchain.* (Zorn's Lemma, first form)

(iv) *Any nonempty POS, P, in which every subchain C has an upper bound in P, i.e., an element x of P such that* $c \leq x$ *for all c in C, must contain a maximal element, i.e., an element m such that for no x in P is* $m < x$. (Zorn's Lemma, second form)

PROOF. (i) implies (ii).

Let A be any nonempty set. Since, by (i), A has a choice function, we may define a function f from $P(A) \cup \{\emptyset\}$, the set of all subsets of A, into A such that for every subset S of A other than A itself, Sf is an element of A not in S, since, for any such S, the complement of S in A is not empty. We shall say that a well-ordering of a subset S of A is compatible with f if for every $a \in S$, we have $a = [\text{IS}(a)]f$. Thus the first element a_1 of a compatibly well-ordered subset S must be $\emptyset f$, the second element a_2 must be $\{a_1\}f$, etc.

Let S and T be any two compatibly well-ordered subsets of A. We assert that either $S = T$ (the same elements with the same order) or else one must be an initial segment of the other. For, by Lemma 3, there must exist an isomorphism h of one, say S, into the other, T. This isomorphism is either onto T or else onto some initial segment of T. If h is not the identity mapping, then let x be the first element of S for which $xh = y \neq x$. (Such an x must exist, since S is well-ordered.) Now $\text{IS}(x)$ is identically the same as $\text{IS}(y)$, since h is the identity on all elements of S less than x. But then $x = [\text{IS}(x)]f = [\text{IS}(y)]f = y$, a contradiction. Hence no such x can exist, h is the identity map on all of S, and our assertion is established.

Now consider the set of all compatibly well-ordered subsets S_i of A. Let W be the union of all the S_i and order W as follows: For any x and y in W, we have $x \in S_i$, $y \in S_j$ and one of S_i, S_j contained in the other, say $S_i \subseteq S_j$. Then both x and y are in S_j, a well-ordered set; so we may define $x \leq y$ or $y \leq x$ in W, according as $x \leq y$ or $y \leq x$ in S_j. (Note that, by the above argument, this definition is independent of the particular S_j chosen.)

This is a linear ordering of W, since for any x and y in W, x and y are comparable. It is also a well-ordering, for, by Lemma 1, it is sufficient to show well-ordering for all elements less than an arbitrary x in W. But x is in some S_i, and S_i must also contain all elements of W which are less than x. Since S_i is well-ordered, and the ordering of elements of S_i is the same whether considered as elements of S_i or of W, the set of elements of W less than x must be well-ordered. Finally, the ordering is compatible with f. For if we take any x in W, then $x = [\text{IS}(x)]f$, where $\text{IS}(x)$ is taken in any S_i containing x. But $\text{IS}(x)$ is the same in W as in S_i. If $W \neq A$, then let $Y = W \cup \{Wf\}$, and order Y by $Wf > x$ for all x in W; otherwise the order of Y is that of W. Then Y is also compatibly well-ordered, and, hence, is an S_i and must be contained in W, a contradiction. Thus $W = A$ and A is well-ordered.

(ii) implies (iii).

Let P be a partially ordered set. We may assume that P is not empty as, otherwise, the result is trivial. P may be well-ordered, say with ordinal λ, by assumption of (ii). By Lemma 2, P can then be indexed by the ordinals less than λ, $P = \{a_0, a_1, \ldots, a_\alpha, \ldots\}$.

Let S be either P or an initial segment of P with respect to this well-ordering. A function $g\colon S \to S$ will be called suitable if (1) $a_1 g = a_1$ and (2) for any other a in S, $ag = a$ if a is comparable in the original partial ordering with all elements of $[\text{IS}(a)]g$ and, otherwise, $ag = a_1$. (Recall that initial segments are defined only with respect to a well-ordering.)

Now if S admits a suitable function, it is unique. For, otherwise, there is an element b of minimal index for which the functions differ, say $bg \neq bg'$. But $[\text{IS}(b)]g$ is identically $[\text{IS}(b)]g'$, which implies that $bg = bg'$, a contradiction.

Let W be the union of all the S_i which admit a suitable function. Then W admits a suitable function, for if x is in W, then x is in S_i for some S_i, and, as an element of S_i, a suitable function g is already defined for x. If there is an element of P, say y, not in W, we may let yg be y or a_1, according as y is comparable with Wg or not. Then we have a suitable function defined on $W \cup \{y\}$ which, thus, must be some S_j. But then y is in W, contrary to assumption. Hence we must have $W = P$.

Wg is, then, the desired maximal subchain in P. For if there were an element not in Wg, say z, comparable with all elements in Wg, then we would have $zg = z$, and z would be in $Wg = Pg$, another contradiction.

(iii) implies (iv).

Let P be a partially ordered set in which every subchain has an upper bound in P. Then by assumption of (iii), P has a maximal subchain C and C has an upper bound m in P. Clearly, m must be in C, since C is maximal. If there exists an element x in P greater than m, then $\{C, x\}$ is a chain properly containing C, which is impossible by the maximality of C. Hence no such x can exist and m is maximal in P.

(iv) implies (i).

Let A be a nonempty partially ordered set and let P be the set of all pairs (M, f), where M is a set of subsets of A and f is a choice function defined on M. We define $(M_1, f_1) \geq (M_2, f_2)$ to mean $M_1 \supseteq M_2$ and f_1 agrees with f_2 on M_2. This makes P a partially ordered set.

We assert that in P any chain $\{(M_i, f_i)\}$ has an upper bound (U, g). For let U be the union of all the M_i for (M_i, f_i) in the chain, and if S is in U, then S is in some M_i, so that we may define $Sg = Sf_i$. This definition is independent of the particular M_i chosen. Moreover, it is easy to see that g is a choice function of U.

Now there is a maximal element (V, h) in P, by (iv). We claim that V is the set of all nonempty subsets of A. For if there were a missing nonempty subset T, then we could enlarge the set V by adding T as another element and extend the choice function h by defining Th to be any element in T, thus contradicting the maximality of (V, h).

The equivalence of the four statements is thus established.

Before giving examples of the use of these set theoretic axioms in abstract algebra, we remark that the union of any ascending chain of ideals in a ring R is, again, an ideal in R. Similarly, the union of any ascending chain of fields is a field.

Theorem A–2. *Let F be any field. Then there exists an algebraically complete algebraic extension field K of F, which is unique to within equivalence over F.*

PROOF. The polynomial domain $F[x]$ can be well-ordered by the Well-Ordering Axiom. Let $F_0 = F$, and for each element f_α of $F[x]$, let F_α be the splitting field of f_α over the union of all F_β with $\beta < \alpha$. We assert that the union K of all the F_α for f_α in $F[x]$ is the desired field. First, K is algebraic over F, since, by the construction of K, every element of K is a root of some polynomial in $F[x]$.

Moreover, K is algebraically complete. For suppose that $g(x)$ is an element of $K[x]$. Then $g(x)$ splits in some algebraic extension field $K(r_1, r_2, \ldots, r_n)$, where the r_i are the roots of $g(x)$. Now each r_i is algebraic over K and K is algebraic over F; hence, by Theorem 4.10, each r_i is algebraic over F. Thus r_i is a root of some f_{α_i} in $F[x]$, which means that r_i is in F_{α_i}. But then r_i is in K and

$$K = K(r_1, r_2, \ldots, r_n),$$

so that every element of $K[x]$ splits in $K[x]$.

Suppose, now, that K and L are two algebraically complete algebraic extensions of F. To show that K and L are equivalent over F, we must show that there is an isomorphism between K and L, $\phi\colon K \to L$, such that $a\phi = a$ for all a in F.

Consider the set P of all triples

$$(K', L', \phi'),$$

where $F \subseteq K' \subseteq K$, $F \subseteq L' \subseteq L$, and $\phi'\colon K' \to L'$ is an isomorphism leaving every element of F fixed. P is a partially ordered set under the order relation

$$(K', L', \phi') \le (K'', L'', \phi''),$$

if $K' \subseteq K''$, $L' \subseteq L''$, and $a\phi' = a\phi''$ for all a in K'. Every subchain C of P clearly has the upper bound (K^*, L^*, ϕ^*), where K^* is the union of all the K' in elements of C, L^* is the union of all the L' in elements of C, and ϕ^* is defined on the element t by considering t as an element of any K' containing t. Then, by Zorn's Lemma, second form, P must have a maximal element $(K^\#, L^\#, \phi^\#)$.

Suppose that there exists an element k in K which is not in $K^\#$. Since k is algebraic over F, k is algebraic over $K^\#$, say with minimum polynomial $p(x)$ in $K^\#[x]$. By Theorem 4.12, the isomorphism $\phi^\#$ of $K^\#$ and $L^\#$ can be extended to an isomorphism of the splitting field of $p(x)$ over $K^\#$ and that of $q(x)$ over $L^\#$, where $q(x)$ is the polynomial corresponding to $p(x)$ under $\phi^\#$. But then the element $(K^\#, L^\#, \phi^\#)$ would not be maximal in P. Hence no such k exists and $K = K^\#$. Thus $K^\#$ is algebraically complete and $L^\#$ is also. But every element of L is algebraic over F and, hence, must be in the algebraically complete field $L^\#$, so that $L = L^\#$. Thus we have that K and L are equivalent over F.

In the development of ideal theory, where one does not assume the ascending chain condition on ideals as one does in the case of Noetherian ideal theory, much use is made of Zorn's Lemma. As an illustration of the type of argument encountered in such applications, we shall prove the following theorem.

Theorem A–3. *Let A be an ideal in a ring R with unity element, $A \neq R$. Then A is contained in a maximal ideal M of R.*

PROOF. Consider the partially ordered set S of ideals A' of R such that $A \subseteq A' \subset R$, the ordering being by inclusion. The union of any ascending chain of ideals is an ideal, and if none of the ideals in the chain is equal to R, then the union must also be different from R. For if the unity element, e, is in the union, it must be in some ideal in the chain, which contradicts the condition that the ideal be unequal to R. Thus every ascending chain of ideals in S has an upper bound in S. Hence, by Zorn's Lemma, there exists a maximal element M in S. M certainly contains A and the definition of S shows at once that if M is maximal in S, then M is a maximal ideal of R.

As an example of the use of Zorn's Lemma in group theory, consider the following: An (additive) Abelian group G is called *divisible* if for any x in G and positive integer n, there exists y in G such that $g = ny$. A subgroup H of G is a divisible subgroup of G if H is divisible as a group. We then have the following theorem.

Theorem A–4. *Any divisible subgroup H of the (additive) Abelian group G is a direct summand, i.e., there exists a subgroup K of G such that $G = H \oplus K$.*

PROOF. The set of all subgroups K' of G such that $H \cap K' = 0$ is a partially ordered set under the inclusion ordering. Since the union of any ascending chain of such subgroups is again such a subgroup, Zorn's Lemma assures us that there exists a maximal such subgroup, K. We now need only show that $H + K = G$.

If, on the contrary, there exists x in G such that $x \notin H + K$, then let $L = (K, x)$. Since L properly contains K (x is not in K) and all elements of L are of the form $mx + k$ for some integer m and some $k \in K$, the maximality of K implies that $mx + k = h \neq 0$ for some $k \in K$ and $h \in H$. Then $mx = h - k$ is in $H + K$. Let m be the least integer such that $mx \in H + K$ and we have $m \geq 2$, since $x \notin H + K$. Thus m is divisible by some prime p and we let $y = (m/p)x$. Since $m/p < m$, $y \notin H + K$, while $py = mx = h - k \in H + K$. Since H is divisible, we have $h = ph'$ for some $h' \in H$, and we let $z = y - h'$. If $z \in H + K$, then $y = z + h' \in H + K$. But, $y \notin H + K$, hence $z \notin H + K$. Thus $z \notin K$ and some nonzero element $nz + k'$ of (K, z) is in H, say $nz + k' = h'' \neq 0$. Now if p divides n, say $n = qp$, then $nz = q(pz) = q(py - ph') = q(py - h) = q(-k) \in K$, which would imply $h'' \in K$, which is not the case. Thus p does not divide n, and we have $ap + bn = 1$ for some integers a and b. But then $z = apz + bnz = a(-k) + b(-k' + h'') \in H + K$, a contradiction. Hence no such x can exist, $H + K = G$ and $G = H \oplus K$.

Ordered Fields

In order to develop the real number system, one must adopt some starting point. If one wishes, one can go back to the theory of sets and develop the whole structure from that point on. Or one may wish to begin with the natural numbers (or positive integers), defining them by means of the Peano Postulates or some other equivalent system of axioms. One would then imbed the additive semi-group of natural numbers in the group of integers by a process very similar to that used to imbed an integral domain in a field, and then define multiplication in terms of natural multiples to obtain the ring of integers. The integers are then imbedded in the rationals. We may note that one usually introduces the concept of order at the stage of the natural numbers if one adopts this procedure, and, of course, must show at each stage of the enlargement process that the order relation can be extended to the larger system. Alternatively, one can delay introducing order until the rationals have been constructed, thus ordering the natural numbers and integers as subsets of the rationals.

The reader should be able to carry out the indicated process up to the stage of the rational number field, and so we shall turn our attention in this section to the passage from the rational number field to the real number field. As a first step, we shall introduce the notion of an ordered field.

Definition. A field F is said to be *ordered* if there exists a partition of the nonzero elements of F into two disjoint classes F_P and F_N such that:

(i) If a is in F_N, then $-a$ is in F_P.

(ii) If a and b are in F_P, then $a + b$ and ab are in F_P.

We write $a > b$ if $a - b$ is in F_P and $a < b$ if $a - b$ is in F_N and call F_P (F_N) the *class of positive* (*negative*) *elements of* F.

One may easily show that if F is an ordered field, a and b are in F_N, and c is in F_P, then $a + b$ and ac are in F_N and ab is in F_P. For we have $-a$ and $-b$ in F_P, whence

$$-(a + b) = (-a) + (-b), (-a)c = -(ac), \text{and } (-a)(-b) = ab$$

are all in F_P, $a + b$ and ac are in F_N.

It is then possible to derive the familiar properties of the relation $a < b$ (in particular, that it is a linear or simple ordering of F) and, likewise, the familiar properties of $|a|$ if we define $|a|$ to be a, $-a$, or 0 according as a is, respectively, positive, negative, or zero. Two ordered fields are called *order isomorphic* if there exists an isomorphism between them which preserves order relations as well as sums and products.

It is clear that in any ordered field, the unity element 1 is positive, since $1 = 1^2$, and a^2 is positive for any nonzero element a of the field. If we consider the field R of rational numbers, it then follows that since $n + 1 > n$ for every integer n, the integers 1, 2, 3, . . . are all positive, and the integers $-1, -2, -3$, . . . are all negative. For an arbitrary element x of R, we may write $x = a/b$, where a and b are integers and b is positive. It then follows that x is positive, zero, or negative, according as a is positive, zero, or negative. Thus the only possible ordering of the field R is the "natural" ordering, and, moreover, any ordered field isomorphic to R must actually be order isomorphic to R. (It should be remembered that the ordering of a field which we are now considering is quite a distinct notion from that of a well-ordering of the set of elements in the field. Thus, while the "natural" order is the only order the rational numbers can have as a field, other order relations are required if we wish to consider the rational numbers as elements of a well-ordered set.)

It also follows readily from the positiveness of 1 that in a field of finite characteristic p, the element

$$-a = (p - 1)a = a + a + \cdots + a$$

must be in the same class as a, whence we conclude that an ordered field cannot have finite characteristic. Thus we see that every ordered field must contain an isomorphic copy of the field R of rational numbers, and the only possible order for this prime subfield of every ordered field is the natural order.

To bring the notion of order closer to that which we customarily think of as the order relation in the real field, we introduce the notion of a field with an Archimedean ordering.

An ordered field K is said to be *Archimedean ordered* if for every element a of K, there exists an integer n greater than a. (Here we are, of course, considering R as the prime field of K, rather than just an isomorphic copy of R.)

The field R is Archimedean ordered. For if a is zero or negative, then we may take $n = 1$. If a is positive, then we may find the desired n by applying a particular case of the following argument:

We claim that for any two positive rational numbers a/b and c/d, where a, b, c, d are positive integers, there exists an integer n such that $n(a/b) > c/d$. This is true by the definition of order in R if and only if $nad > bc$. This we obtain, in turn, as a particular case of the result that, for any two positive integers r and s, there exists an integer n such that $nr > s$. This latter property follows at once if we take $n = s + 1$, since then

$$nr = (s + 1)r \geq s + 1 > s.$$

(We note that these results for positive rational numbers and positive integers which extend easily to any pairs of nonzero rationals or, respectively, integers, are frequently known as the Archimedean laws for the rationals and integers, whence comes the term Archimedean ordered field. We shall see that a similar property holds in the real number field.)

One property of an Archimedean ordered field K will be particularly useful later on. If $\epsilon > 0$ in K, then we may find a positive integer n such that $n > \epsilon^{-1}$. It follows that $\epsilon > n^{-1} > 0$ for the rational number n^{-1}. We may also find a positive integer m (e.g., $m = n$) such that $2^m > n$, whence, $\epsilon > 2^{-m}$. The similarity of these results to certain frequently used facts in analysis will be obvious.

We next generalize the notion of absolute value to that of a valuation of a field.

Consider a function ϕ from the field F to an Archimedean ordered field K. ϕ is a *valuation of F* if:

(i) $0\phi = 0$ and $a\phi > 0$ if $a \neq 0$ in F (ϕ is positive definite).

(ii) $(ab)\phi = (a\phi)(b\phi)$ for all a, b in F (ϕ is multiplicative).

(iii) $(a + b)\phi \leq a\phi + b\phi$ (ϕ is subadditive).

From these defining properties of a valuation, we may derive the further properties:

$1\phi = (-1)\phi = 1.$

$a\phi = (-a)\phi$ for any a in F.

$n\phi \leq n$ for any integer n in F.

$a\phi \leq b\phi + (a - b)\phi$ for all a, b in F.

$|a\phi - b\phi| \leq (a - b)\phi$, all a, b in F, where $|k|$ is the absolute value of the element k of the Archimedean ordered field K.

The valuation ϕ is called *nontrivial* if $a\phi \neq 0, 1$ for some a in F. If F is a finite field, then the nonzero elements of F form a cyclic group, say of order q, and, for all nonzero x in F, we have

$$(x^q)\phi = (x\phi)^q = 1\phi = 1,$$

whence it follows that $x\phi = 1$ and the valuation is trivial.

Two fields F and H with respective valuations $\phi: F \to K$ and $\psi: H \to K$ are called *analytically equivalent* if there is an isomorphism $\alpha: F \to H$ such that

$$f\phi = (f\alpha)\psi$$

for all f in F. Two valuations $\phi: F \to K$ and $\psi: F \to K$ of the same field F are thus equivalent if

$$a\phi < b\phi \text{ iff } a\psi < b\psi$$

for all a, b in F.

The next step in building up the concepts which we shall need to develop the real number system from the rationals is to introduce the notion of an infinite sequence, in particular, of a regular, or Cauchy sequence. With the introduction of these ideas, our development may be said to pass from the strictly algebraic to a combination of algebraic and analytic methods.

The infinite sequence $\alpha = \{a_n\} = \{a_1, a_2, \ldots, a_n, \ldots\}$ of elements a_i in the field F with valuation $\phi: F \to K$ is called a *regular* or *Cauchy sequence* if, for every $\epsilon > 0$ in K, there exists some integer n_ϵ such that $(a_p - a_q)\phi < \epsilon$ for all p and q greater than n_ϵ.

By arguments entirely similar to those of elementary analysis, one may then show that:

(i) Every Cauchy sequence (in F) is bounded (in K), i.e., if $\alpha = \{a_n\}$ is Cauchy, then there exists m_α in K such that $a_n\phi < m_\alpha$ for all positive integers n.

(ii) If $\alpha = \{a_n\}$ and $\beta = \{b_n\}$ are Cauchy, then

$$\alpha + \beta = \{a_n + b_n\} \text{ and}$$
$$\alpha\beta = \{a_nb_n\}$$

are Cauchy.

(iii) If $\delta = \{d\}$ is the Cauchy sequence all of whose elements are d, and $\alpha = \{a_n\}$ is Cauchy, then $\delta\alpha = \{da_n\}$ is Cauchy, and we will write $\delta\alpha = d\alpha$.

(iv) The sequences $0 = \{0\}$ and $1 = \{1\}$ are Cauchy.

(v) If α and β are Cauchy, then so are

$$-\alpha = \{-a_n\} \text{ and } \alpha - \beta = a + (-\beta).$$

(vi) If α and $\alpha - \beta$ are Cauchy, then so is β.

(vii) The distributive law holds for sequences, i.e.,

$$\alpha(\beta + \gamma) = \{a_n(b_n + c_n)\} = \{a_nb_n + a_nc_n\} = \alpha\beta + \alpha\gamma.$$

As a consequence of the above properties of Cauchy sequences in the elements of a field with valuation ϕ, we see that the set A of all such Cauchy sequences is a commutative ring with unity element. Also, if we identify the sequence $\{d\}$ with the element d in F, we may say that the ring A contains the field F. However, A is not, in general, a field, and what we are after is to obtain a field which contains F and is, in an as yet undefined sense, complete. To this end, we introduce the notion of a null sequence in a field F with a valuation ϕ.

A sequence $\alpha = \{a_n\}$ of the field F with valuation ϕ is *null* if for any $\epsilon > 0$ in K, there exists some positive integer n_ϵ such that $a_n\phi < \epsilon$ for all $n > n_\epsilon$.

It follows, at once, that a null sequence is Cauchy, and that if α is Cauchy and β is null, then $\alpha - \beta$ is Cauchy, and that if α is Cauchy and $\alpha - \beta$ is null, then β is Cauchy.

Note that $\alpha = \{a_n\}$ not a null sequence implies that there exists $\epsilon > 0$ in K such that, for any positive integer m, we have $a_n\phi \geq \epsilon$ for infinitely many $n > m$. For, if this were not the case, i.e., if for each $\epsilon > 0$, there is some m such that there are only a finite number of such n, then let n_ϵ be the largest of them and we would have $a_n\phi < \epsilon$ for all $n > n_\epsilon$, a contradiction of the assumption that α is not null.

Theorem A–5. *The set N of all null sequences of a field F with valuation ϕ is a maximal ideal of the set A of all Cauchy sequences of F, and, hence, the residue class ring A/N is a field F_ϕ, called the derived field of F.*

PROOF. That N is actually a proper ideal of A is trivially true, so that our argument reduces to showing that N is maximal in A. Suppose that $\alpha = \{a_n\}$ is Cauchy but not null, so that $M = (\alpha, N)$ properly contains N. We shall show that in this case $M = A$ by showing that M contains the constant sequence 1 and, hence, every element of A. To see that 1 is in M, we shall construct a sequence $\gamma = \{c_n\}$ in M none of whose elements are zero and such that the sequence $\{c_n^{-1}\}$ is Cauchy, whence the product sequence, 1, will be in M.

Now for every $\epsilon > 0$ in K, K the Archimedean ordered field into which ϕ maps F, we may find n_ϵ such that $a_p\phi - \epsilon < a_q\phi$ for all p and q greater than n_ϵ. Since α is not null, there exists some $\epsilon_0 > 0$ such that for infinitely many $p > n_{\epsilon_0} = n_0$, we have $a_p\phi \geq 2\epsilon_0$. Now we let $n_1 =$ maximum (n_0, n_ϵ), pick some fixed one of the infinitely many $p > n_1$ for which $a_p\phi \geq 2\epsilon_0$, and have

$$a_q\phi > a_p\phi - \epsilon_0 = \delta \geq \epsilon_0, \qquad \text{all } q > n_0.$$

Let $a = a_{n_0+1}$ so that $a\phi > \delta > 0$, and define a null sequence $\tau = \{t_n\}$ by $t_n = a_n - a$ for $n \leq n_0$ and $t_n = 0$ for all $n > n_0$. Since τ is null, $\gamma = \alpha - \tau$ is Cauchy and is in M. Moreover, for all c_n in $\{c_n\} = \gamma$, we have $c_n \neq 0$, since $c_n\phi > \delta > 0$.

Thus we may define the sequence $\beta = \{b_n\}$ by $b_n = c_n^{-1}$. Now β is Cauchy, since given any $\epsilon > 0$, we may choose n_ϵ such that $(c_p - c_q)\phi < \delta^2\epsilon$ for all p and q greater than n_ϵ. But then

$$(b_p - b_q)\phi = (c_p^{-1} - c_q^{-1})\phi = (c_p^{-1}c_q^{-1})\phi(c_p - c_q)\phi < \epsilon$$

for all p and q greater than n_ϵ. Hence β is Cauchy and in A, and $\beta\gamma$ is in M. But $\beta\gamma = \{1\} = 1$, and it follows that every Cauchy sequence is in M and, hence, $M = A$. Thus N is maximal in the commutative ring A with unity element. The result then follows by Corollary 3.40.1.

Now let K be a field with valuation ϕ, containing the field F. Clearly ϕ is also a valuation on F and, hence, both K_ϕ and F_ϕ are defined. However, K_ϕ will, in general, not contain all the elements of F_ϕ, since if N_F and N_K are the sets of all null sequences in F and K, respectively, then N_F is, in general, properly contained in N_K. Hence if $\alpha + N_F$ is an element of F_ϕ not in F, i.e., α is not null, then $\alpha + N_F$ is not even an element of K_ϕ. But if we consider the correspondence

$$\alpha + N_F \leftrightarrow \alpha + N_K,$$

we readily see that it is an isomorphism of F_ϕ onto a subfield of K_ϕ. Thus we may identify K_ϕ with an isomorphic field actually containing F_ϕ. This we shall agree to do in all such cases, and, thus, if K with valuation ϕ contains F, we shall have $K_\phi \supseteq F_\phi$.

We are now in a position to define the concept of *completeness* of a field with a valuation which we referred to earlier.

Definition. A field F with valuation ϕ is *complete* if $F_\phi = F$. That is, F is complete if for any Cauchy sequence $\alpha = \{a_n\}$, a_n in F, there exists an element a in F such that $\{a\}$ and $\{a_n\}$ define the same class

$$[\alpha] = \alpha + N = a + N = a \quad \text{in} \quad F_\phi.$$

We shall adopt the notation $[\alpha]$ for the equivalence class $\alpha + N$. If, as above,

$$[\alpha] = [a] = a,$$

we shall say that a is the *limit of the sequence* $\{a_n\}$, or $\lim_{n\to\infty} a_n = a$. Thus a field with valuation is complete if every Cauchy sequence of elements of the field has a limit in the field.

From this definition of limit in a complete field F, it follows that $\lim_{n\to\infty} a_n = a$ if and only if for every $\epsilon > 0$ (in the Archimedean ordered field K into which ϕ maps F), there exists n_ϵ such that $(a_n - a)\phi < \epsilon$ for all $n > n_\epsilon$, the customary form of the definition in analysis. We may now obtain the basic theorem concerning limits in a complete field.

Theorem A–6. *Let F be a complete field. Then there exists an element a in F such that $\lim_{n\to\infty} a_n = a$ if and only if $\{a_n\}$ is Cauchy, and, in this case, the limit a is unique.*

PROOF. Immediate from the above definition and remarks.

Now consider the situation where F is itself an Archimedean ordered field. We may then define $a\phi = |a|$ and let F' be the derived field of F for this absolute value valuation. We now wish to obtain an Archimedean ordering of F' preserving that of F, and, thus, a valuation of F' preserving that of F.

The Cauchy sequence $\{a_n\}$ in the Archimedean ordered field F is called *positive* if there exists $\epsilon > 0$ in F and an integer n_ϵ such that $a_n > \epsilon$ for all $n > n_\epsilon$.

Theorem A–7. *Let F' be the derived field of the Archimedean ordered field F, F'_P the set of all classes $[\alpha]$ of F' all of whose sequences are positive, and F'_N the set of all other nonzero elements $[\beta]$ of F'. Then F'_P and F'_N give an Archimedean ordering of F' which preserves that of F.*

PROOF. If $\tau = \{t_n\}$ is a null sequence, then τ cannot be positive; hence the zero element, N, of F' is not in F'_P.

If α is a positive sequence, then $\alpha + \tau$ is also positive, since for given $\epsilon > 0$, we may choose n_ϵ such that for $n > n_\epsilon$, both $a_n > \epsilon$ and $|t_n| < \epsilon/2$, whence

$$a_n + t_n \geq a_n - |t_n| > \epsilon/2.$$

Thus for any positive α, we have $[\alpha]$ in F'_P.

Now suppose that $[\alpha]$ is in F'_N; that is, the Cauchy sequence α is neither null nor positive. Then, as in the proof of the maximality of the ideal N, we have that $|a_n| > \delta > 0$ for all $n > n_0$. Hence for each $n > n_0$, either $a_n > \delta > 0$ or $-a_n > \delta > 0$. Since α is not positive, we cannot have $a_n > \delta > 0$ for all $n > n_0$.

Suppose now that for every $n_1 > n_0$, there exist p and q both greater than n_1 such that

$$a_p > \delta > 0 \text{ and } -a_q > \delta > 0.$$

Then

$$|a_p - a_q| = a_p - a_q > 2\delta,$$

which contradicts the fact that α is Cauchy, and is impossible. The only remaining possibility is that $-a_n > \delta > 0$ for all $n > n_0$ and $-\alpha$ is positive; $[-\alpha]$ is in F'_P.

Thus we have an ordering of F' if we can show that if $[\alpha]$ and $[\beta]$ are in F'_P, then so are

$$[\alpha] + [\beta] = [\alpha + \beta]$$

and

$$[\alpha][\beta] = [\alpha\beta].$$

Now there exist $\epsilon_1 > 0$ and $\epsilon_2 > 0$, together with positive integers n_{ϵ_1} and n_{ϵ_2}, such that for all n greater than both n_{ϵ_1} and n_{ϵ_2}, we have

$$a_n + b_n > \epsilon_1 + \epsilon_2 > 0$$

and

$$a_n b_n > \epsilon_1\epsilon_2 > 0,$$

whence the desired conclusion follows and F' is ordered.

It is clear that if a is in F, then $\{a\}$ defines an element $[a] = a$ of F' and $[a]$ is positive, zero, or negative, according as a is positive, zero, or negative, so that the ordering of F' preserves that of F.

To complete the proof, we must show that the ordering of F' is Archimedean; that is, for every $[\alpha]$ in F', there exists an integer n such that $n > [\alpha]$. But this is true if we can show that there exists an a in F such that $a > [\alpha]$, since F is Archimedean, and, hence, there is some n in F such that $n > a$. Now, since $\alpha = \{a_n\}$ is Cauchy, α is also bounded, and there exists b in F such that $|a_n| < b$ for all n. Now choose any fixed $c > 0$ in F and let $a = b + c$. Then $\{a\}$ is Cauchy and $a - a_n \geq a - |a_n| > c > 0$, so that $a - \alpha$ is positive and, hence, $a > [\alpha]$. This completes the proof.

Since every Archimedean ordered field F contains a subfield isomorphic to the rational number field R, we may assume without loss of generality that $F \supseteq R$ and then obtain the following important result.

Theorem A–8. *Every element* $[\gamma]$ *of the derived field* F' *of an Archimedean ordered field* F *is the equivalence class of a sequence* $\alpha = \{a_n\}$, *where the elements* a_n *are all in the rational number field* R.

PROOF. It is sufficient to consider only positive elements of F', since if $[\gamma]$ is negative, we may write $[\gamma] = -[-\gamma]$ where $[-\gamma]$ is positive, while for $[\gamma] = 0$, we simply take all the $a_n = 0$.

If γ is any positive sequence, then there must exist $\epsilon > 0$ and n_ϵ such that

$$c_n > \epsilon \qquad \text{for all } n > n_\epsilon.$$

If we then let

$$t_n = |c_n| + \epsilon \qquad \text{for } n \leq n_\epsilon$$

and

$$t_n = 0 \qquad \text{for all } n > n_\epsilon,$$

we have that $\tau = \{t_n\}$ is null; hence γ and $\beta = \gamma + \tau$ define the same element of F'. But every element of β is greater than ϵ and, hence, greater than 0. Thus, as a representative of a positive element $[\gamma]$, we may take a sequence β such that

$$b_n > \epsilon > 0 \qquad \text{for all } n.$$

We now wish to obtain a sequence α of rational numbers a_n such that $\beta - \alpha$ is null, that is, find rational "approximations" to the elements b_n of the sequence β where we are assuming that $b_n > \epsilon > 0$ for all n. Since F is Archimedean, we can find an integer greater than $2^n b_n$, and, indeed, a least such integer m_n. Then we have

$$m_n - 1 \leq 2^n b_n < m_n,$$

from which it follows that

$$0 \leq b_n - 2^{-n}(m_n - 1) < 2^{-n}.$$

Now $a_n = 2^{-n}(m_n - 1)$ is a rational number, and $\{b_n\} - \{a_n\}$ is null, since for any $\epsilon' > 0$, we may choose $n_{\epsilon'}$ such that $0 < 2^{-n} < \epsilon'$ for all $n > n_{\epsilon'}$, whence $0 \leq b_n - a_n < \epsilon'$ for all $n > n_{\epsilon'}$. Then $\alpha = \{a_n\}$ and $\beta = \{b_n\}$ define the same element $[\gamma]$ of F', and α has all rational elements.

Definition. The *real number field* R' is the derived field of the rational number field R under the absolute value valuation.

This defines R' uniquely, since we know that R has a unique Archimedean ordering; hence a unique absolute value is defined for R. R' is unique in the further sense that it contains, to within order isomorphism, every Archimedean ordered field and is, moreover, the essentially unique completion of every Archimedean ordered field, as is established by the next theorem.

Theorem A–9. *The derived field F' of any Archimedean ordered field F is complete, and is order isomorphic to the field R' of real numbers.*

PROOF. We may assume that F contains R. Now R has the natural order as its only ordering, and the derived field of R under the valuation of R, induced by the absolute value valuation of F, is order isomorphic to R'. As before, we may replace F' by an order isomorphic field or, equally well, assume that F' actually contains R'. But, by the previous theorem, every Cauchy sequence in F determines the same element of F' as is determined by some Cauchy sequence in R. Thus every element of F' is also in R', and we conclude that

$$F' = R'.$$

To complete the proof, it remains only to show that R' is complete. For this purpose we put

$$R' = F$$

and, from the argument just given, obtain that

$$(R')' = F' = R'.$$

Thus R' is its own derived field and is, therefore, complete.

We have now developed the real number system from the rational number system by the method of Cauchy sequences. As the reader is doubtless aware, the method of Dedekind cuts could equally well have been used. Having obtained the essential uniqueness of the real number field, we could, at this point, leave the further development of the properties of the system with regard to order to the subject of analysis. However, we shall include one more theorem in our treatment, partly because of its vital importance for analytic and other arguments, and partly because if we had chosen to give a postulational definition of the real numbers rather than obtaining them from the rationals, then this theorem would very likely have been included as one of the postulates.

In an ordered field F, the nonempty subset S is said to have an *upper bound* a in F if for all x in S, we have

$$x \leq a.$$

S has a *least upper bound* (l.u.b.) b in F if b is an upper bound of S, and for any upper bound a of S, we have

$$b \leq a.$$

(It follows, at once, that if S has a l.u.b., then this l.u.b. is unique.) *Lower bounds* and *greatest lower bounds* (g.l.b.) are similarly defined.

Theorem A–10. *In a complete Archimedean ordered field F (i.e., in a field order isomorphic to the real number field), any nonempty subset S which has an upper bound in F has a least upper bound in F.*

PROOF. Let s be an upper bound of S. Then, since F is Archimedean ordered, there exists an integer $M > s$, and M is also an upper bound of S. For any given positive integer p, consider the set T_p of integers k for which both $k2^{-p} \leq M$ and $k2^{-p}$ is an upper bound of S. T_p is not empty, since if we take $k_0 = M2^p$, then $k_0 2^{-p} = M$ and, hence, k_0 is in T_p. Moreover, T_p is finite, since for any element x of S, there exists an integer m such that $m > -x$ or $-m < x$, whence, if we let $k_1 = -m2^p$, then all $k < k_1$ are not in T_p. Thus there must exist a smallest integer k_p in T_p. Hence a smallest rational number $a_p = k_p 2^{-p}$, of the form $k2^{-p}$, such that $a_p \leq M$ and a_p is an upper bound of S must also exist. Then $a_p - 2^{-p} = (k_p - 1)2^{-p}$ is not an upper bound for S.

Now for all integers $q > p$, we have $a_p - 2^{-p} < a_q$, since a_q is an upper bound for S, and, also, $a_q \leq a_p$, since for every integer k in T_p, $2^{q-p}k$ is an integer in T_q and, thus,

$$a_q \leq (2^{q-p}k_p)2^{-q} = k_p 2^{-p} = a_p.$$

It follows that

$$|a_p - a_q| < 2^{-p}, \text{ all } q > p, \text{ or}$$
$$|a_p - a_q| < 2^{-n}, \text{ all } p, q > n.$$

Thus $\{a_n\}$ is Cauchy and defines an element $[\alpha] = a$ of F', which is in F, since F is complete. We have $a_p - 2^{-p} \leq a \leq a_p$ for all positive integers p.

Then a is an upper bound for S. For if not, say x in S is greater than a. We could then find a positive integer p such that $2^p > (x - a)^{-1}$, or $2^{-p} < x - a$. Since $a_p - 2^{-p} < a$, we would obtain $a_p < x$, which is impossible, since a_p is an upper bound for S.

Finally, a is the least upper bound of S. For if b were also an upper bound of S with $a - b > 0$, then we could, again, find p such that $2^p > (a - b)^{-1}$, or $2^{-p} < a - b$. Now there would exist some x in S such that

$$a_p - 2^{-p} < x < b.$$

But this would imply that $a_p < a$, which is, again, an impossibility.

References

For collateral reading and further study

GENERAL

Albert, A. A., *Fundamental Concepts of Higher Algebra.* Chicago: The University of Chicago Press, 1956.

Birkhoff, G., and MacLane, S., *A Survey of Modern Algebra,* Revised Edition. New York: The Macmillan Company, 1953.

Bourbaki, N., *Éléments de Mathematique,* Livre II, *Algèbre.* Paris: Hermann, 1942–1959.

Chevalley, C., *Fundamental Concepts of Algebra.* New York: Academic Press, Inc., 1956.

Dubriel, P., and Dubriel-Jacotin, M., *Leçons d'Algèbre Moderne.* Paris: Dunod, 1961.

Jacobson, N., *Lectures in Abstract Algebra,* Vol. I, *Basic Concepts.* Princeton: D. Van Nostrand Company, Inc., 1951.

Johnson, R. E., *First Course in Abstract Algebra.* Englewood Cliffs, New Jersey: Prentice-Hall, Inc., 1953.

McCoy, N. H., *Introduction to Modern Algebra.* Boston: Allyn and Bacon, Inc., 1960.

Miller, K. S., *Elements of Modern Abstract Algebra.* New York: Harper & Brothers, 1958.

Redei, L., *Algebra,* Part 1. Leipzig: Geest & Portig, 1959.

Smirnov, V., *Linear Algebra and Group Theory,* revised, adapted and edited by R. A. Silverman. New York: McGraw-Hill Book Company, Inc., 1961.

Van der Waerden, B. L., *Modern Algebra,* 2 vols. New York: Frederick Ungar Publishing Company, Inc.; Vol. I, 1953; Vol. II, 1950.

Zariski, O., and Samuel, P., *Commutative Algebra,* Vol. I. Princeton: D. Van Nostrand Company, Inc., 1958.

SETS, FUNCTIONS

Fraenkel, A. A., *Abstract Set Theory,* 2d ed. Amsterdam: North Holland Publishing Company, 1961.

Halmos, P. R., *Naive Set Theory.* Princeton: D. Van Nostrand Company, Inc., 1960.

Hamilton, N. T., and Landin, J., *Set Theory: The Structure of Arithmetic.* Boston: Allyn and Bacon, Inc., 1961.

Kamke, E., *Theory of Sets,* trans. from 2d German ed. by F. Bagemihl. New York: Dover Publications, Inc., 1950.

Kuratowski, K., *Introduction to Set Theory and Topology.* Reading, Massachusetts: Addison-Wesley Publishing Company, Inc., 1962.

Landau, E., *Foundations of Analysis,* trans. by F. Steinhardt. New York: Chelsea Publishing Company, 1951.

Stoll, R. R., *Sets, Logic, and Axiomatic Theories.* San Francisco: W. H. Freeman and Company, 1961.

Thurston, H. A., *The Number System.* New York: Interscience Publishers, a division of John Wiley & Sons, Inc., 1956.

GROUPS

Fuchs, L., *Abelian Groups.* New York: Pergamon Press, 1960.

Hall, M., Jr., *The Theory of Groups.* New York: The Macmillan Company, 1959.

Kaplanski, I., *Infinite Abelian Groups.* Ann Arbor: The University of Michigan Press, 1954.

Kurosh, A., *The Theory of Groups,* 2 vols., trans. by K. A. Hirsch, 2d English ed. New York: Chelsea Publishing Company, 1960.

Ledermann, W., *Introduction to the Theory of Finite Groups,* 4th rev. ed. New York: Interscience Publishers, a division of John Wiley & Sons, Inc., 1961.

Zassenhaus, H. J., *The Theory of Groups,* 2d ed. New York: Chelsea Publishing Company, 1958.

RINGS

Artin, E., Nesbitt, C. J., and Thrall, R. M., *Rings with Minimum Condition.* Ann Arbor: The University of Michigan Press, 1944.

Jacobson, N., *The Theory of Rings.* New York: American Mathematical Society, 1943.

McCoy, N. H., *Rings and Ideals.* Buffalo: The Mathematical Association of America; La Salle, Illinois: The Open Court Publishing Company, 1948.

Northcott, D. G., *Ideal Theory.* Cambridge: Cambridge University Press, 1953.

Zariski, O., and Samuel, P., *Commutative Algebra,* Vol. II. Princeton: D. Van Nostrand Company, Inc., 1960.

FIELDS

Artin, E., *Galois Theory,* Notre Dame Mathematical lectures, no. 2, 2d ed., revised. Notre Dame, Indiana: University of Notre Dame Press, 1944.

Schilling, O., *The Theory of Valuations.* New York: American Mathematical Society, 1950.

Steinitz, E., *Algebraische Theorie der Koerper.* New York: Chelsea Publishing Company, 1950.

Tschebotaroew, N., and Schwerdtfeger, H., *Grundzuege der Galois'schen Theorie.* Groningen: Noordhoff, 1950.

LINEAR ALGEBRA

Finkbeiner, D. T., II, *Introduction to Matrices and Linear Transformations.* San Francisco: W. H. Freeman and Company, 1960.

Halmos, P. R., *Finite-Dimensional Vector Spaces.* Princeton: D. Van Nostrand Company, Inc., 1958.

Hoffman, K., and Kunze, R., *Linear Algebra.* Englewood Cliffs, New Jersey: Prentice-Hall, Inc., 1961.

Jacobson, N., *Lectures in Abstract Algebra,* Vol. II, Linear Algebra. Princeton: D. Van Nostrand Company, Inc., 1953.

Murdoch, D. C., *Linear Algebra for Undergraduates.* New York: John Wiley & Sons, Inc., 1957.

Paige, L. J., and Swift, J. D., *Elements of Linear Algebra.* Boston: Ginn and Company, 1961.

Schreier, O., and Sperner, E., *Introduction to Modern Algebra and Matrix Theory,* 2d ed. New York: Chelsea Publishing Company, 1959.

Thrall, R. M., and Tornheim, L., *Vector Spaces and Matrices.* New York: John Wiley & Sons, Inc., 1957.

Index

Abel, Niels Henrik, 186
Abelian group, 17, 70
Additive notation for a group, 18
Addition modulo n, 27
Adjunction to a field, 151
Algebraic element, 151
Algebraic extension field, 151, 158
Algebraic numbers, field of, 161
Algebraic system or structure, 14
Algebraically closed or complete, 191, 197
Alternating group, 38
Analytically equivalent fields, 201
Annihilator or order of an ideal, 93
Antecedent, 8
Anti-isomorphic, 36
Archimedean laws, 200
Archimedean order, 200
Arithmetic, fundamental laws of, 12
Ascending chain condition, 113
Associate elements, 116
Associated prime ideal, 128, 135
Associativity, 12, 17, 24
Automorphism, 14
  of a group, 33
  of a ring, 89
Automorphism group of a field, 181
Axiom of choice, Zermelo's, 195

Basis, of extension field, 157, 159
  of ideal, 113
  of module, 142
Basis theorem, Hilbert, 131
Binary operation or composition, 9
Binary relation, 5
Bound, greatest lower, 207
  least upper, 207

Cancellation law of addition, 13
Cancellation properties of a ring, 83
Cardinal number, 194
Cardinally equivalent sets, 8
Cauchy or regular sequence, 202
Center of a group, 50, 73
Chain, 193
Chain conditions, ascending, 113
  descending, for groups, 41
    for ideals, 113
Characteristic of a ring, 138
Characteristic series, 58
Characteristic subgroup, 52
Chief or principal series, 58
Choice, Zermelo's axiom of, 195
Choice function, 194
Class, conjugate, 45
  equivalence, 6
  of positive (negative) elements, 199
Class equation of a group, conjugate, 74
Closure of operation, 10
Common divisor, 115
Commutative group, 17
Commutative ring, 78
Commutator, 50
Compatible operation, 10
Complement, 4
Complete, algebraically, 191, 197
Complete inverse image, 9
Complete ordered field, 204
Component or factor of direct product, 62
Composite or product mapping, 9
Composition. *See* Operation
Composition series, 58
Congruence modulo a subgroup, 39
Congruence modulo an ideal, 86
Congruence modulo n, 26
Conjugate class, 45
Conjugate element, 41
Conjugate subgroup, 41
Content of a polynomial, 122
Correspondence, 8
Coset, 39
Cycle, 29, 31
Cyclic group, 26, 34
Cyclic module, 142
Cyclic permutation, 31
Cyclotomic polynomial, 171, 176

Dedekind's modular law, 94
Degree, of algebraic element, 152
  of extension field, 157
  of polynomial, 104
Derivative mapping, 165
Derived field, 203
Derived group, 62
Descending chain condition, for groups, 41
  for ideals, 113
Difference or factor module, 142
Dimension of vector space, 146
Direct product of groups, 62
  component or factor of, 62
  interior, 66
  weak, 63

Direct sum of groups, 63
Disjoint sets, 6
Distributive laws, for modules, 141
  for natural numbers, 12
  for rings, 77
Divisible subgroup, 198
Division ring, 78
Division algorithm for integers, 118
  for natural numbers, 13
  for polynomials, 105
  for rings, 119
Divisor, common, 115
Divisor, of an ideal, 112
  of a polynomial, left or right, 107
  of a ring element, 115
  of zero, 78
Domain, integral, 78
Domain of a function, 8
Duplication of cube, 161

Eisenstein's irreducibility criterion, 170
Element or member of a set, 2
Empty or null set, 3
Endomorphism, 15
  of a group, 33
  of a ring, 89
Equivalence class, 6
Equivalence relation, 5
  mapping determined by, 9
Equivalent fields, 163
Euclidean algorithm, 119
Euclidean domain, 119
Euclidean ring, 119
Euler extension of the Fermat Theorem, 88
Even permutation, 38
Extension, of isomorphism, 97
  by radicals, 186
Extension field, 151
  algebraic, 151, 158
  degree of, 157
  finite, 157
  normal, 181
  separable, 164
  simple, 151
  transcendental, 151, 158
Extension ring, 97
External composition or operation, 10

Factor or component of direct product, 62
Factor or divisor of a polynomial, right or left, 107
Factor group, 46
Factor or difference module, 142
Factor ring, 87
Factor set, 6
Factorization into primes, 117
Factors of a series, 58
Fermat's theorem, 88, 140

Field, 78
  of algebraic numbers, 161
  of quotients, 99
  of rational functions, 150
  of rational numbers, 100, 102
  of real numbers, 206
Finite basis condition (for ideals), 113
Finite dimensional vector space, 146
Finite extension of a field, 157
Finitely generated group, 67, 70
Finitely generated module, 142
Fixed field, 179
Fully invariant series, 58
Fully invariant subgroup, 52
Function. *See* Mapping
Function, choice, 195
Fundamental homomorphism theorems, 47, 53, 90
Fundamental laws of arithmetic, 12
Fundamental theorem of algebra, 188
Fundamental theorem of Galois theory, 184

Galois field, 174
Galois group, 181, 186
Gauss's Lemma, 122
Gauss's proof for the Fundamental Theorem of Algebra, 188
Generators, 26
Generating system, for ideal, 85
  for subgroup, 39
  for submodule, 142
Greatest common divisor, 115, 121
Greatest lower bound, 207
Group, 17
Group with operator, 51
Groupoid, 24

Hilbert basis theorem, 131
Homomorphism, 15
  of groups, 33, 53
  of rings, 89
Homomorphism theorem, for groups, 47, 53
  for rings, 90

Ideal, 84
  generated by a subset, 85
Ideals, quotient of, 93
Idempotent, 21
Identity coset, 40
Identity or unity element, 17
  left, 21
  right, 21
  ring with, 78
  uniqueness of, 20
Identity transformation, 28, 31
Image, 8
  complete inverse, 9
Imbedded primes of an ideal, 135

Imbedding in an extension ring, 97
Indeterminate, 103
Index of a subgroup, 40
Induction, principle of mathematical or finite, 11
  second principle of, 11
Initial segment, 194
Inner automorphism, 41
Integers modulo n, group of, 27
Integral domain, 78
Interior direct product, 66
Internal operation or composition, 10
Intersection, 3
  of ideals, 85
  of subgroups, 42
Invariant subgroup or normal subgroup, 42
Inverse element, 17
Inverse image, complete, 9
Inverse mapping, 8
Irreducible element, 116
Irreducible ideal, 132
Irreducible polynomial, 121, 152, 168
Irreducibility criterion, Eisenstein's, 170
Irredundant or reduced primary representation, 133
Isolated component, 136
Isolated primary component, 136
Isolated or minimal prime of an ideal, 133
Isomorphic series, 58
Isomorphism, 14
  of groups, 33, 53
  of rings, 89
Isomorphism theorems for groups, 54–56
Isomorphism theorems for rings, 91–92
Isomorphisms, linearly independent, 179

Jordan-Hölder theorem, 60

Kernel of homomorphism, 47, 90
Kronecker, Leopold, 154, 169

Lagrange's theorem, 40
Leading coefficient, 104
Leading term, 104
Least upper bound, 207
Left ideal, 84
Left identity element, 21
Left inverse, 21
Left quotient, 106
Left remainder, 106
Length of a cycle, 31
Length of a series, 58
Limit of a sequence, 204
Linear combination, 142
Linear homogeneous equations, system of, 147
Linearly dependent, 142
Linearly independent, 142
Linearly independent isomorphisms, 179
Linearly or simply ordered set, 193
Loop, 24
Lower bound of a sequence, 207

Mapping, 8
  composite or product, 9
  determined by equivalence relation, 9
  inverse, 8
  one-to-one, 8
  onto, 8
  successor, of natural numbers, 11
Matrix, 80
Maximal condition, 113
Maximal ideal, 125
Maximal subgroup, 54
Member or element of a set, 2
Minimal condition, 113
Minimal generating system, 67
Minimal or isolated prime of an ideal, 133
Minimum polynomial, 152
Modular field, 150
Modular law, Dedekind's, 94
Module, 141
Monic polynomial, 104
Monomial, 109
Multiple of an ideal, 112
Multiplication, scalar, 51, 143
Multiplicative group, 18
Multiplicative system, 129
Mutually disjoint sets, 6

n-ary relation, 5
Natural homomorphism, 48, 90
Natural isomorphism, 48
Natural multiple, 18, 85, 138
Natural numbers, 11
Negative elements, class of, 199
Nilpotent, 88
Noetherian ring, 131
Normal extension field, 181
Normal series, 58
Normal subgroup, 41
Normalizer, 73
Null sequence, 202
Null or empty set, 3
Number of zeros of polynomial, 107
Numbers, algebraic, 161
  cardinal, 194
  natural, 11
  rational, 100, 102
  real, 206

Odd permutation, 38
One-to-one mapping, 8
Onto mapping, 8
Operation, 9
  well-defined, 19, 26

Operator automorphism, 53
Operator endomorphism, 53
Operator homomorphism, 53
Operator isomorphism, 53
Operator subgroup, 52
Operators, group with, 51
Order, Archimedean, 200
  or annihilator of ideal, 93
  of element, 39
  of group, 34, 71, 72
  of root of unity, 175
Order isomorphism, 193, 199
Ordered field, 199
Ordinal number, 194
Outer automorphism, 41

p-group, 70
Parallelogram law of vector addition, 144
Partially ordered set, 193
Partition, 6
Peano's postulates, 11
Permutation, 31
Permutation group, 32, 35
Polynomial, 103
  in several indeterminates, 108
Polynomial domain, 121
Polynomial ring, 103
Positive elements, class of, 199
Positive sequence, 204
Primary component, of an ideal, 135
  isolated, 136
Primary group, 70
Primary ideal, 127
Primary representation of ideal, 133
Prime element, 116
Prime factorization, 117
Prime field, 149
Prime ideal, 125
  imbedded, 135
  isolated or minimal, 133
Prime subfield, 149
Primitive polynomial, 122
Primitive root of unity, 175
Principal or chief series, 58
Principal ideal, 85
Principal ideal domain, 111
Principal ideal ring, 111
Product, of ideals, 93
  of subgroups, 42
Product or composite mapping, 9
Product set, 4
Projection homomorphism, 66
Proper ideal, 84
Proper subgroup, 37

Quasi-field, 78
Quasi-group, 24
Quaternions, 81
Quotient, of ideals, 93
  of polynomials, 106
Quotient field, 99
Quotient group, 46

Radical, 88, 95
  of an ideal, 95
  of a primary ideal, 127
Radicals, extension by, 186
  solvable by, 186
Rational function field, 150
Rational number field, 100, 102
Real number field, 206
Reduced or irredundant primary representation, 133
Reducible ideal, 132
Refinement of a series, 58
Refinement theorem, Schreier, 58
Reflexivity, 5
Regular or Cauchy sequence, 202
Regular representation, 36
Relations, 5
Relatively prime, 116
Remainder, 106
Remainder theorem, 106
Representation, of group, 36
  of ideal, 133
Residue class, 86
Residue or remainder class ring, 87
Right ideal, 84
Right identity element, 21
Right inverse, 21
Right quotient, 106
Right remainder, 106
Ring, 77
  extension, 97
  factor, 87
  of polynomials, 103, 109
  of residue or remainder classes, 87
  with unity, 78
Root, of polynomial, 107, 154
  of unity, 175

Scalar, 143
Scalar multiple, 51, 143
Schreier refinement theorem, 58
Self-conjugate subgroup, 42
Semi-group, 24
Separability, 164
Sequence, regular or Cauchy, 202
Series, composition, 58
Set, 2
Set inclusion, 2
Set of operators, 51
Sfield, 78
Simple extension field, 151
Simple group, 41
Simply or linearly ordered set, 193

Skew-field, 78
Solvable group, 62
  by radicals, 186
Splitting field, 162
Square, group of symmetries of the, 28
Steinitz exchange principle, 146
Subdirect sum of groups, 66
Subdirect product of groups, 66
Subfield, 149
Subgroup, 37
Subinvariant series, 58
Submodule, 141
Subring, 81
Subset, 2
Subspace, 143
Successor mapping, 11
Sum, of ideals, 92
  of vectors, 144
Superfield, 151
Sylow subgroup, 72
Sylow theorems, 73
Symmetric group, 31
Symmetry, 5
Symmetries of the square, 27, 44, 48
System, algebraic, 14
System of linear homogeneous equations, 147

Torsion group, 70
Transcendental element, 151
Transcendental extension field, 151, 158
Transformation, 8
Transformation group, 27
Transitive group, 186
Transitivity, 5
Transposition, 39
Trivial module, 141
Trisection of angle, 160
Two-sided ideal, 84

Unary operation, 9
Union, 3
Unique factorization domain, 118
Unique factorization of polynomials, 121
Uniqueness, of identity, 20
  of inverse, 20
Unit, 78
Unitary module, 141
Unity or identity element, 17, 78
Universe set, 2
Upper bound of sequence, 207

Valuation, 119, 201
Vector space, 143
  dimension of, 146
Virtual degree, 104
Virtual leading coefficient, 104
Virtual leading term, 104

Weak direct product, 63
Wedderburn's theorem, 177
Well-defined operation, 19, 26
Well-ordered set, 193
Well-ordering axiom, 195
Well-ordering of natural numbers, 11

Zassenhaus's theorem, 56
Zermelo's axiom of choice, 195
Zero element, 18, 79
Zero or root of a polynomial, 107
Zero-divisor, 78
Zorn's lemmas, 195